The William Lowell Putnam Mathematical Competition 2001–2016

Problems, Solutions, and Commentary

AMS/MAA | PROBLEM BOOKS

VOL **37**

The William Lowell Putnam Mathematical Competition 2001–2016

Problems, Solutions, and Commentary

Kiran S. Kedlaya
Daniel M. Kane
Jonathan M. Kane
Evan M. O'Dorney

MAA PRESS

An Imprint of the AMERICAN MATHEMATICAL SOCIETY

Providence, Rhode Island

2010 *Mathematics Subject Classification.* Primary 97U40, 97D50.

For additional information and updates on this book, visit
www.ams.org/bookpages/prb-37

Library of Congress Cataloging-in-Publication Data
Names: Kedlaya, Kiran Sridhara, 1974- author. | Kane, Daniel M., 1986- author.
Title: The William Lowell Putnam mathematical competition 2001–2016 : problems, solutions, and
    commentary / Kiran S. Kedlaya, Daniel M. Kane, Jonathan M. Kane, Evan M. O'Dorney.
Description: Providence, Rhode Island : American Mathematical Society, [2020] | Series: Problem
    books ; volume 37 | Includes bibliographical references and index.
Identifiers: LCCN 2020023499 | ISBN 9781470454272 (paperback) | ISBN 9781470462604 (ebook)
Subjects: LCSH: William Lowell Putnam Mathematical Competition. | Mathematics–Problems, ex-
    ercises, etc. | AMS: Mathematics education – Educational material and media, educational tech-
    nology – Problem books. Competitions. Examinations. | Mathematics education – Education
    and instruction in mathematics – Teaching problem solving and heuristic strategies For research
    aspects, see 97Cxx.
Classification: LCC QA43 .K375 2020 | DDC 510.76–dc23
LC record available at https://lccn.loc.gov/2020023499

Dedicated to the Putnam contestants

Contents

Contents

Introduction

This book is the fourth collection of William Lowell Putnam Mathematical Competition problems and solutions, following in the footsteps of [**PutnamI**] (1938–1964), [**PutnamII**] (1965-1984), and [**PutnamIII**] (1985-2000). We have largely followed the structure of the third collection, by including multiple solutions and commentary putting the problems in a broader mathematical context.

The Putnam Competition. The William Lowell Putnam Mathematical Competition (a/k/a "the Putnam") is the preeminent mathematics competition for undergraduate college students in the United States and Canada, and one of the oldest and most prominent such competitions in the world. The first competition was held in 1938; this book covers the 62nd–77th competitions, held in the years 2001–2016. Since 1962, the competition has been held on the first Saturday in December, consisting of two three-hour sessions of six problems each (A1–A6 in the morning, B1–B6 in the afternoon). For more information about the history of the Putnam Competition, see the articles of Garrett Birkhoff and L. E. Bush in [**PutnamI**], and also [**Arney**].

The competition is open to regularly enrolled undergraduates in the U.S. and Canada who have not yet received a college degree; the 2016 competition saw more than 4000 contestants from over 500 institutions. No individual may participate in the competition more than four times.

Since its origin, the competition has been organized by the Mathematical Association of America and funded by the William Lowell Putnam Prize Fund for the Promotion of Scholarship. From 1975 to 2017, the competition was administered by Leonard Klosinski (director) and Gerald Alexanderson (associate director) at Santa Clara University; from 1985 to 2017, Loren Larson also served as an associate director. As of the 2017 competition (not included in this volume), the competition is being administered directly by the MAA, with Daniel Ullman as director and Mark Krusemeyer as associate director.

The problems. The competition is meant to cover the standard undergraduate mathematics curriculum; at present, this is generally taken to mean calculus, linear algebra, differential equations, real analysis, abstract algebra, number theory, probability, and combinatorics. (In some cases, in addition to the intended solution, a problem may admit an alternate solution using more advanced mathematics.) However, problems often involve nonroutine applications of these tools, to the extent that a standard mathematical education is not necessarily the best preparation for the competition; experience with high-school competitions such as the USA Mathematical Olympiad (USAMO) and the International Mathematical Olympiad (IMO) is somewhat more transferable, although those competitions generally exclude calculus and some other advanced topics.

The problems are set by the Questions Committee, typically consisting of three mathematicians appointed by the MAA for staggered three-year terms, with the member whose term is closest to expiration serving as Chair; the committee is assisted in this effort by the associate director. For each competition included in this book, we have included the membership of the Questions Committee together with the problem statements. (The Questions Committee does not issue attributions for individual problems.)

Results of the competition. While each contestant takes the exam individually, the competition includes both individual and team aspects. On the individual side, top-scoring contestants are recognized in the following tiers. (The size of each group is only indicative; it is subject to small fluctuations due to tied scores.)

- The top 5 contestants, designated as Putnam Fellows. These receive a cash prize; one of the Putnam Fellows is also awarded the William Lowell Putnam Prize Scholarship at Harvard.

- The next 10 contestants. These receive a cash prize.

- The next 10 contestants. These receive a cash prize.

- The remaining contestants[1] among the top 100 finishers. These are designated Honorable Mentions.

- The remaining contestants among the top 200 finishers.

- The remaining contestants among the top 500 finishers.

Beginning in 1992, the Elizabeth Lowell Putnam Prize has been awarded in some years to a woman whose performance has been deemed particularly meritorious. The winner receives a cash prize.

On the team side, each participating college or university with at least three participants is awarded a team score equal to the sum of the top three scores from

---

[1]This is the definition in use at the time of writing. Previously, in addition to the top 100, there was a smaller Honorable Mention tier; the official competition reports reflect this distinction.

that institution.[2] The top 5 teams are recognized as such (in order), with cash prizes awarded both to the mathematics departments of the institutions and to the team members. The next 5 teams are designated Honorable Mentions.

An Announcement of Winners, including all of the designations listed above, is released by the MAA several months after the competition. An official report of each competition is published in the *American Mathematical Monthly* in the September or October issue of the following year; this report includes the problems, a complete set of solutions, individual results (through Honorable Mention, plus the Elizabeth Lowell Putnam Prize), and team results. It also includes, for each problem, a breakdown of how many of the top 200 contestants obtained each possible score on each problem; note that while problems are graded out of 10 points each, generally only the scores 0, 1, 2, 8, 9, 10 are used.[3]

It should be emphasized that the competition is intended not merely to identify winners, but also to provide a challenge to all of the contestants. As scores can be quite low (the median score is commonly 0), even solving a single problem is a notable result!

Structure of this book. The first section contains the problems, as they originally appeared in the competition. Next is a section containing a brief hint for each problem. The hints may often be more mystifying than enlightening. Nonetheless, we hope that they encourage readers to spend more time wrestling with a problem before turning to the solutions section.

The heart of this book is in the solutions. (Beware that in certain instances, our standard notation disagrees with the problem statement; these are described at the front of the solutions section.) For each problem, we include one or more solutions; multiple solutions generally illustrate distinct ideas, although the later solutions are compressed when they partly repeat an earlier solution. We also include commentary in the form of remarks on the various solutions. In addition, with each problem's solution we give the "score vector" consisting of the number of participants from among the top 200 finishers achieving each possible score on the problem; for ease of reference, we also indicate the percentage of the top 200 finishers achieving a score of 8–10, which we call the *success rate*. (See the first page of the solutions section for a precise definition of the score vector.)

After the solutions comes a tabulation of competition results for the years 2001–2016, including tables of various score cutoffs, including the individual tiers of recognition listed above; a list of Putnam Fellows; the top 5 schools in the team competition; and a detailed analysis of the results by Joe Gallian. More detailed

---

[2]This is the rule in use at the time of writing. During the years covered in this volume, a different system was used; see the team results section for details.

[3]This restriction was phased out as of the 2018 competition, but scores in the 3–7 range are likely to remain rare in the future.

year-by-year results can be found at the Putnam Archive (see below) and in the official competition reports in the *American Mathematical Monthly* (see above).

In addition to a standard keyword index, we have also included a topic index for the problems. This constitutes a rough (and necessarily subjective) identification of which topics from the undergraduate mathematics curriculum pertain to each problem treated in this book.

Acknowledgments. Our primary source for problem statements and competition results, and a secondary source for problem solutions, is the official competition reports (see above). We thank the Mathematical Association of America and the William Lowell Putnam Mathematical Competition for the use of the problems and results from the various Competitions.

Our primary source for the solutions published in this volume has been the online Putnam Archive, maintained by one of us (Kedlaya) at

http://kskedlaya.org/putnam-archive.

The Putnam Archive includes solutions compiled by Kedlaya together with Manjul Bhargava and Lenhard Ng; we thank Bhargava and Ng for their permission to use that material as the basis for this book. We are also grateful to the many individuals who have shared ideas that are incorporated into the solutions, including the Art of Problem Solving (AoPS) online community at http://artofproblemsolving.com; we have attributed these contributions to the best of our ability. Special recognition is due to Kent Merryfield, who built the AoPS Putnam forum into a definitive presence, and maintained it as such until his untimely passing in November 2018; his efforts will be dearly missed.

We thank Joe Gallian for helping to assemble the competition results and with making his analysis available to us for inclusion. We also wish to acknowledge Joe's continuing role as unofficial William Lowell Putnam Competition historian as well as his mentoring of undergraduate students, from which all four of us have benefited directly.

We thank Steve Kennedy for his continued support of this project, and the AMS/MAA Problem Books editorial board for their detailed feedback on a draft of this book.

We thank the Mathematical Association of America for continuing to organize the competition; the past directors Gerald Alexanderson, Leonard Klosinski, and Loren Larson for their extended service to the mathematical community; the current director Daniel Ullman and associate director Mark Krusemeyer for carrying this work forward; numerous unnamed volunteers who have participated in the grading of the competition; and the Putnam family for its continued support of the competition over so many years.

Problems

The Sixty-Second William Lowell Putnam Mathematical Competition—December 1, 2001

Questions Committee: Eugene Luks (Chair), Titu Andreescu, Andrew J. Granville, and Carl Pomerance
See page 55 for hints.

A1.

Consider a set S and a binary operation $*$, that is, for each $a, b \in S, a*b \in S$. Assume $(a * b) * a = b$ for all $a, b \in S$. Prove that $a * (b * a) = b$ for all $a, b \in S$.

(page 73)

A2.

You have coins $C_1, C_2, \ldots, C_n$. For each k, C_k is biased so that, when tossed, it has probability $\frac{1}{2k+1}$ of falling heads. If the n coins are tossed, what is the probability that the number of heads is odd? Express the answer as a rational function of n.

(page 73)

A3.

For each integer m, consider the polynomial

$$P_m(x) = x^4 - (2m + 4)x^2 + (m - 2)^2.$$

For what values of m is $P_m(x)$ the product of two nonconstant polynomials with integer coefficients?

(page 73)

A4.

Triangle ABC has area 1. Points E, F, G lie, respectively, on sides BC, CA, AB such that AE bisects BF at point R, BF bisects CG at point S, and CG bisects AE at point T. Find the area of the triangle RST.

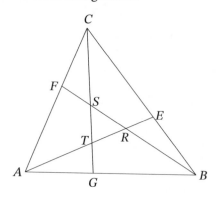

(page 74)

A5.
   Prove that there are unique positive integers a, n such that
$$a^{n+1} - (a+1)^n = 2001.$$

(page 76)

A6.
   Can an arc of a parabola inside a circle of radius 1 have a length greater than 4?

(page 76)

B1.
   Let n be an even positive integer. Write the numbers $1, 2, \ldots, n^2$ in the squares of an $n \times n$ grid so that the kth row, from left to right, is
$$(k-1)n + 1, (k-1)n + 2, \ldots, (k-1)n + n.$$
Color the squares of the grid so that half of the squares in each row and in each column are red and the other half are black (a checkerboard coloring is one possibility). Prove that for each coloring, the sum of the numbers on the red squares is equal to the sum of the numbers on the black squares.

(page 77)

B2.
   Find all pairs of real numbers (x, y) satisfying the system of equations
$$\frac{1}{x} + \frac{1}{2y} = (x^2 + 3y^2)(3x^2 + y^2)$$
$$\frac{1}{x} - \frac{1}{2y} = 2(y^4 - x^4).$$

(page 78)

B3.
   For any positive integer n, let $\langle n \rangle$ denote the closest integer to $\sqrt{n}$. Evaluate
$$\sum_{n=1}^{\infty} \frac{2^{\langle n \rangle} + 2^{-\langle n \rangle}}{2^n}.$$

(page 79)

B4.

Let S denote the set of rational numbers different from $-1, 0$, and 1. Define $f : S \to S$ by $f(x) = x - 1/x$. Prove or disprove:

$$\bigcap_{n=1}^{\infty} f^{(n)}(S) = \emptyset,$$

where $f^{(n)} = \underbrace{f \circ f \circ \cdots \circ f}_{n \text{ times}}$.

(Note: $f(S)$ denotes the set of all values $f(s)$ for $s \in S$.)

(page 80)

B5.

Let a and b be real numbers in the interval $(0, \frac{1}{2})$ and let g be a continuous real-valued function such that $g(g(x)) = ag(x) + bx$ for all real x. Prove that $g(x) = cx$ for some constant c.

(page 81)

B6.

Assume that $(a_n)_{n \geq 1}$ is an increasing sequence of positive real numbers such that $\lim \frac{a_n}{n} = 0$. Must there exist infinitely many positive integers n such that

$$a_{n-i} + a_{n+i} < 2a_n \quad \text{for } i = 1, 2, \ldots, n - 1?$$

(page 81)

The Sixty-Third William Lowell Putnam
Mathematical Competition—December 7, 2002

Questions Committee: Andrew J. Granville and Carl Pomerance (Chairs),
David Callan, and Byron L. Walden
See page 56 for hints.

A1.

Let k be a fixed positive integer. The nth derivative of $\frac{1}{x^k-1}$ has the form $\frac{P_n(x)}{(x^k-1)^{n+1}}$, where $P_n(x)$ is a polynomial. Find $P_n(1)$.

(page 83)

A2.

Given any five points on a sphere, show that some four of them must lie on a closed hemisphere.

(page 84)

A3.

Let $n \geq 2$ be an integer and T_n be the number of nonempty subsets S of $\{1, 2, 3, \ldots, n\}$ with the property that the average of the elements of S is an integer. Prove that $T_n - n$ is always even.

(page 84)

A4.

In Determinant Tic-Tac-Toe, Player 1 enters a 1 in an empty 3×3 matrix. Player 0 counters with a 0 in a vacant position, and play continues in turn until the 3×3 matrix is completed with five 1's and four 0's. Player 0 wins if the determinant is 0 and player 1 wins otherwise. Assuming both players pursue optimal strategies, who will win and how?

(page 84)

A5.

Define a sequence by $a_0 = 1$, together with the rules $a_{2n+1} = a_n$ and $a_{2n+2} = a_n + a_{n+1}$ for each integer $n \geq 0$. Prove that every positive rational number appears in the set

$$\left\{ \frac{a_{n-1}}{a_n} : n \geq 1 \right\} = \left\{ \frac{1}{1}, \frac{1}{2}, \frac{2}{1}, \frac{1}{3}, \frac{3}{2}, \ldots \right\}.$$

(page 85)

A6.

Fix an integer $b \geq 2$. Let $f(1) = 1$, $f(2) = 2$, and for each $n \geq 3$, define $f(n) = nf(d)$, where d is the number of base-b digits of n. For which values of b

does

$$\sum_{n=1}^{\infty} \frac{1}{f(n)}$$

converge?

(page 86)

B1.

Shanille O'Keal shoots free throws on a basketball court. She hits the first and misses the second, and thereafter the probability that she hits the next shot is equal to the proportion of shots she has hit so far. What is the probability she hits exactly 50 of her first 100 shots?

(page 88)

B2.

Consider a polyhedron with at least five faces such that exactly three edges emerge from each of its vertices. Two players play the following game:

> Each player, in turn, signs his or her name on a previously unsigned face. The winner is the player who first succeeds in signing three faces that share a common vertex.

Show that the player who signs first will always win by playing as well as possible.

(page 88)

B3.

Show that, for all integers $n > 1$,

$$\frac{1}{2ne} < \frac{1}{e} - \left(1 - \frac{1}{n}\right)^n < \frac{1}{ne}.$$

(page 89)

B4.

An integer n, unknown to you, has been randomly chosen in the interval $[1, 2002]$ with uniform probability. Your objective is to select n in an **odd** number of guesses. After each incorrect guess, you are informed whether n is higher or lower, and you **must** guess an integer on your next turn among the numbers that are still feasibly correct. Show that you have a strategy so that the chance of winning is greater than 2/3.

(page 90)

B5.

A palindrome in base b is a positive integer whose base-b digits read the same backwards and forwards; for example, 2002 is a 4-digit palindrome in base 10.

Note that 200 is not a palindrome in base 10, but it is the 3-digit palindrome 242 in base 9, and 404 in base 7. Prove that there is an integer which is a 3-digit palindrome in base b for at least 2002 different values of b.

(page 91)

B6.

Let p be a prime number. Prove that the determinant of the matrix

$$\begin{pmatrix} x & y & z \\ x^p & y^p & z^p \\ x^{p^2} & y^{p^2} & z^{p^2} \end{pmatrix}$$

is congruent modulo p to a product of polynomials of the form $ax+by+cz$, where a, b, c are integers. (We say two integer polynomials are congruent modulo p if corresponding coefficients are congruent modulo p.)

(page 92)

The Sixty-Fourth William Lowell Putnam Mathematical Competition—December 6, 2003

Questions Committee: David Callan (Chair),
Hugh Montgomery, and Byron L. Walden
See page 57 for hints.

A1.

Let n be a fixed positive integer. How many ways are there to write n as a sum of positive integers,

$$n = a_1 + a_2 + \cdots + a_k,$$

with k an arbitrary positive integer, and $a_1 \leq a_2 \leq \cdots \leq a_k \leq a_1 + 1$? For example, with $n = 4$ there are four ways: $4, 2+2, 1+1+2, 1+1+1+1$.

(page 95)

A2.

Let $a_1, a_2, \ldots, a_n$ and $b_1, b_2, \ldots, b_n$ be nonnegative real numbers. Show that

$$(a_1 a_2 \cdots a_n)^{1/n} + (b_1 b_2 \cdots b_n)^{1/n} \leq [(a_1 + b_1)(a_2 + b_2) \cdots (a_n + b_n)]^{1/n}.$$

(page 95)

A3.

Find the minimum value of

$$|\sin x + \cos x + \tan x + \cot x + \sec x + \csc x|$$

for real numbers x.

(page 97)

A4.

Suppose that a, b, c, A, B, C are real numbers, $a \neq 0$ and $A \neq 0$, such that

$$|ax^2 + bx + c| \leq |Ax^2 + Bx + C|$$

for all real numbers x. Show that

$$|b^2 - 4ac| \leq |B^2 - 4AC|.$$

(page 99)

A5.

A Dyck n-path is a lattice path of n upsteps $(1, 1)$ and n downsteps $(1, -1)$ that starts at the origin O and never dips below the x-axis. A return is a maximal sequence of contiguous downsteps that terminates on the x-axis. For example, the Dyck 5-path illustrated has two returns, of length 3 and 1 respectively.

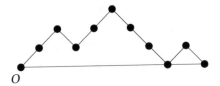

Show that there is a one-to-one correspondence between the Dyck n-paths with no return of even length and the Dyck $(n-1)$-paths.

(page 100)

A6.

For a set S of nonnegative integers, let $r_S(n)$ denote the number of ordered pairs (s_1, s_2) such that $s_1 \in S$, $s_2 \in S$, $s_1 \neq s_2$, and $s_1 + s_2 = n$. Is it possible to partition the nonnegative integers into two sets A and B in such a way that $r_A(n) = r_B(n)$ for all n?

(page 102)

B1.

Do there exist polynomials $a(x), b(x), c(y), d(y)$ such that

$$1 + xy + x^2 y^2 = a(x)c(y) + b(x)d(y)$$

holds identically?

(page 104)

B2.

Let n be a positive integer. Starting with the sequence $1, \frac{1}{2}, \frac{1}{3}, \ldots, \frac{1}{n}$, form a new sequence of $n-1$ entries $\frac{3}{4}, \frac{5}{12}, \ldots, \frac{2n-1}{2n(n-1)}$ by taking the averages of two consecutive entries in the first sequence. Repeat the averaging of neighbors on the second sequence to obtain a third sequence of $n-2$ entries and continue until the final sequence produced consists of a single number x_n. Show that $x_n < 2/n$.

(page 105)

B3.

Show that for each positive integer n,

$$n! = \prod_{i=1}^{n} \operatorname{lcm}\{1, 2, \ldots, \lfloor n/i \rfloor\}.$$

(Here lcm denotes the least common multiple, and $\lfloor x \rfloor$ denotes the greatest integer $\leq x$.)

(page 106)

B4.

Let $f(z) = az^4 + bz^3 + cz^2 + dz + e = a(z - r_1)(z - r_2)(z - r_3)(z - r_4)$ where a, b, c, d, e are integers, $a \neq 0$. Show that if $r_1 + r_2$ is a rational number and $r_1 + r_2 \neq r_3 + r_4$, then $r_1 r_2$ is a rational number.

(page 107)

B5.

Let $A, B,$ and C be equidistant points on the circumference of a circle of unit radius centered at O, and let P be any point in the circle's interior. Let a, b, c be the distance from P to A, B, C, respectively. Show that there is a triangle with side lengths a, b, c, and that the area of this triangle depends only on the distance from P to O.

(page 108)

B6.

Let $f(x)$ be a continuous real-valued function defined on the interval $[0, 1]$. Show that

$$\int_0^1 \int_0^1 |f(x) + f(y)| \, dx \, dy \geq \int_0^1 |f(x)| \, dx.$$

(page 109)

The Sixty-Fifth William Lowell Putnam
Mathematical Competition—December 4, 2004

Questions Committee: Byron L. Walden (Chair),
Hugh Montgomery, and Steven Tschanz
See page 58 for hints.

A1.

Basketball star Shanille O'Keal's team statistician keeps track of the number, $S(N)$, of successful free throws she has made in her first N attempts of the season. Early in the season, $S(N)$ was less than 80% of N, but by the end of the season, $S(N)$ was more than 80% of N. Was there necessarily a moment in between when $S(N)$ was exactly 80% of N?

(page 114)

A2.

For $i = 1, 2$ let T_i be a triangle with side lengths a_i, b_i, c_i, and area A_i. Suppose that $a_1 \le a_2, b_1 \le b_2, c_1 \le c_2$, and that T_2 is an acute triangle. Does it follow that $A_1 \le A_2$?

(page 114)

A3.

Define a sequence $\{u_n\}_{n=0}^{\infty}$ by $u_0 = u_1 = u_2 = 1$, and thereafter by the condition that

$$\det \begin{pmatrix} u_n & u_{n+1} \\ u_{n+2} & u_{n+3} \end{pmatrix} = n!$$

for all $n \ge 0$. Show that u_n is an integer for all n. (By convention, $0! = 1$.)

(page 116)

A4.

Show that for any positive integer n there is an integer N such that the product $x_1 x_2 \cdots x_n$ can be expressed identically in the form

$$x_1 x_2 \cdots x_n = \sum_{i=1}^{N} c_i (a_{i1} x_1 + a_{i2} x_2 + \cdots + a_{in} x_n)^n$$

where the c_i are rational numbers and each a_{ij} is one of the numbers $-1, 0, 1$.

(page 116)

A5.

An $m \times n$ checkerboard is colored randomly: each square is independently assigned red or black with probability $1/2$. We say that two squares, p and q, are in the same connected monochromatic region if there is a sequence of squares, all of the same color, starting at p and ending at q, in which successive squares in the sequence share a common side. Show that the expected number of connected monochromatic regions is greater than $mn/8$.

(page 117)

A6.

Suppose that $f(x, y)$ is a continuous real-valued function on the unit square $0 \le x \le 1, 0 \le y \le 1$. Show that

$$\int_0^1 \left(\int_0^1 f(x,y)dx \right)^2 dy + \int_0^1 \left(\int_0^1 f(x,y)dy \right)^2 dx$$

$$\le \left(\int_0^1 \int_0^1 f(x,y)dx\, dy \right)^2 + \int_0^1 \int_0^1 [f(x,y)]^2 dx\, dy.$$

(page 119)

B1.

Let $P(x) = c_n x^n + c_{n-1} x^{n-1} + \cdots + c_0$ be a polynomial with integer coefficients. Suppose that r is a rational number such that $P(r) = 0$. Show that the n numbers

$$c_n r, \ c_n r^2 + c_{n-1} r, \ c_n r^3 + c_{n-1} r^2 + c_{n-2} r,$$

$$\ldots, \ c_n r^n + c_{n-1} r^{n-1} + \cdots + c_1 r$$

are integers.

(page 120)

B2.

Let m and n be positive integers. Show that

$$\frac{(m+n)!}{(m+n)^{m+n}} < \frac{m!}{m^m} \frac{n!}{n^n}.$$

(page 120)

B3.

Determine all real numbers $a > 0$ for which there exists a nonnegative continuous function $f(x)$ defined on $[0, a]$ with the property that the region

$$R = \{(x, y) : 0 \le x \le a, 0 \le y \le f(x)\}$$

has perimeter k units and area k square units for some real number k.

(page 122)

B4.

Let n be a positive integer, $n \geq 2$, and put $\theta = 2\pi/n$. Define points $P_k = (k, 0)$ in the xy-plane, for $k = 1, 2, \ldots, n$. Let R_k be the map that rotates the plane counterclockwise by the angle θ about the point P_k. Let R denote the map obtained by applying, in order, R_1, then $R_2, \ldots$, then R_n. For an arbitrary point (x, y), find, and simplify, the coordinates of $R(x, y)$.

(page 123)

B5.

Evaluate

$$\lim_{x \to 1^-} \prod_{n=0}^{\infty} \left(\frac{1 + x^{n+1}}{1 + x^n} \right)^{x^n}.$$

(page 124)

B6.

Let $\mathcal{A}$ be a nonempty set of positive integers, and let $N(x)$ denote the number of elements of $\mathcal{A}$ not exceeding x. Let $\mathcal{B}$ denote the set of positive integers b that can be written in the form $b = a - a'$ with $a \in \mathcal{A}$ and $a' \in \mathcal{A}$. Let $b_1 < b_2 < \cdots$ be the members of $\mathcal{B}$, listed in increasing order. Show that if the sequence $b_{i+1} - b_i$ is unbounded, then

$$\lim_{x \to \infty} N(x)/x = 0.$$

(page 126)

The Sixty-Sixth William Lowell Putnam
Mathematical Competition—December 3, 2005

Questions Committee: Hugh L. Montgomery (Chair),
Titu Andreescu, and Steven Tschanz
See page 59 for hints.

A1.

Show that every positive integer is a sum of one or more numbers of the form $2^r 3^s$, where r and s are nonnegative integers and no summand divides another. (For example, $23 = 9 + 8 + 6$.)

(page 128)

A2.

Let $S = \{(a, b) : a = 1, 2, \ldots, n, b = 1, 2, 3\}$. A *rook tour* of S is a polygonal path made up of line segments connecting points $p_1, p_2, \ldots, p_{3n}$ in sequence such that

(i) $p_i \in S$,

(ii) p_i and p_{i+1} are a unit distance apart, for $1 \le i < 3n$,

(iii) for each $p \in S$ there is a unique i such that $p_i = p$.

How many rook tours are there that begin at $(1, 1)$ and end at $(n, 1)$? (An example of such a rook tour for $n = 5$ is depicted.)

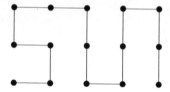

(page 128)

A3.

Let $p(z)$ be a polynomial of degree n all of whose zeros have absolute value 1 in the complex plane. Put $g(z) = p(z)/z^{n/2}$. Show that all zeros of $g'(z) = 0$ have absolute value 1.

(page 131)

A4.

Let H be an $n \times n$ matrix all of whose entries are ± 1 and whose rows are mutually orthogonal. Suppose H has an $a \times b$ submatrix whose entries are all 1. Show that $ab \le n$.

(page 132)

A5.

Evaluate $\int_0^1 \frac{\ln(x+1)}{x^2+1}\,dx$.

(page 133)

A6.

Let n be given, $n \geq 4$, and suppose that $P_1, P_2, \ldots, P_n$ are n randomly, independently and uniformly, chosen points on a circle. Consider the convex n-gon whose vertices are the P_i. What is the probability that at least one of the vertex angles of this polygon is acute?

(page 136)

B1.

Find a nonzero polynomial $P(x, y)$ such that $P(\lfloor a \rfloor, \lfloor 2a \rfloor) = 0$ for all real numbers a. (Note: $\lfloor v \rfloor$ is the greatest integer less than or equal to v.)

(page 137)

B2.

Find all positive integers $n, k_1, \ldots, k_n$ such that $k_1 + \cdots + k_n = 5n - 4$ and

$$\frac{1}{k_1} + \cdots + \frac{1}{k_n} = 1.$$

(page 138)

B3.

Find all differentiable functions $f : (0, \infty) \to (0, \infty)$ for which there is a positive real number a such that

$$f'\left(\frac{a}{x}\right) = \frac{x}{f(x)}$$

for all $x > 0$.

(page 139)

B4.

For positive integers m and n, let $f(m, n)$ denote the number of n-tuples $(x_1, x_2, \ldots, x_n)$ of integers such that $|x_1| + |x_2| + \cdots + |x_n| \leq m$. Show that $f(m, n) = f(n, m)$.

(page 140)

B5.

Let $P(x_1, \ldots, x_n)$ denote a polynomial with real coefficients in the variables $x_1, \ldots, x_n$, and suppose that

$$\left(\frac{\partial^2}{\partial x_1^2} + \cdots + \frac{\partial^2}{\partial x_n^2} \right) P(x_1, \ldots, x_n) = 0 \quad \text{(identically)}$$

and that

$$x_1^2 + \cdots + x_n^2 \text{ divides } P(x_1, \ldots, x_n).$$

Show that $P = 0$ identically.

(page 142)

B6.

Let S_n denote the set of all permutations of the numbers $1, 2, \ldots, n$. For $\pi \in S_n$, let $\sigma(\pi) = 1$ if π is an even permutation and $\sigma(\pi) = -1$ if π is an odd permutation. Also, let $\nu(\pi)$ denote the number of fixed points of π. Show that

$$\sum_{\pi \in S_n} \frac{\sigma(\pi)}{\nu(\pi) + 1} = (-1)^{n+1} \frac{n}{n+1}.$$

(page 143)

**The Sixty-Seventh William Lowell Putnam
Mathematical Competition—December 2, 2006**

December 2, 2006

*Questions Committee: Steven Tschanz (Chair),
Titu Andreescu, and Greg Kuperberg
See page 60 for hints.*

A1.

Find the volume of the region of points (x, y, z) such that

$$(x^2 + y^2 + z^2 + 8)^2 \leq 36(x^2 + y^2).$$

(page 146)

A2.

Alice and Bob play a game in which they take turns removing stones from a heap that initially has n stones. The number of stones removed at each turn must be one less than a prime number. The winner is the player who takes the last stone. Alice plays first. Prove that there are infinitely many n such that Bob has a winning strategy. (For example, if $n = 17$, then Alice might take 6 leaving 11; then Bob might take 1 leaving 10; then Alice can take the remaining stones to win.)

(page 146)

A3.

Let $1, 2, 3, \ldots, 2005, 2006, 2007, 2009, 2012, 2016, \ldots$ be a sequence defined by $x_k = k$ for $k = 1, 2, \ldots, 2006$ and $x_{k+1} = x_k + x_{k-2005}$ for $k \geq 2006$. Show that the sequence has 2005 consecutive terms each divisible by 2006.

(page 147)

A4.

Let $S = \{1, 2, \ldots, n\}$ for some integer $n > 1$. Say a permutation π of S has a *local maximum* at $k \in S$ if

(i) $\pi(k) > \pi(k + 1)$ for $k = 1$;

(ii) $\pi(k - 1) < \pi(k)$ and $\pi(k) > \pi(k + 1)$ for $1 < k < n$;

(iii) $\pi(k - 1) < \pi(k)$ for $k = n$.

(For example, if $n = 5$ and π takes values at $1, 2, 3, 4, 5$ of $2, 1, 4, 5, 3$, then π has a local maximum of 2 at $k = 1$, and a local maximum of 5 at $k = 4$.) What is the average number of local maxima of a permutation of S, averaging over all permutations of S?

(page 148)

A5.

Let n be a positive odd integer and let θ be a real number such that θ/π is irrational. Set $a_k = \tan(\theta + k\pi/n)$, $k = 1, 2, \ldots, n$. Prove that

$$\frac{a_1 + a_2 + \cdots + a_n}{a_1 a_2 \cdots a_n}$$

is an integer, and determine its value.

(page 149)

A6.

Four points are chosen uniformly and independently at random in the interior of a given circle. Find the probability that they are the vertices of a convex quadrilateral.

(page 150)

B1.

Show that the curve $x^3 + 3xy + y^3 = 1$ contains only one set of three distinct points, A, B, and C, which are vertices of an equilateral triangle, and find its area.

(page 154)

B2.

Prove that, for every set $X = \{x_1, x_2, \ldots, x_n\}$ of n real numbers, there exists a nonempty subset S of X and an integer m such that

$$\left| m + \sum_{s \in S} s \right| \le \frac{1}{n+1}.$$

(page 155)

B3.

Let S be a finite set of points in the plane. A *linear partition* of S is an unordered pair $\{A, B\}$ of subsets of S such that $A \cup B = S$, $A \cap B = \emptyset$, and A and B lie on opposite sides of some straight line disjoint from S (A or B may be empty). Let L_S be the number of linear partitions of S. For each positive integer n, find the maximum of L_S over all sets S of n points.

(page 156)

B4.

Let Z denote the set of points in $\mathbb{R}^n$ whose coordinates are 0 or 1. (Thus Z has 2^n elements, which are the vertices of a unit hypercube in $\mathbb{R}^n$.) Given a vector subspace V of $\mathbb{R}^n$, let $Z(V)$ denote the number of members of Z that lie in V. Let k be given, $0 \le k \le n$. Find the maximum, over all vector subspaces $V \subseteq \mathbb{R}^n$ of dimension k, of the number of points in $V \cap Z$.

(page 158)

B5.

For each continuous function $f : [0,1] \to \mathbb{R}$, let $I(f) = \int_0^1 x^2 f(x)\,dx$ and $J(x) = \int_0^1 x(f(x))^2\,dx$. Find the maximum value of $I(f) - J(f)$ over all such functions f.

(page 159)

B6.

Let k be an integer greater than 1. Suppose $a_0 > 0$, and define

$$a_{n+1} = a_n + \frac{1}{\sqrt[k]{a_n}}$$

for $n > 0$. Evaluate

$$\lim_{n\to\infty} \frac{a_n^{k+1}}{n^k}.$$

(page 160)

The Sixty-Eighth William Lowell Putnam Mathematical Competition—December 1, 2007

Questions Committee: Titu Andreescu (Chair),
Greg Kuperberg, and Mark Krusemeyer
See page 61 for hints.

A1.

Find all values of α for which the curves $y = \alpha x^2 + \alpha x + \frac{1}{24}$ and $x = \alpha y^2 + \alpha y + \frac{1}{24}$ are tangent to each other.

A2.

Find the least possible area of a convex set in the plane that intersects both branches of the hyperbola $xy = 1$ and both branches of the hyperbola $xy = -1$. (A set S in the plane is called *convex* if for any two points in S the line segment connecting them is contained in S.)

(page 165)

A3.

Let k be a positive integer. Suppose that the integers $1, 2, 3, \ldots, 3k + 1$ are written down in random order. What is the probability that at no time during this process, the sum of the integers that have been written up to that time is a positive integer divisible by 3? Your answer should be in closed form, but may include factorials.

(page 167)

A4.

A *repunit* is a positive integer whose digits in base 10 are all ones. Find all polynomials f with real coefficients such that if n is a repunit, then so is $f(n)$.

(page 167)

A5.

Suppose that a finite group has exactly n elements of order p, where p is a prime. Prove that either $n = 0$ or p divides $n + 1$.

(page 169)

A6.

A *triangulation* $\mathcal{T}$ of a polygon P is a finite collection of triangles whose union is P, and such that the intersection of any two triangles is either empty, or a shared vertex, or a shared side. Moreover, each side is a side of exactly one triangle in $\mathcal{T}$. Say that $\mathcal{T}$ is *admissible* if every internal vertex is shared by six or more triangles. For example

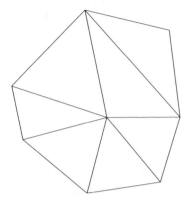

Prove that there is an integer M_n, depending only on n, such that any admissible triangulation of a polygon P with n sides has at most M_n triangles.

(page 169)

B1.
Let f be a polynomial with positive integer coefficients. Prove that if n is a positive integer, then $f(n)$ divides $f(f(n) + 1)$ if and only if $n = 1$.

(page 171)

B2.
Suppose that $f : [0, 1] \to \mathbb{R}$ has a continuous derivative and that $\int_0^1 f(x)\, dx = 0$. Prove that for every $\alpha \in (0, 1)$,

$$\left| \int_0^\alpha f(x)\, dx \right| \le \frac{1}{8} \max_{0 \le x \le 1} |f'(x)|.$$

(page 171)

B3.
Let $x_0 = 1$ and for $n \ge 0$, let $x_{n+1} = 3x_n + \lfloor x_n \sqrt{5} \rfloor$. In particular, $x_1 = 5$, $x_2 = 26$, $x_3 = 136$, $x_4 = 712$. Find a closed-form expression for x_{2007}. ($\lfloor a \rfloor$ means the largest integer $\le a$.)

(page 172)

B4.
Let n be a positive integer. Find the number of pairs P, Q of polynomials with real coefficients such that

$$(P(X))^2 + (Q(X))^2 = X^{2n} + 1$$

and $\deg P > \deg Q$.

(page 173)

B5.

Let k be a positive integer. Prove that there exist polynomials $P_0(n)$, $P_1(n)$, ..., $P_{k-1}(n)$ (which may depend on k) such that for any integer n,

$$\left\lfloor \frac{n}{k} \right\rfloor^k = P_0(n) + P_1(n)\left\lfloor \frac{n}{k} \right\rfloor + \cdots + P_{k-1}(n)\left\lfloor \frac{n}{k} \right\rfloor^{k-1}.$$

(page 174)

B6.

For each positive integer n, let $f(n)$ be the number of ways to make $n!$ cents using an unordered collection of coins, each worth $k!$ cents for some k, $1 \le k \le n$. Prove that for some constant C, independent of n,

$$n^{n^2/2 - Cn} e^{-n^2/4} \le f(n) \le n^{n^2/2 + Cn} e^{-n^2/4}.$$

(page 174)

**The Sixty-Ninth William Lowell Putnam
Mathematical Competition—December 6, 2008**

*Questions Committee: Greg Kuperberg (Chair),
Mark Krusemeyer, and Bjorn Poonen
See page 62 for hints.*

A1.

Let $f : \mathbb{R}^2 \to \mathbb{R}$ be a function such that $f(x,y) + f(y,z) + f(z,x) = 0$ for all real numbers x, y, and z. Prove that there exists a function $g : \mathbb{R} \to \mathbb{R}$ such that $f(x,y) = g(x) - g(y)$ for all real numbers x and y.

(page 176)

A2.

Alan and Barbara play a game in which they take turns filling entries of an initially empty 2008×2008 array. Alan plays first. At each turn, a player chooses a real number and places it in a vacant entry. The game ends when all the entries are filled. Alan wins if the determinant of the resulting matrix is nonzero; Barbara wins if it is zero. Which player has a winning strategy?

(page 176)

A3.

Start with a finite sequence $a_1, a_2, \ldots, a_n$ of positive integers. If possible, choose two indices $j < k$ such that a_j does not divide a_k, and replace a_j and a_k by $\gcd(a_j, a_k)$ and $\mathrm{lcm}(a_j, a_k)$, respectively. Prove that if this process is repeated, it must eventually stop and the final sequence does not depend on the choices made. (Note: gcd means greatest common divisor and lcm means least common multiple.)

(page 176)

A4.

Define $f : \mathbb{R} \to \mathbb{R}$ by

$$f(x) = \begin{cases} x & \text{if } x \le e, \\ xf(\ln x) & \text{if } x > e. \end{cases}$$

Does $\sum_{n=1}^{\infty} \frac{1}{f(n)}$ converge?

(page 179)

A5.

Let $n \ge 3$ be an integer. Let $f(x)$ and $g(x)$ be polynomials with real coefficients such that the points $(f(1), g(1)), (f(2), g(2)), \ldots, (f(n), g(n))$ in $\mathbb{R}^2$ are the vertices of a regular n-gon in counterclockwise order. Prove that at least one of $f(x)$ and $g(x)$ has degree greater than or equal to $n-1$.

(page 180)

A6.

Prove that there exists a constant $c > 0$ such that in every nontrivial finite group G there exists a sequence of length at most $c \log |G|$ with the property that each element of G equals the product of some subsequence. (The elements of G in the sequence are not required to be distinct. A *subsequence* of a sequence is obtained by selecting some of the terms, not necessarily consecutive, without reordering them; for example, $4, 4, 2$ is a subsequence of $2, 4, 6, 4, 2$, but $2, 2, 4$ is not.)

(page 181)

B1.

What is the maximum number of rational points that can lie on a circle in $\mathbb{R}^2$ whose center is not a rational point? (A *rational point* is a point both of whose coordinates are rational numbers.)

(page 183)

B2.

Let $F_0(x) = \ln x$. For $n \geq 0$ and $x > 0$, let $F_{n+1}(x) = \int_0^x F_n(t)\,dt$. Evaluate

$$\lim_{n\to\infty} \frac{n!\, F_n(1)}{\ln n}.$$

(page 184)

B3.

What is the largest possible radius of a circle contained in a 4-dimensional hypercube of side length 1?

(page 184)

B4.

Let p be a prime number. Let $h(x)$ be a polynomial with integer coefficients such that $h(0), h(1), \ldots, h(p^2-1)$ are distinct modulo p^2. Show that $h(0), h(1), \ldots, h(p^3 - 1)$ are distinct modulo p^3.

(page 186)

B5.

Find all continuously differentiable functions $f : \mathbb{R} \to \mathbb{R}$ such that for every rational number q, the number $f(q)$ is rational and has the same denominator as

q. (The denominator of a rational number q is the unique positive integer b such that $q = a/b$ for some integer a with $\gcd(a, b) = 1$.) (Note: gcd means greatest common divisor.)

(page 187)

B6.

Let n and k be positive integers. Say that a permutation σ of $\{1, 2, \ldots, n\}$ is *k-limited* if $|\sigma(i) - i| \leq k$ for all i. Prove that the number of k-limited permutations of $\{1, 2, \ldots, n\}$ is odd if and only if $n \equiv 0$ or $1 \pmod{2k + 1}$.

(page 188)

**The Seventieth William Lowell Putnam
Mathematical Competition—December 5, 2009**

*Questions Committee: Mark Krusemeyer (Chair),
Izabella Laba, and Bjorn Poonen
See page 63 for hints.*

A1.

Let f be a real-valued function on the plane such that for every square $ABCD$ in the plane, $f(A) + f(B) + f(C) + f(D) = 0$. Does it follow that $f(P) = 0$ for all points P in the plane?

(page 193)

A2.

Functions f, g, h are differentiable on some open interval around 0 and satisfy the equations and initial conditions

$$f' = 2f^2 gh + \frac{1}{gh}, \quad f(0) = 1,$$

$$g' = fg^2 h + \frac{4}{fh}, \quad g(0) = 1,$$

$$h' = 3fgh^2 + \frac{1}{fg}, \quad h(0) = 1.$$

Find an explicit formula for $f(x)$, valid in some open interval around 0.

(page 193)

A3.

Let d_n be the determinant of the $n \times n$ matrix whose entries, from left to right and then from top to bottom, are $\cos 1, \cos 2, \dots, \cos n^2$. (For example,

$$d_3 = \begin{vmatrix} \cos 1 & \cos 2 & \cos 3 \\ \cos 4 & \cos 5 & \cos 6 \\ \cos 7 & \cos 8 & \cos 9 \end{vmatrix}.$$

The argument of cos is always in radians, not degrees.) Evaluate $\lim_{n \to \infty} d_n$.

(page 194)

A4.

Let S be a set of rational numbers such that

(a) $0 \in S$;

(b) If $x \in S$, then $x + 1 \in S$ and $x - 1 \in S$; and

(c) If $x \in S$ and $x \notin \{0, 1\}$, then $\frac{1}{x(x-1)} \in S$.

Must S contain all rational numbers?

(page 195)

A5.

Is there a finite abelian group G such that the product of the orders of all its elements is 2^{2009}?

(page 196)

A6.

Let $f : [0,1]^2 \to \mathbb{R}$ be a continuous function on the closed unit square such that $\frac{\partial f}{\partial x}$ and $\frac{\partial f}{\partial y}$ exist and are continuous on the interior $(0,1)^2$. Let $a = \int_0^1 f(0,y)\,dy$, $b = \int_0^1 f(1,y)\,dy$, $c = \int_0^1 f(x,0)\,dx$, $d = \int_0^1 f(x,1)\,dx$. Prove or disprove: There must be a point (x_0, y_0) in $(0,1)^2$ such that

$$\frac{\partial f}{\partial x}(x_0, y_0) = b - a \quad \text{and} \quad \frac{\partial f}{\partial y}(x_0, y_0) = d - c.$$

(page 197)

B1.

Show that every positive rational number can be written as a quotient of products of factorials of (not necessarily distinct) primes. For example,

$$\frac{10}{9} = \frac{2! \cdot 5!}{3! \cdot 3! \cdot 3!}.$$

(page 198)

B2.

A game involves jumping to the right on the real number line. If a and b are real numbers and $b > a$, the cost of jumping from a to b is $b^3 - ab^2$. For what real numbers c can one travel from 0 to 1 in a finite number of jumps with total cost exactly c?

(page 199)

B3.

Call a subset S of $\{1, 2, \ldots, n\}$ *mediocre* if it has the following property: Whenever a and b are elements of S whose average is an integer, that average is also an element of S. Let $A(n)$ be the number of mediocre subsets of $\{1, 2, \ldots, n\}$. [For instance, every subset of $\{1, 2, 3\}$ except $\{1, 3\}$ is mediocre, so $A(3) = 7$.] Find all positive integers n such that $A(n+2) - 2A(n+1) + A(n) = 1$.

(page 200)

B4.

Say that a polynomial with real coefficients in two variables, x, y, is *balanced* if the average value of the polynomial on each circle centered at the origin is 0. The balanced polynomials of degree at most 2009 form a vector space V over $\mathbb{R}$. Find the dimension of V.

(page 201)

B5.

Let $f : (1, \infty) \to \mathbb{R}$ be a differentiable function such that

$$f'(x) = \frac{x^2 - f(x)^2}{x^2(f(x)^2 + 1)} \qquad \text{for all } x > 1.$$

Prove that $\lim_{x \to \infty} f(x) = \infty$.

(page 202)

B6.

Prove that for every positive integer n, there is a sequence of integers $a_0, a_1, \ldots, a_{2009}$ with $a_0 = 0$ and $a_{2009} = n$ such that each term after a_0 is either an earlier term plus 2^k for some nonnegative integer k, or of the form $b \bmod c$ for some earlier positive terms b and c. [Here $b \bmod c$ denotes the remainder when b is divided by c, so $0 \le (b \bmod c) < c$.]

(page 203)

**The Seventy-First William Lowell Putnam
Mathematical Competition—December 4, 2010**

*Questions Committee: Bjorn Poonen (Chair),
Izabella Laba, and George T. Gilbert
See page 64 for hints.*

A1.

Given a positive integer n, what is the largest k such that the numbers $1, 2, \ldots, n$ can be put into k boxes so that the sum of the numbers in each box is the same? [When $n = 8$, the example $\{1, 2, 3, 6\}, \{4, 8\}, \{5, 7\}$ shows that the largest k is *at least* 3.]

(page 206)

A2.

Find all differentiable functions $f : \mathbb{R} \to \mathbb{R}$ such that

$$f'(x) = \frac{f(x+n) - f(x)}{n}$$

for all real numbers x and all positive integers n.

(page 206)

A3.

Suppose that the function $h : \mathbb{R}^2 \to \mathbb{R}$ has continuous partial derivatives and satisfies the equation

$$h(x, y) = a\frac{\partial h}{\partial x}(x, y) + b\frac{\partial h}{\partial y}(x, y)$$

for some constants a, b. Prove that if there is a constant M such that $|h(x, y)| \le M$ for all $(x, y) \in \mathbb{R}^2$, then h is identically zero.

(page 207)

A4.

Prove that for each positive integer n, the number $10^{10^{10^n}} + 10^{10^n} + 10^n - 1$ is not prime.

(page 207)

A5.

Let G be a group, with operation $*$. Suppose that

(i) G is a subset of $\mathbb{R}^3$ (but $*$ need not be related to addition of vectors);

(ii) For each $\mathbf{a}, \mathbf{b} \in G$, either $\mathbf{a} \times \mathbf{b} = \mathbf{a} * \mathbf{b}$ or $\mathbf{a} \times \mathbf{b} = \mathbf{0}$ (or both), where $\times$ is the usual cross product in $\mathbb{R}^3$.

Prove that $\mathbf{a} \times \mathbf{b} = \mathbf{0}$ for all $\mathbf{a}, \mathbf{b} \in G$.

(page 207)

A6.

Let $f : [0, \infty) \to \mathbb{R}$ be a strictly decreasing continuous function such that $\lim_{x \to \infty} f(x) = 0$. Prove that $\int_0^\infty \frac{f(x) - f(x+1)}{f(x)} \, dx$ diverges.   (page 208)

B1.

Is there an infinite sequence of real numbers $a_1, a_2, a_3, \ldots$ such that

$$a_1^m + a_2^m + a_3^m + \cdots = m$$

for every positive integer m?

(page 211)

B2.

Given that A, B, and C are noncollinear points in the plane with integer coordinates such that the distances AB, AC, and BC are integers, what is the smallest possible value of AB?

(page 213)

B3.

There are 2010 boxes labeled $B_1, B_2, \ldots, B_{2010}$, and $2010n$ balls have been distributed among them, for some positive integer n. You may redistribute the balls by a sequence of moves, each of which consists of choosing an i and moving *exactly* i balls from box B_i into any one other box. For which values of n is it possible to reach the distribution with exactly n balls in each box, regardless of the initial distribution of balls?

(page 214)

B4.

Find all pairs of polynomials $p(x)$ and $q(x)$ with real coefficients for which

$$p(x)q(x+1) - p(x+1)q(x) = 1.$$

(page 214)

B5.

Is there a strictly increasing function $f : \mathbb{R} \to \mathbb{R}$ such that $f'(x) = f(f(x))$ for all x?

(page 216)

B6.

Let A be an $n \times n$ matrix of real numbers for some $n \geq 1$. For each positive integer k, let $A^{[k]}$ be the matrix obtained by raising each entry to the kth power. Show that if $A^k = A^{[k]}$ for $k = 1, 2, \ldots, n + 1$, then $A^k = A^{[k]}$ for all $k \geq 1$.

(page 217)

The Seventy-Second William Lowell Putnam Mathematical Competition—December 3, 2011

Questions Committee: Izabella Laba (Chair),
George T. Gilbert, and Djordje Milićević
See page 65 for hints.

A1.

Define a *growing spiral* in the plane to be a sequence of points with integer coordinates $P_0 = (0,0), P_1, \ldots, P_n$ such that $n \geq 2$ and:

a.   the directed line segments $P_0P_1, P_1P_2, \ldots, P_{n-1}P_n$ are in the successive coordinate directions east (for P_0P_1), north, west, south, east, etc.;

b.   the lengths of these line segments are positive and strictly increasing.

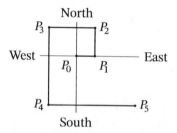

How many of the points (x,y) with integer coordinates $0 \leq x \leq 2011, 0 \leq y \leq 2011$ *cannot* be the last point, P_n of any growing spiral?

(page 219)

A2.

Let $a_1, a_2, \ldots$ and $b_1, b_2, \ldots$ be sequences of positive real numbers such that $a_1 = b_1 = 1$ and $b_n = b_{n-1}a_n - 2$ for $n = 2, 3, \ldots$. Assume that the sequence (b_j) is bounded. Prove that

$$S = \sum_{n=1}^{\infty} \frac{1}{a_1 \cdots a_n}$$

converges, and evaluate S.

(page 220)

A3.

Find a real number c and a positive number L for which

$$\lim_{r \to \infty} \frac{r^c \displaystyle\int_0^{\pi/2} x^r \sin x \, dx}{\displaystyle\int_0^{\pi/2} x^r \cos x \, dx} = L.$$

(page 221)

A4.

For which positive integers n is there an $n \times n$ matrix with integer entries such that every dot product of a row with itself is even, while every dot product of two different rows is odd?

(page 222)

A5.

Let $F : \mathbb{R}^2 \to \mathbb{R}$ and $g : \mathbb{R} \to \mathbb{R}$ be twice continuously differentiable functions with the following properties:

- $F(u, u) = 0$ for every $u \in \mathbb{R}$;

- for every $x \in \mathbb{R}$, $g(x) > 0$ and $x^2 g(x) \le 1$;

- for every $(u, v) \in \mathbb{R}^2$, the vector $\nabla F(u, v)$ is either $\mathbf{0}$ or parallel to the vector $\langle g(u), -g(v) \rangle$.

Prove that there exists a constant C such that for every $n \ge 2$ and any $x_1, \ldots, x_{n+1} \in \mathbb{R}$, we have

$$\min_{i \ne j} |F(x_i, x_j)| \le \frac{C}{n}.$$

(page 222)

A6.

Let G be an abelian group with n elements, and let

$$\{g_1 = e, g_2, \ldots, g_k\} \subsetneqq G$$

be a (not necessarily minimal) set of distinct generators of G. A special die, which randomly selects one of the elements $g_1, g_2, \ldots, g_k$ with equal probability, is rolled m times, and the selected elements are multiplied to produce an element $g \in G$. Prove that there exists a real number $b \in (0, 1)$ such that

$$\lim_{m \to \infty} \frac{1}{b^{2m}} \sum_{x \in G} \left(\text{Prob}(g = x) - \frac{1}{n} \right)^2$$

is positive and finite.

(page 223)

B1.

Let h and k be positive integers. Prove that for every $\epsilon > 0$, there are positive integers m and n such that

$$\epsilon < |h\sqrt{m} - k\sqrt{n}| < 2\epsilon.$$

(page 225)

B2.

Let S be the set of all ordered triples (p, q, r) of prime numbers for which at least one rational number x satisfies $px^2 + qx + r = 0$. Which primes appear in seven or more elements of S?

(page 226)

B3.

Let f and g be (real-valued) functions defined on an open interval containing 0, with g nonzero and continuous at 0. If fg and f/g are differentiable at 0, must f be differentiable at 0?

(page 227)

B4.

In a tournament, 2011 players meet 2011 times to play a multiplayer game. Every game is played by all 2011 players together and ends with each of the players either winning or losing. The standings are kept in two 2011×2011 matrices, $T = (T_{hk})$ and $W = (W_{hk})$. Initially, $T = W = 0$. After every game, for every (h, k) (including for $h = k$), if players h and k tied (that is, both won or both lost), the entry T_{hk} is increased by 1, while if player h won and player k lost, the entry W_{hk} is increased by 1 and W_{kh} is decreased by 1.

Prove that at the end of the tournament, $\det(T + iW)$ is a nonnegative integer divisible by 2^{2010}.

(page 228)

B5.

Let $a_1, a_2, \ldots$ be real numbers. Suppose that there is a constant A such that for all n,

$$\int_{-\infty}^{\infty} \left(\sum_{i=1}^{n} \frac{1}{1 + (x - a_i)^2} \right)^2 dx \leq An.$$

Prove there is a constant $B > 0$ such that for all n,

$$\sum_{i,j=1}^{n} (1 + (a_i - a_j)^2) \geq Bn^3.$$

(page 228)

B6.

Let p be an odd prime. Show that for at least $(p+1)/2$ values of n in $\{0, 1, 2, \ldots, p-1\}$,

$$\sum_{k=0}^{p-1} k!\, n^k \qquad \text{is not divisible by } p.$$

(page 230)

The Seventy-Third William Lowell Putnam Mathematical Competition—December 1, 2012

Questions Committee: George T. Gilbert (Chair), Djordje Milićević, and Hugh Montgomery
See page 66 for hints.

A1.

Let $d_1, d_2, \ldots, d_{12}$ be real numbers in the open interval $(1, 12)$. Show that there exist distinct indices i, j, k such that d_i, d_j, d_k are the side lengths of an acute triangle.

(page 232)

A2.

Let $*$ be a commutative and associative binary operation on a set S. Assume that for every x and y in S, there exists z in S such that $x * z = y$. (This z may depend on x and y.) Show that if a, b, c are in S and $a * c = b * c$, then $a = b$.

(page 232)

A3.

Let $f : [-1, 1] \to \mathbb{R}$ be a continuous function such that

(i) $f(x) = \frac{2-x^2}{2} f\left(\frac{x^2}{2-x^2}\right)$ for every x in $[-1, 1]$,

(ii) $f(0) = 1$, and

(iii) $\lim_{x \to 1-} \frac{f(x)}{\sqrt{1-x}}$ exists and is finite.

Prove that f is unique, and express $f(x)$ in closed form.

(page 232)

A4.

Let q and r be integers with $q > 0$, and let A and B be intervals on the real line. Let T be the set of all $b + mq$ where b and m are integers with b in B, and let S be the set of all integers a in A such that ra is in T. Show that if the product of the lengths of A and B is less than q, then S is the intersection of A with some arithmetic progression.

(page 234)

A5.

Let $\mathbb{F}_p$ denote the field of integers modulo a prime p, and let n be a positive integer. Let v be a fixed vector in $\mathbb{F}_p^n$, let M be an $n \times n$ matrix with entries in $\mathbb{F}_p$, and define $G : \mathbb{F}_p^n \to \mathbb{F}_p^n$ by $G(x) = v + Mx$. Let $G^{(k)}$ denote the k-fold composition of G with itself, that is, $G^{(1)}(x) = G(x)$ and $G^{(k+1)}(x) = G(G^{(k)}(x))$.

Determine all pairs p, n for which there exist v and M such that the p^n vectors $G^{(k)}(0), k = 1, 2, \ldots, p^n$ are distinct.

(page 236)

A6.

Let $f(x, y)$ be a continuous, real-valued function on $\mathbb{R}^2$. Suppose that, for every rectangular region R of area 1, the double integral of $f(x, y)$ over R equals 0. Must $f(x, y)$ be identically 0?

(page 237)

B1.

Let S be a class of functions from $[0, \infty)$ to $[0, \infty)$ that satisfies:

(i) The functions $f_1(x) = e^x - 1$ and $f_2(x) = \ln(x + 1)$ are in S;

(ii) If $f(x)$ and $g(x)$ are in S, the functions $f(x) + g(x)$ and $f(g(x))$ are in S;

(iii) If $f(x)$ and $g(x)$ are in S and $f(x) \geq g(x)$ for all $x \geq 0$, then the function $f(x) - g(x)$ is in S.

Prove that if $f(x)$ and $g(x)$ are in S, then the function $f(x)g(x)$ is also in S.

(page 239)

B2.

Let P be a given (nondegenerate) polyhedron. Prove that there is a constant $c(P) > 0$ with the following property: If a collection of n balls whose volumes sum to V contains the entire surface of P, then $n > c(P)/V^2$.

(page 240)

B3.

A round-robin tournament among $2n$ teams lasted for $2n-1$ days, as follows. On each day, every team played one game against another team, with one team winning and one team losing in each of the n games. Over the course of the tournament, each team played every other team exactly once. Can one necessarily choose one winning team from each day without choosing any team more than once?

(page 240)

B4.

Suppose that $a_0 = 1$ and that $a_{n+1} = a_n + e^{-a_n}$ for $n = 0, 1, 2, \ldots$. Does $a_n - \log n$ have a finite limit as $n \to \infty$? (Here $\log n = \log_e n = \ln n$.)

(page 241)

B5.

Prove that, for any two bounded functions $g_1, g_2 : \mathbb{R} \to [1, \infty)$, there exist functions $h_1, h_2 : \mathbb{R} \to \mathbb{R}$ such that, for every $x \in \mathbb{R}$,

$$\sup_{s \in \mathbb{R}} (g_1(s)^x g_2(s)) = \max_{t \in \mathbb{R}} (x h_1(t) + h_2(t)).$$

(page 242)

B6.

Let p be an odd prime number such that $p \equiv 2 \pmod 3$. Define a permutation π of the residue classes modulo p by $\pi(x) \equiv x^3 \pmod p$. Show that π is an even permutation if and only if $p \equiv 3 \pmod 4$. (page 243)

The Seventy-Fourth William Lowell Putnam Mathematical Competition—December 7, 2013

Questions Committee: Djordje Milićević (Chair),
Hugh Montgomery, and David Savitt
See page 67 for hints.

A1.

Recall that a regular icosahedron is a convex polyhedron having 12 vertices and 20 faces; the faces are congruent equilateral triangles. On each face of a regular icosahedron is written a nonnegative integer such that the sum of all 20 integers is 39. Show that there are two faces that share a vertex and have the same integer written on them.

(page 246)

A2.

Let S be the set of all positive integers that are *not* perfect squares. For n in S, consider choices of integers $a_1, a_2, \ldots, a_r$ such that $n < a_1 < a_2 < \cdots < a_r$ and $n \cdot a_1 \cdot a_2 \cdots a_r$ is a perfect square, and let $f(n)$ be the minimum of a_r over all such choices. For example, $2 \cdot 3 \cdot 6$ is a perfect square, while $2 \cdot 3, 2 \cdot 4, 2 \cdot 5$, $2 \cdot 3 \cdot 4, 2 \cdot 3 \cdot 5, 2 \cdot 4 \cdot 5$, and $2 \cdot 3 \cdot 4 \cdot 5$ are not, and so $f(2) = 6$. Show that the function f from S to the integers is one-to-one.

(page 246)

A3.

Suppose that the real numbers $a_0, a_1, \ldots, a_n$ and x, with $0 < x < 1$, satisfy

$$\frac{a_0}{1-x} + \frac{a_1}{1-x^2} + \cdots + \frac{a_n}{1-x^{n+1}} = 0.$$

Prove that there exists a real number y with $0 < y < 1$ such that

$$a_0 + a_1 y + \cdots + a_n y^n = 0.$$

(page 247)

A4.

A finite collection of digits 0 and 1 is written around a circle. An *arc* of length $L \geq 0$ consists of L consecutive digits around the circle. For each arc w, let $Z(w)$ and $N(w)$ denote the number of 0's in w and the number of 1's in w, respectively. Assume that $|Z(w) - Z(w')| \leq 1$ for any two arcs w, w' of the same length. Suppose that some arcs $w_1, \ldots, w_k$ have the property that

$$Z = \frac{1}{k}\sum_{j=1}^{k} Z(w_j) \text{ and } N = \frac{1}{k}\sum_{j=1}^{k} N(w_j)$$

are both integers. Prove that there exists an arc w with $Z(w) = Z$ and $N(w) = N$.

(page 247)

A5.

For $m \geq 3$, a list of $\binom{m}{3}$ real numbers a_{ijk} ($1 \leq i < j < k \leq m$) is said to be *area definite* for $\mathbb{R}^n$ if the inequality

$$\sum_{1 \leq i < j < k \leq m} a_{ijk} \cdot \text{Area}(\triangle A_i A_j A_k) \geq 0$$

holds for every choice of m points $A_1, \ldots, A_m$ in $\mathbb{R}^n$. For example, the list of four numbers $a_{123} = a_{124} = a_{134} = 1$, $a_{234} = -1$ is area definite for $\mathbb{R}^2$. Prove that if a list of $\binom{m}{3}$ numbers is area definite for $\mathbb{R}^2$, then it is area definite for $\mathbb{R}^3$.

(page 249)

A6.

Define a function $w : \mathbb{Z} \times \mathbb{Z} \to \mathbb{Z}$ as follows. For $|a|, |b| \leq 2$, let $w(a, b)$ be as in the table shown; otherwise, let $w(a, b) = 0$.

$w(a,b)$		b			
		-2	-1	0	1	2
	-2	-1	-2	2	-2	-1
	-1	-2	4	-4	4	-2
a	0	2	-4	12	-4	2
	1	-2	4	-4	4	-2
	2	-1	-2	2	-2	-1

For every finite subset S of $\mathbb{Z} \times \mathbb{Z}$, define

$$A(S) = \sum_{(\mathbf{s}, \mathbf{s}') \in S \times S} w(\mathbf{s} - \mathbf{s}').$$

Prove that if S is any finite nonempty subset of $\mathbb{Z} \times \mathbb{Z}$, then $A(S) > 0$. (For example, if $S = \{(0, 1), (0, 2), (2, 0), (3, 1)\}$, then the terms in $A(S)$ are $12, 12, 12, 12, 4, 4, 0, 0, 0, 0, -1, -1, -2, -2, -4, -4$.)

(page 250)

B1.

For positive integers n, let the numbers $c(n)$ be determined by the rules $c(1) = 1$, $c(2n) = c(n)$, and $c(2n + 1) = (-1)^n c(n)$. Find the value of

$$\sum_{n=1}^{2013} c(n) c(n + 2).$$

(page 251)

B2.

Let $\mathcal{C} = \bigcup_{N=1}^{\infty} \mathcal{C}_N$, where $\mathcal{C}_N$ denotes the set of those 'cosine polynomials' of the form

$$f(x) = 1 + \sum_{n=1}^{N} a_n \cos(2\pi n x)$$

for which:

(i) $f(x) \geq 0$ for all real x, and

(ii) $a_n = 0$ whenever n is a multiple of 3.

Determine the maximum value of $f(0)$ as f ranges through $\mathcal{C}$, and prove that this maximum is attained.

(page 252)

B3.

Let $\mathcal{P}$ be a nonempty collection of subsets of $\{1, \ldots, n\}$ such that:

(i) if $S, S' \in \mathcal{P}$, then $S \cup S' \in \mathcal{P}$ and $S \cap S' \in \mathcal{P}$, and

(ii) if $S \in \mathcal{P}$ and $S \neq \emptyset$, then there is a subset $T \subset S$ such that $T \in \mathcal{P}$ and T contains exactly one fewer element than S.

Suppose that $f : \mathcal{P} \to \mathbb{R}$ is a function such that $f(\emptyset) = 0$ and

$$f(S \cup S') = f(S) + f(S') - f(S \cap S') \text{ for all } S, S' \in \mathcal{P}.$$

Must there exist real numbers $f_1, \ldots, f_n$ such that

$$f(S) = \sum_{i \in S} f_i$$

for every $S \in \mathcal{P}$?

(page 252)

B4.

For any continuous real-valued function f defined on the interval $[0, 1]$, let

$$\mu(f) = \int_0^1 f(x)\,dx,$$

$$\mathrm{Var}(f) = \int_0^1 \left(f(x) - \mu(f)\right)^2 dx,$$

$$M(f) = \max_{0 \leq x \leq 1} |f(x)|.$$

Show that if f and g are continuous real-valued functions defined on the interval $[0, 1]$, then

$$\mathrm{Var}(fg) \leq 2\mathrm{Var}(f)M(g)^2 + 2\mathrm{Var}(g)M(f)^2.$$

(page 254)

B5.

Let $X = \{1, 2, \ldots, n\}$, and let $k \in X$. Show that there are exactly $k \cdot n^{n-1}$ functions $f : X \to X$ such that for every $x \in X$ there is a $j \geq 0$ such that $f^{(j)}(x) \leq k$. [Here $f^{(j)}$ denotes the jth iterate of f, so that $f^{(0)}(x) = x$ and $f^{(j+1)}(x) = f(f^{(j)}(x))$.]

(page 255)

B6.

Let $n \geq 1$ be an odd integer. Alice and Bob play the following game, taking alternating turns, with Alice playing first. The playing area consists of n spaces, arranged in a line. Initially all spaces are empty. At each turn, a player either

- places a stone in an empty space, or

- removes a stone from a nonempty space s, places a stone in the nearest empty space to the left of s (if such a space exists), and places a stone in the nearest empty space to the right of s (if such a space exists).

Furthermore, a move is permitted only if the resulting position has not occurred previously in the game. A player loses if he or she is unable to move. Assuming that both players play optimally throughout the game, what moves may Alice make on her first turn?

(page 257)

The Seventy-Fifth William Lowell Putnam
Mathematical Competition—December 6, 2014

Questions Committee: Hugh Montgomery (Chair),
Henry Cohn, and David Savitt
See page 68 for hints.

A1.

Prove that every nonzero coefficient of the Taylor series of

$$(1 - x + x^2)e^x$$

about $x = 0$ is a rational number whose numerator (in lowest terms) is either 1 or a prime number.

(page 260)

A2.

Let A be the $n \times n$ matrix whose entry in the ith row and jth column is

$$\frac{1}{\min(i, j)}$$

for $1 \le i, j \le n$. Compute $\det(A)$.

(page 260)

A3.

Let $a_0 = 5/2$ and $a_k = a_{k-1}^2 - 2$ for $k \ge 1$. Compute

$$\prod_{k=0}^{\infty} \left(1 - \frac{1}{a_k}\right)$$

in closed form.

(page 262)

A4.

Suppose X is a random variable that takes on only nonnegative integer values, with $E[X] = 1$, $E[X^2] = 2$, and $E[X^3] = 5$. (Here $E[Y]$ denotes the expectation of the random variable Y.) Determine the smallest possible value of the probability of the event $X = 0$.

(page 263)

A5.

Let

$$P_n(x) = 1 + 2x + 3x^2 + \cdots + nx^{n-1}.$$

Prove that the polynomials $P_j(x)$ and $P_k(x)$ are relatively prime for all positive integers j and k with $j \ne k$.

(page 264)

A6.

Let n be a positive integer. What is the largest k for which there exist $n \times n$ matrices $M_1, \ldots, M_k$ and $N_1, \ldots, N_k$ with real entries such that for all i and j, the matrix product $M_i N_j$ has a zero entry somewhere on its diagonal if and only if $i \neq j$?

(page 267)

B1.

A *base*-10 *over-expansion* of a positive integer N is an expression of the form

$$N = d_k 10^k + d_{k-1} 10^{k-1} + \cdots + d_0 10^0$$

with $d_k \neq 0$ and $d_i \in \{0, 1, 2, \ldots, 10\}$ for all i. For instance, the integer $N = 10$ has two base-10 over-expansions: $10 = 10 \cdot 10^0$ and the usual base-10 expansion $10 = 1 \cdot 10^1 + 0 \cdot 10^0$. Which positive integers have a unique base-10 over-expansion?

(page 268)

B2.

Suppose that f is a function on the interval $[1, 3]$ such that $-1 \leq f(x) \leq 1$ for all x and $\int_1^3 f(x) \, dx = 0$. How large can $\int_1^3 \frac{f(x)}{x} \, dx$ be?

(page 268)

B3.

Let A be an $m \times n$ matrix with rational entries. Suppose that there are at least $m + n$ distinct prime numbers among the absolute values of the entries of A. Show that the rank of A is at least 2.

(page 269)

B4.

Show that for each positive integer n, all the roots of the polynomial

$$\sum_{k=0}^{n} 2^{k(n-k)} x^k$$

are real numbers.

(page 271)

B5.

In the 75th annual Putnam Games, participants compete at mathematical games. Patniss and Keeta play a game in which they take turns choosing an element from the group of invertible $n \times n$ matrices with entries in the field $\mathbb{Z}/p\mathbb{Z}$ of integers modulo p, where n is a fixed positive integer and p is a fixed prime number. The rules of the game are:

(1) A player cannot choose an element that has been chosen by either player on any previous turn.

(2) A player can only choose an element that commutes with all previously chosen elements.

(3) A player who cannot choose an element on his/her turn loses the game.

Patniss takes the first turn. Which player has a winning strategy? (Your answer may depend on n and p.)   (page 272)

B6.

Let $f : [0,1] \to \mathbb{R}$ be a function for which there exists a constant $K > 0$ such that $|f(x) - f(y)| \leq K|x - y|$ for all $x, y \in [0,1]$. Suppose also that for each rational number $r \in [0,1]$, there exist integers a and b such that $f(r) = a + br$. Prove that there exist finitely many intervals $I_1, \ldots, I_n$ such that f is a linear function on each I_i and $[0,1] = \bigcup_{i=1}^{n} I_i$.

(page 274)

The Seventy-Sixth William Lowell Putnam
Mathematical Competition—December 5, 2015

Questions Committee: David Savitt (Chair),
Henry Cohn, and Byron Walden
See page 69 for hints.

A1.

Let A and B be points on the same branch of the hyperbola $xy = 1$. Suppose that P is a point lying between A and B on this hyperbola, such that the area of the triangle APB is as large as possible. Show that the region bounded by the hyperbola and the chord AP has the same area as the region bounded by the hyperbola and the chord PB.

(page 276)

A2.

Let $a_0 = 1$, $a_1 = 2$, and $a_n = 4a_{n-1} - a_{n-2}$ for $n \geq 2$. Find an odd prime factor of a_{2015}.

(page 277)

A3.

Compute

$$\log_2 \left(\prod_{a=1}^{2015} \prod_{b=1}^{2015} (1 + e^{2\pi i ab/2015}) \right)$$

Here i is the imaginary unit (that is, $i^2 = -1$).

(page 278)

A4.

For each real number x, let

$$f(x) = \sum_{n \in S_x} \frac{1}{2^n},$$

where S_x is the set of positive integers n for which $\lfloor nx \rfloor$ is even. What is the largest real number L such that $f(x) \geq L$ for all $x \in [0, 1)$? (As usual, $\lfloor z \rfloor$ denotes the greatest integer less than or equal to z.)

(page 279)

A5.

Let q be an odd positive integer, and let N_q denote the number of integers a such that $0 < a < q/4$ and $\gcd(a, q) = 1$. Show that N_q is odd if and only if q is of the form p^k with k a positive integer and p a prime congruent to 5 or 7 modulo 8.

(page 280)

A6.

Let n be a positive integer. Suppose that A, B, and M are $n \times n$ matrices with real entries such that $AM = MB$, and such that A and B have the same characteristic polynomial. Prove that $\det(A - MX) = \det(B - XM)$ for every $n \times n$ matrix X with real entries.

(page 282)

B1.

Let f be a three times differentiable function (defined on $\mathbb{R}$ and real-valued) such that f has at least five distinct real zeros. Prove that $f + 6f' + 12f'' + 8f'''$ has at least two distinct real zeros.

(page 285)

B2.

Given a list of the positive integers $1, 2, 3, 4, \ldots$, take the first three numbers $1, 2, 3$ and their sum 6 and cross all four numbers off the list. Repeat with the three smallest remaining numbers $4, 5, 7$ and their sum 16. Continue in this way, crossing off the three smallest remaining numbers and their sum, and consider the sequence of sums produced: $6, 16, 27, 36, \ldots$. Prove or disprove that there is some number in the sequence whose base-10 representation ends with 2015.

(page 285)

B3.

Let S be the set of all 2×2 real matrices

$$M = \begin{pmatrix} a & b \\ c & d \end{pmatrix}$$

whose entries a, b, c, d (in that order) form an arithmetic progression. Find all matrices M in S for which there is some integer $k > 1$ such that M^k is also in S.

(page 287)

B4.

Let T be the set of all triples (a, b, c) of positive integers for which there exist triangles with side lengths a, b, c. Express

$$\sum_{(a,b,c) \in T} \frac{2^a}{3^b 5^c}$$

as a rational number in lowest terms.

(page 288)

B5.

Let P_n be the number of permutations π of $\{1, 2, \ldots, n\}$ such that

$$|i - j| = 1 \text{ implies } |\pi(i) - \pi(j)| \leq 2$$

for all i, j in $\{1, 2, \ldots, n\}$. Show that for $n \geq 2$, the quantity

$$P_{n+5} - P_{n+4} - P_{n+3} + P_n$$

does not depend on n, and find its value.

(page 290)

B6.

For each positive integer k, let $A(k)$ be the number of odd divisors of k in the interval $[1, \sqrt{2k})$. Evaluate

$$\sum_{k=1}^{\infty} (-1)^{k-1} \frac{A(k)}{k}.$$

(page 292)

The Seventy-Seventh William Lowell Putnam Mathematical Competition—December 3, 2016

Questions Committee: Henry Cohn (Chair),
Byron Walden, and Harm Derksen
See page 70 for hints.

A1.

Find the smallest positive integer j such that for every polynomial $p(x)$ with integer coefficients and for every integer k, the integer

$$p^{(j)}(k) = \frac{d^j}{dx^j} p(x)\Big|_{x=k}$$

(the jth derivative of $p(x)$ at k) is divisible by 2016.

(page 295)

A2.

Given a positive integer n, let $M(n)$ be the largest integer m such that

$$\binom{m}{n-1} > \binom{m-1}{n}.$$

Evaluate

$$\lim_{n\to\infty} \frac{M(n)}{n}.$$

(page 295)

A3.

Suppose that f is a function from $\mathbb{R}$ to $\mathbb{R}$ such that

$$f(x) + f\left(1 - \frac{1}{x}\right) = \arctan x$$

for all real $x \neq 0$. (As usual, $y = \arctan x$ means $-\pi/2 < y < \pi/2$ and $\tan y = x$.) Find

$$\int_0^1 f(x)\,dx.$$

(page 296)

A4.

Consider a $(2m-1)\times(2n-1)$ rectangular region, where m and n are integers such that $m, n \geq 4$. This region is to be tiled using tiles of the two types shown:

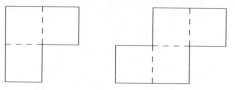

(The dotted lines divide the tiles into 1×1 squares.) The tiles may be rotated and reflected, as long as their sides are parallel to the sides of the rectangular region. They must all fit within the region, and they must cover it completely without overlapping.

What is the minimum number of tiles required to tile the region?

(page 297)

A5.

Suppose that G is a finite group generated by the two elements g and h, where the order of g is odd. Show that every element of G can be written in the form

$$g^{m_1} h^{n_1} g^{m_2} h^{n_2} \cdots g^{m_r} h^{n_r}$$

with $1 \leq r \leq |G|$ and $m_1, n_1, m_2, n_2, \ldots, m_r, n_r \in \{-1, 1\}$. (Here $|G|$ is the number of elements of G.)

(page 299)

A6.

Find the smallest constant C such that for every real polynomial $P(x)$ of degree 3 that has a root in the interval $[0, 1]$,

$$\int_0^1 |P(x)| \, dx \leq C \max_{x \in [0,1]} |P(x)|.$$

(page 301)

B1.

Let $x_0, x_1, x_2, \ldots$ be the sequence such that $x_0 = 1$ and for $n \geq 0$,

$$x_{n+1} = \ln(e^{x_n} - x_n)$$

(as usual, the function ln is the natural logarithm). Show that the infinite series

$$x_0 + x_1 + x_2 + \cdots$$

converges and find its sum.

(page 302)

B2.

Define a positive integer n to be *squarish* if either n is itself a perfect square or the distance from n to the nearest perfect square is a perfect square. For example, 2016 is squarish, because the nearest perfect square to 2016 is $45^2 = 2025$ and $2025 - 2016 = 9$ is a perfect square. (Of the positive integers between 1 and 10, only 6 and 7 are not squarish.)

For a positive integer N, let $S(N)$ be the number of squarish integers between 1 and N, inclusive. Find positive constants α and β such that

$$\lim_{N \to \infty} \frac{S(N)}{N^{\alpha}} = \beta,$$

or show that no such constants exist.

(page 303)

B3.

Suppose that S is a finite set of points in the plane such that the area of triangle $\triangle ABC$ is at most 1 whenever A, B, and C are in S. Show that there exists a triangle of area 4 that (together with its interior) covers the set S.

(page 304)

B4.

Let A be a $2n \times 2n$ matrix, with entries chosen independently at random. Every entry is chosen to be 0 or 1, each with probability 1/2. Find the expected value of $\det(A - A^t)$ (as a function of n), where A^t is the transpose of A.

(page 305)

B5.

Find all functions f from the interval $(1, \infty)$ to $(1, \infty)$ with the following property: if $x, y \in (1, \infty)$ and $x^2 \le y \le x^3$, then $f(x)^2 \le f(y) \le f(x)^3$.

(page 307)

B6.

Evaluate

$$\sum_{k=1}^{\infty} \frac{(-1)^{k-1}}{k} \sum_{n=0}^{\infty} \frac{1}{k2^n + 1}.$$

(page 308)

Hints

The Sixty-Second William Lowell Putnam
Mathematical Competition—December 1, 2001

A1. In $(a * b) * a = b$, replace a with various expressions involving the $*$ operation.

A2. Find a recursive relation for P_n, the desired probability for n coins.

A3. Find the roots of $P_m(x)$ and think about how one or two of these roots could be the roots of a divisor of $P_m(x)$.

A4. Create variables for EC/BC, FA/CA, GB/AB and relate them by computing areas of relevant triangles.

A5. Note that $2001 = a^{n+1} - (a + 1)^n \equiv -1 \pmod{a}$. Possible values of a, n can be cut down by similar tricks.

A6. Consider a skinny parabola with vertex on the boundary of the disc and axis of symmetry along its diameter.

B1. Decompose the number on each square into a portion that is constant within each row and a portion that is constant within each column.

B2. Start by considering the sum and the difference of the two given equations.

B3. Group terms based on their value of $\langle n \rangle$.

B4. Let $H(p/q) = |p| + |q|$, where $\gcd(p, q) = 1$. Show that $H(f(x)) > H(x)$ for all x.

B5. *Hint 1 of 2.* Prove that g is bijective.   *Hint 2 of 2.* For $x_0 \in \mathbb{R}$ and $n \in \mathbb{Z}$, find a formula for the nth iterate $x_n = g^{(n)}(x_0)$.

B6. Find the value of n for which $a_n - cn$ is maximal for some $c > 0$.

The Sixty-Third William Lowell Putnam
Mathematical Competition—December 7, 2002

A1. Find P_n recursively.

A2. Draw a great circle through two of the five given points.

A3. Consider the number of subsets with average equal to k for each $1 \le k \le n$.

A4. Try to complete a row/column or 2×2 square of 0's as Player 0.

A5. Prove by induction that if p and q are relatively prime positive integers, then there exists an n so that $a_n = p$ and $a_{n+1} = q$.

A6. Group terms in the sum based on their value of d. Then relate back to the original sum.

B1. Find the probability that she makes k of her first $n > k$ shots inductively.

B2. Show that the polyhedron must have a face with at least four sides. Then show that, if the first player chooses a face with at least four sides on the first move, the first player can win on their third move.

B3. Take logarithms and compare the Taylor series.

B4. Construct a sequence of guesses where each guess is close to the smallest remaining possibility.

B5. Produce many representations as $([d^2][2d^2][d^2])_b$ or as $(1x1)_b$.

B6. Compare the determinant (as a polynomial in x, y, z) with a product of known linear factors.

The Sixty-Fourth William Lowell Putnam
Mathematical Competition—December 6, 2003

A1. Count the ways with k summands, for a fixed $k \le n$.

A2. Divide both sides of the inequality by the right side. Then apply the arithmetic mean/geometric mean inequality to both terms on the left side.

A3. Write the expression as a function of $\sin(x) + \cos(x)$.

A4. Split into cases based on which of the polynomials have real roots.

A5. Given a Dyck $(n-1)$-path, turn it into a Dyck n-path, making the last even-length return one longer and getting rid of the returns before it.

A6. There is only one such partition. Guess the pattern by working it out explicitly for small integers.

B1. Fix various values of y to obtain three linearly independent polynomials in x.

B2. Calculate the value of x_n explicitly.

B3. Count the exponent to which each prime p divides each side of the equation.

B4. Write $b/a, c/a, d/a$ as polynomials in $r_1 + r_2, r_1 \cdot r_2, r_3 + r_4, r_3 \cdot r_4$.

B5. Rotate the segments $\overline{PA}$, $\overline{PB}$, and $\overline{PC}$ by 0, 120, and 240 degrees before reassembling.

B6. Split $[0, 1]$ into the sets where $f(x) \ge 0$ and where $f(x) \le 0$. Then consider the size of the integral over each set.

The Sixty-Fifth William Lowell Putnam Mathematical Competition—December 4, 2004

A1. Determine what $\frac{S(N)}{N} < \frac{4}{5}$ and $\frac{S(N)+1}{N+1} > \frac{4}{5}$ say about the value of $5S(N)$.

A2. *Hint 1 of 2.* Use the fact that a triangle with side lengths x and y and included angle θ has area $\frac{1}{2}xy\sin\theta$.

    Hint 2 of 2. Show that the triangles T_1 and T_2 have a pair of corresponding angles θ_1 and θ_2 with $\sin(\theta_1) \le \sin(\theta_2)$.

A3. Show that u_n equals $(n-1)(n-3)(n-5)\cdots 2$ or $(n-1)(n-3)(n-5)\cdots 1$ depending on whether n is even or odd.

A4. Arrange things so that the right-hand side is an odd function of x_i for each i.

A5. Think of the squares as initially separated and gluing adjacent squares of the same color together to form monochromatic regions. What is the expected number of gluings?

A6. Relate the difference of the two sides to $\int F(x,y,z,w)^2\,dx\,dy\,dz\,dw$ where $F(x,y,z,w)$ is some linear combination of values of f. This might be easier to do for a discrete analogue of the original question.

B1. Write
$$c_n r^{n-k} + c_{n-1}r^{n-k-1} + \cdots + c_{k+1}r = -(c_k + c_{k-1}r^{-1} + \cdots + c_0 r^{-k})$$
where r is represented as p/q in lowest terms.

B2. Apply the binomial theorem to $(m+n)^{m+n}$.

B3. What is the biggest possible ratio of area to perimeter of R as a function of a?

B4. Put the points in the complex plane. Write R_k as a linear function on $\mathbb{C}$ using $\zeta = e^{2\pi i/n}$.

B5. Use logarithms to convert the product into a sum, then approximate each term in the sum with something easier to work with.

B6. Assuming that $\lim_{x\to\infty} N(x)/x \ne 0$, find a maximal set of disjoint translates of $\mathcal{A}$.

The Sixty-Sixth William Lowell Putnam
Mathematical Competition—December 3, 2005

A1. Use strong induction, handling even and odd cases separately.

A2. Show that the set of rook tours can be put in a one-to-one correspondence with the subsets of $\{1, 2, 3, \ldots, n\}$ that contain n and have an even number of elements.

A3. Write $p(z)$ as a product of linear factors and find an expression for $g'(z)/g(z)$.

A4. *Hint 1 of 2.* Consider the sum of the rows containing the given submatrix.
   Hint 2 of 2. Show the dot product of this sum with itself is both equal to *an* and is at least $a^2 b$.

A5. Consider $f(t) = \int_0^1 \frac{\ln(xt+1)}{1+x^2} dx$. Find $f'(t)$.

A6. Look at the probability that the angle at any given P_i is acute but that the angle counterclockwise of it is not.

B1. Note that either $\lfloor 2a \rfloor = 2\lfloor a \rfloor$ or $\lfloor 2a \rfloor = 2\lfloor a \rfloor + 1$.

B2. Apply the Cauchy-Schwarz inequality to the sequences $k_1, k_2, \ldots, k_n$ and $1/k_1, 1/k_2, \ldots, 1/k_n$ to bound n. Then analyze each option for n separately.

B3. Find a differential equation satisfied by $g(y) = \log(f(e^y))$.

B4. Count the number of such expressions with exactly k nonzero x_i.

B5. Reduce to the case where P is homogeneous and divisible by $x_1^2 + x_2^2 + \cdots + x_n^2$ exactly m times.

B6. For any $S \subset \{1, 2, 3, \ldots, n\}$ with $|S| < n - 1$, the sum of $\sigma(\pi)$ over all permutations π fixing S is 0. Use the inclusion/exclusion principle to write the desired sum as a linear combination of such sums over various sets S.

The Sixty-Seventh William Lowell Putnam Mathematical Competition—December 2, 2006

A1. Switch to cylindrical coordinates.

A2. Assuming that the set of n for which Bob has a winning strategy has a maximum value M, show that Alice cannot have a winning strategy for every $n > M$.

A3. Prove that $\{x_n\}$ is periodic modulo 2006.

A4. What is the probability that a random π has a local maximum at some particular k?

A5. Find the polynomial whose roots are the a_i.

A6. Find the expected area of ABC. Then relate this to the areas of AOB, BOC, COA.

B1. Factor the polynomial $x^3 + 3xy + y^3 - 1 = 0$.

B2. *Hint 1 of 2.* Sort the sums $s_i = x_1 + x_2 + x_3 + \cdots + x_i$ into increasing order by their fractional parts $\{s\} = s - \lfloor s \rfloor$.

Hint 2 of 2. Show that either the difference between two of these fractional parts, or the difference between 1 and the greatest of the fractional parts, must be less than or equal to $1/(n+1)$.

B3. Consider how the number of linear partitions of S increases as the number of points in S increases by 1.

B4. Write the defining equations of V in row-reduced form.

B5. Consider the inner product $\langle f, g \rangle = \int_0^1 x f(x) g(x) dx$.

B6. Use the Taylor series for $(1+x)^m$ to approximate $a_{n+1}^{(k+1)/k} - a_n^{(k+1)/k}$.

The Sixty-Eighth William Lowell Putnam
Mathematical Competition—December 1, 2007

A1. The two cases are when the two curves are both tangent to the line $x = y$, and when they are both perpendicular to the line $x = y$.

A2. Calculate the area of a quadrilateral with one vertex on each branch of the hyperbolas directly. Then bound it from below using the arithmetic mean/geometric mean inequality.

A3. What are the possiblities for the order of the numbers modulo 3?

A4. Consider polynomials $t(n)$ that give a power of 10 for each n that is a repunit, and then polynomials $r(n)$ that give a repunit for each n that is a power of 10.

A5. Consider the set of p-tuples of elements whose product is the identity. Count the number of elements in this set in two different ways.

A6. Use Euler's formula to prove that the average degree of a boundary vertex is small. Then use this to reduce to the case of a smaller polygon.

B1. Find the remainder when $f(f(n) + 1)$ is divided by $f(n)$.

B2. Show that one can assume that the maximum of the integral occurs at $\alpha \in [0, 1/2]$. Then use the maximum value of $|f'(x)|$ to bound $|f(x)|$ by a linear function.

B3. Find a recurrence relation that x_n satisfies.

B4. Factor $P^2 + Q^2$ over the complex numbers.

B5. For any n, there are only k possible values of $n - \left\lfloor \frac{n}{k} \right\rfloor$. Use this to find a degree-k polynomial in $\left\lfloor \frac{n}{k} \right\rfloor$ and n that vanishes for every n.

B6. Count the number of sequences $a_2, a_3, \ldots, a_n$ where a_k is a nonnegative integer bounded by either $n!/k!$ or $(n-1)!/k!$.

The Sixty-Ninth William Lowell Putnam
Mathematical Competition—December 6, 2008

A1. Fix a value of y in $f(x,y)$.

A2. Show that Barbara can construct a singular matrix.

A3. Consider what this process does to the number of times p divides each of the a_i.

A4. Replace the sum by an integral and compare $\int_a^b \frac{dx}{f(x)}$ to $\int_{ea}^{eb} \frac{dx}{f(x)}$.

A5. Consider the polynomial $h(x) = f(x) + ig(x)$.

A6. For a sequence $a_1, a_2, \ldots, a_k$ count the number of possible subsequence products. Show that if this number is small, one can add a single element to increase the number of possibilities by a constant factor.

B1. Show that a triangle with vertices at rational points has a rational point for its circumcenter by expressing the coordinates of the circumcenter in terms of the coordinates of the vertices.

B2. Find an explicit formula for the integral by induction on n.

B3. Parameterize the circle as $v_0 + v_1 \sin(\theta) + v_2 \cos(\theta)$. When does this fit inside a cube?

B4. How does $h(a) - h(a+p)$ (mod p^2) relate to $h(a) - h(a + p^2)$ (mod p^3)?

B5. Relate $f(q)$ to $f(q + 1/n)$ for n large and relatively prime to the denominator of q. What does this say about $f'(q)$?

B6. Relate the parity in question to the determinant of an appropriate matrix.

The Seventieth William Lowell Putnam
Mathematical Competition—December 5, 2009

A1. Compare the values of P at the vertices of several squares that have some vertices in common.

A2. Find a differential equation satisfied by the function fgh.

A3. Use row and/or column operations to show that d_n is zero for suitably large n.

A4. Generate a few values that are forced to belong to S, and find a simple value $\frac{r}{s}$ that is missing. Then show that the complement of $\{n + \frac{r}{s} | n \in \mathbb{Z}\}$ satisfies the conditions on S.

A5. Write the given group as a product of cyclic groups and come up with a formula for the product of the orders of the elements in terms of these factors. Then use this formula to control the number of factors.

A6. Consider examples of the form $f(x, y) = g(x)h(y)$.

B1. Show by induction that this can be done for each prime factor of the numerator and denominator of the rational number.

B2. Compare costs to Riemann sums for the integral $\int_0^1 t^2 dt$.

B3. Note that $A(n+1) - A(n)$ counts mediocre subsets of $\{1, \ldots, n+1\}$ containing $n + 1$.

B4. Look separately at the homogeneous polynomials of each degree.

B5. Argue that $|f(x)| < x$ for large x. Then use this to control $f'(x)$ and deduce that $\lim_{x \to +\infty} f(x)$ exists.

B6. Exploit the congruence $(x + 1)^n \equiv 1 + nx \pmod{x^2}$.

The Seventy-First William Lowell Putnam
Mathematical Competition—December 4, 2010

A1. Consider separately the cases where n is even and n is odd.

A2. Show that $f'(x)$ is periodic.

A3. Consider the restrictions of f to lines in $\mathbb{R}^2$.

A4. Let 2^m be the largest factor of 2 dividing n, and consider the reduction of $N = 10^{10^{10^n}} + 10^{10^n} + 10^n - 1$ modulo $10^{2^m} + 1$.

A5. Study $\mathbf{x} * \mathbf{x}$ for $\mathbf{x} \in G$.

A6. Obtain a lower bound on $\int_a^b \frac{f(x)-f(x+1)}{f(x)} \, dx$ for conveniently chosen a and b.

B1. Separate into cases according to whether or not $a_k^2 \leq 1$ for all k.

B2. Consider triangles whose shortest side has length 1, 2, or 3.

B3. Under what conditions is there always at least one possible move?

B4. Compare the given equation with the corresponding equation where x has been replaced by $x - 1$.

B5. Use the given equation to obtain a linear upper bound on $f(x)$ for sufficiently large x.

B6. Use the Cayley-Hamilton theorem.

The Seventy-Second William Lowell Putnam
Mathematical Competition—December 3, 2011

A1. Find all possible points that could be P_1, P_2, or P_3.

A2. Use the fact that $1/a_j = b_{j-1}/(b_j + 2)$ to rewrite S in terms of the b_j.

A3. Bound $\sin x$ and $\cos x$ by polynomials that achieve good approximations near $x = \pi/2$, where the integrands are greatest.

A4. For M a matrix as in the problem statement, consider the product MM^T.

A5. Consider the function $G(x) = \int_0^x g(t)\,dt$ and the function $H(x, y) = F(G^{-1}(x), G^{-1}(y))$.

A6. Interpret the probability in question as an entry of the mth power of a certain matrix.

B1. Given n, consider the smallest m for which $h\sqrt{m} > k\sqrt{n} + \epsilon$.

B2. Consider the discriminant of the quadratic polynomial $px^2 + qx + r$.

B3. If $f(0) > 0$, write $f = \sqrt{(fg) \cdot (f/g)}$ on a suitable domain containing 0.

B4. Write $T + iW = \overline{A}^T A$ for a suitable matrix A.

B5. Show that for some constant C,

$$\int_{-\infty}^{\infty} \frac{dx}{(1 + x^2)(1 + (x + y)^2)} \geq \frac{C}{1 + y^2}.$$

B6. Count roots of the polynomial $\sum_{k=0}^{p-1} \frac{x^k}{k!}$, including multiplicity.

The Seventy-Third William Lowell Putnam
Mathematical Competition—December 1, 2012

A1. If the sides of a triangle are a, b, c with $a \leq b \leq c$ and $a^2 + b^2 \leq c^2$, then the triangle is not acute. If this holds for every three of the $d_i \leq d_j \leq d_k$, how large is the largest d_n?

A2. Assume that $a * c = b * c$ and investigate properties of $d \in S$ for which $(a * c) * d = a$.

A3. If f and f_0 are two such functions, what does (i) say about the ratio f / f_0?

A4. Show that S is a segment of an arithmetic progression by verifying that for any $a, b, c \in S$ with $a \leq b \leq c$, one also has $a + c - b \in S$.

A5. First prove that $M - I$ is nilpotent, where I is the identity matrix.

A6. Differentiate the given condition to get information about the integrals of f over line segments.

B1. Given f and g in S, use the given properties to show that $\ln(f(x) + 1) + \ln(g(x) + 1)$ is in S.

B2. Assume that F is covered by a collection of balls, and express the total volume of the balls and the maximum planar area that the balls can cover in terms of the radii of the balls.

B3. Use *Hall's marriage theorem*: a bipartite graph with parts A and B has a matching that covers A if and only if every subset $S \subseteq A$ has at least $|S|$ neighbors in B.

B4. First prove that $a_n > \log(n + 1)$.

B5. Prove that the left-hand side is a convex function of x.

B6. Reorder the elements $0, 1, 2, \ldots, p-2$ in a convenient way before computing the sign of π.

The Seventy-Fourth William Lowell Putnam
Mathematical Competition—December 7, 2013

A1. Find the minimum sum of the numbers on the faces meeting at a particular vertex.

A2. Suppose $f(n) = f(m)$ for some $n < m$, and $n < a_1 < a_2 < \cdots < a_r = f(n)$ and $m < b_1 < b_2 < \cdots < b_s = f(m)$ are sequences whose products are perfect squares. Multiply the two products together and cancel repeated factors.

A3. Note that $\dfrac{a_k}{1 - x^{k+1}}$ is the sum of a certain geometric series.

A4. Arcs of length k must have either z_k or $z_k + 1$ zeros, for some integer z_k. Guess, then prove, a formula for z_k.

A5. How is the area of a triangle in $\mathbb{R}^3$ related to the expected value of the area of its projection to a randomly oriented plane?

A6. Write the answer as the constant coefficient of a Laurent polynomial. Then pick out this coefficient by averaging over the unit circle.

B1. Compare $c(2k + 1)c(2k + 3)$ with $c(2k)c(2k + 2)$.

B2. Consider the value of $f(1/3)$ for any $f \in \mathcal{C}$ in order to guess the maximum value of $f(0)$.

B3. Define $f_i = f(S \cup \{i\}) - f(S)$ for a suitable choice of S.

B4. Note that $\mathrm{Var}(fg) \leq \int \left(f(x)g(x) - \mu' \right)^2 dx$ for any $\mu' \in \mathbb{R}$.

B5. When k is changed to $k - 1$, what kinds of functions must now be counted?

B6. *Hint 1 of 2.* Which positions can actually occur repeatedly, if the rule forbidding repetitions is disregarded?

   Hint 2 of 2. Watch how the sum of the coordinates of the occupied squares changes at each move.

The Seventy-Fifth William Lowell Putnam
Mathematical Competition—December 6, 2014

A1. Find a general formula for the coefficient of x^n by adding the series for e^x, $-xe^x$, x^2e^x.

A2. Subtract adjacent rows to produce a triangular matrix.

A3. Prove that $a_k = 2^{2^k} + 2^{-2^k}$.

A4. Compute the expected value of $(1 - X)(2 - X)(3 - X)$.

A5. *Hint 1 of 2.* If $1/w$ is a root of P_{n-1}, show that $w^{2n} = nw + n - 1$.
   Hint 2 of 2. Compare the third derivatives of $\log |w^{2n}|$ and $\log |nw + n - 1|$ as functions of n.

A6. Consider the tensor product of the rows of M_i. That is, consider the vector of length n^n whose entries are the products of one entry from each row of M_i.

B1. Show that the base-10 over-expansion is unique for N exactly when the usual base-10 expansion for N contains no digits equal to 0.

B2. Show that the optimal function is 1 for $1 \le x \le 2$ and -1 for $2 < x \le 3$.

B3. If A has rank at most 1, then $A = vw^T$ for some column vectors v and w.

B4. For $n \ge 3$, show that the polynomial takes values with alternating signs at $x = -2^n, -2^{n-2}, \ldots, -2^{-n+2}, -2^{-n}$.

B5. Show that a first move $g \in GL_n(\mathbb{F}_p)$ is a winning move for Patniss if and only if the centralizer of g in $GL_n(\mathbb{F}_p)$ has odd order.

B6. Let f_n be the piecewise linear function connecting the points $(a/b, f(a/b))$ where a and b are integers with $0 \le a \le b \le n$. Show that if n is large, then $f_n = f_{n-1}$.

The Seventy-Sixth William Lowell Putnam
Mathematical Competition—December 5, 2015

A1. Given points $A = (a, 1/a)$ and $B = (b, 1/b)$, find the areas by direct calculation.

A2. Solve the given recurrence relation for a_n. Then consider ratios of the form a_{kn}/a_n.

A3. Compute $\prod_{b=1}^{n}(1 + e^{2\pi i ab/n})$ for n odd, starting with the case $a = 1$.

A4. Guess the optimal value of L by trying $x = \frac{r}{s} \pm \epsilon$ where $\frac{r}{s}$ is a simple rational number and ϵ is small.

A5. Use inclusion/exclusion to rewrite N_q in terms of divisors of q.

A6. First check the case where one of A or B is invertible. Then reduce to this case by reformulating the problem in terms of verifying a polynomial identity.

B1. Find g so that $f(x)g(x)$ has an appropriate third derivative.

B2. Show that the removed sums consist of one element from each sequence of 10 positive integers. Then identify those sums.

B3. Write the elements of S as linear combinations of two convenient generators.

B4. For fixed b and c, compute the sum over all allowable a.

B5. Classify the permutations counted by P_n according to how n appears. Then derive some recurrence relations relating permutations of $\{1, 2, \ldots, n\}$ and $\{1, 2, \ldots, n + 1\}$ of the desired form.

B6. Convert the sum into a double sum, then carefully interchange the order of summation.

The Seventy-Seventh William Lowell Putnam
Mathematical Competition—December 3, 2016

A1. Consider the jth derivative of x^r for $r \geq j$.

A2. Solve the inequality $\binom{m}{n-1} > \binom{m-1}{n}$ for m.

A3. Iterate the substitution $x \mapsto 1 - \frac{1}{x}$ in the given equation.

A4. Color some of the squares in such a way that no tile can cover more than one colored square.

A5. First show that this can be done for some r, without requiring that $r \leq |G|$, by considering the set of all elements of G with representations of the given form.

A6. Reduce to the case where $P(0) = 0$ and $P(x) \geq 0$ for $0 < x \leq 1$. Then find a more useful expression for $\int_0^1 P(x)\,dx$.

B1. Exponentiate the two sides of the given recursive relation to obtain $x_n = e^{x_n} - e^{x_{n+1}}$.

B2. Find the number of squarish numbers in the interval $[n^2 - n - 1, n^2 + n]$, and write $S(N)$ as a sum of these numbers. Then estimate $S(N)$ as an integral.

B3. Choose three points in S so as to maximize the area of the triangle ABC. Then describe the given triangle in terms of this one.

B4. Write the determinant as a sum over permutations and figure out which permutations make a nonzero contribution.

B5. Make a change of variables to put the given inequality into a more useful form.

B6. Rearrange the sum into a form where some convenient cancellation takes place.

Solutions

For each problem, we report on the aggregate results of the top 200 contestants (up to rounding). We first list the *score vector*, defined as the tuple $(n_{10}, n_9, n_8, \ldots, n_2, n_1, n_0, n_\emptyset)$ in which n_i of these contestants scored i points, while $n_\emptyset$ of these contestants did not attempt the problem. (The scores 3–7 were never assigned.) We then give the *success rate*, defined as the percentage of these contestants who scored 8–10 on the problem.

Two sources come up often enough that we have chosen to abbreviate them. "AoPS" is the Art of Problem Solving forums:

https://artofproblemsolving.com/community

and "OEIS" is the On-Line Encyclopedia of Integer Sequences:

https://oeis.org/

Beware that some notations are used differently in the solutions than in the problem statements.

- We write $\log x$ rather than $\ln x$ for the natural logarithm of x.

- For two points A, B in the plane, we write AB for the distance from A to B, $\overline{AB}$ for the line segment from A to B, and $\overleftrightarrow{AB}$ for the line through A and B.

**The Sixty-Second William Lowell Putnam
Mathematical Competition—December 1, 2001**

A1. $(189, 1, 0, \ldots, 0, 0, 8, 2)$ 95.0%
　　Consider a set S and a binary operation $*$; that is, for each $a, b \in S$, $a * b \in S$. Assume $(a * b) * a = b$ for all $a, b \in S$. Prove that $a * (b * a) = b$ for all $a, b \in S$.

Solution. Replacing a by $b * a$ in the condition implies $((b * a) * b) * (b * a) = b$ for all $a, b \in S$, and hence because $(b * a) * b = a$, it follows that $a * (b * a) = b$ for all $a, b \in S$.

A2. $(163, 6, 5, \ldots, 1, 1, 14, 10)$ 87.0%
　　You have coins $C_1, C_2, \ldots, C_n$. For each k, C_k is biased so that, when tossed, it has probability $\frac{1}{2k+1}$ of falling heads. If the n coins are tossed, what is the probability that the number of heads is odd? Express the answer as a rational function of n.

Answer. The probability is $n/(2n + 1)$.

Solution 1. Let P_n denote the desired probability. Then $P_1 = 1/3$. For $j > 1$ there are two ways to obtain an odd number of heads when flipping the first j coins: either there were an odd number of heads in the first $j - 1$ coins, and the jth coin is a head, or there were an even number of heads in the first $j - 1$ coins, and the jth coin is a tail. Thus for $j > 1$,

$$P_j = \left(\frac{2j}{2j+1}\right)P_{j-1} + \left(\frac{1}{2j+1}\right)(1 - P_{j-1})$$
$$= \left(\frac{2j-1}{2j+1}\right)P_{j-1} + \frac{1}{2j+1}.$$

The recurrence yields $P_2 = 2/5$, $P_3 = 3/7$, and simple induction shows that $P_j = j/(2j + 1)$ for general j.

Solution 2. (Richard Stanley) The following is a noninductive argument. Put $f(x) = \prod_{k=1}^{n}(x+2k)/(2k+1)$. Then the coefficient of x^i in $f(x)$ is the probability of getting exactly i heads. Thus the required probability is $(f(1) - f(-1))/2$, and both values of f can be computed directly: $f(1) = 1$, and

$$f(-1) = \frac{1}{3} \cdot \frac{3}{5} \cdot \ldots \cdot \frac{2n-1}{2n+1} = \frac{1}{2n+1}.$$

A3. $(97, 33, 5, \ldots, 24, 22, 7, 12)$ 67.5%
　　For each integer m, consider the polynomial

$$P_m(x) = x^4 - (2m + 4)x^2 + (m - 2)^2.$$

For what values of m is $P_m(x)$ the product of two nonconstant polynomials with integer coefficients?

Answer. $P_m(x)$ can be written as such a product if and only if m is either a perfect square or twice a perfect square.

Solution. By the quadratic formula, if $P_m(x) = 0$, then $x^2 = m \pm 2\sqrt{2m} + 2$, and hence the four roots of P_m are given by $S = \{\pm\sqrt{m} \pm \sqrt{2}\}$. If P_m factors into two nonconstant polynomials over the integers, then some one- or two-element subset of S gives the roots of a polynomial with integer coefficients.

If this subset has a single element, say $\sqrt{m} \pm \sqrt{2}$, it is the root of a linear polynomial with integer coefficients, so it must be a rational number. Then $(\sqrt{m} \pm \sqrt{2})^2 = 2 + m \pm 2\sqrt{2m}$ is an integer, so m is twice a perfect square, say $m = 2n^2$. But $\sqrt{m} \pm \sqrt{2} = (n \pm 1)\sqrt{2}$ is only rational if $n = \pm 1$, that is, only if $m = 2$.

If the subset contains two elements, then it is one of the six subsets $\{\sqrt{m}\pm\sqrt{2}\}$, $\{\sqrt{2}\pm\sqrt{m}\}$, or $\{\pm(\sqrt{m}+\sqrt{2})\}$. In all cases, the sum and the product of the elements of the subset must be rational numbers. In the first case, this means $2\sqrt{m} \in \mathbb{Q}$, so m is a perfect square. In the second case, $2\sqrt{2} \in \mathbb{Q}$, which is a contradiction. In the third case, $(\sqrt{m} + \sqrt{2})^2 \in \mathbb{Q}$, or $m + 2 + 2\sqrt{2m} \in \mathbb{Q}$, which means that m is twice a perfect square.

Therefore $P_m(x)$ factors into two nonconstant polynomials over the integers only if m is either a square or twice a square. However, in either of these cases, one can see directly that $P_m(x)$ does actually factor. If m is a perfect square, then $(x - \sqrt{m} - \sqrt{2})(x - \sqrt{m} + \sqrt{2}) = x^2 - 2\sqrt{m}x + (m - 2)$ is a factor of $P_m(x)$ with integer coefficients. If m is twice a square, then $(x - \sqrt{m} - \sqrt{2})(x + \sqrt{m} + \sqrt{2}) = x^2 - (m + 2\sqrt{2m} + 2)$ is a factor with integer coefficients. This completes the proof.

Reinterpretation. If m is neither a square nor twice a square, then the number fields $\mathbb{Q}(\sqrt{m})$ and $\mathbb{Q}(\sqrt{2})$ are distinct quadratic fields, so their compositum $\mathbb{Q}(\sqrt{m}, \sqrt{2})$ is a number field of degree 4, whose Galois group acts transitively on $\{\pm\sqrt{m} \pm \sqrt{2}\}$. Thus P_m is irreducible.

A4. $(29, 7, 8, \ldots, 10, 10, 47, 89)\ 22.0\%$

Triangle ABC has area 1. Points E, F, G lie, respectively, on sides BC, CA, AB such that AE bisects BF at point R, BF bisects CG at point S, and CG bisects AE at point T. Find the area of the triangle RST.

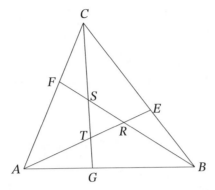

Answer. The area of RST is $\frac{7-3\sqrt{5}}{4}$.

Solution. Choose r, s, t so that $EC = rBC, FA = sCA, GB = tAB$, and let $[XYZ]$ denote the area of triangle XYZ. Then $[ABE] = [AFE]$ since the triangles have the same altitude ($FR = BR$) and a common base AE. By the sine formula for the area of a triangle,

$$[ABE] = \frac{1}{2}(AB)(BE)\sin(\angle ABE) = (BE/BC)[ABC] = 1 - r$$

and

$$[ECF] = \frac{1}{2}(EC)(CF)\sin(\angle ECF) = (EC/BC)(CF/CA)[ABC] = r(1 - s).$$

Adding this all up yields

$$1 = [ABE] + [AFE] + [ECF]$$
$$= 2(1 - r) + r(1 - s) = 2 - r - rs$$

or $r(1 + s) = 1$. Similarly, $s(1 + t) = t(1 + r) = 1$.

Let $f : [0, \infty) \to [0, \infty)$ be the function given by $f(x) = 1/(1 + x)$; then $f(f(f(r))) = r$. However, $f(x)$ is strictly decreasing in x, so $f(f(x))$ is increasing and $f(f(f(x)))$ is decreasing. Thus there is at most one x such that $f(f(f(x))) = x$. Since the equation $f(z) = z$ has a positive root $z = (-1 + \sqrt{5})/2$, it must be that $r = s = t = z$.

Now compute

$$[ABF] = (AF/AC)[ABC] = z,$$
$$[ABR] = (BR/BF)[ABF] = z/2,$$
$$[BCS] = [CAT] = z/2,$$

and

$$[RST] = |[ABC] - [ABR] - [BCS] - [CAT]| = |1 - 3z/2| = \frac{7 - 3\sqrt{5}}{4}.$$

Remark. The key relation $r(1 + s) = 1$ can also be derived using homogeneous coordinates or vectors.

A5. $(12, 9, 10, \ldots, 9, 41, 33, 86)$ 15.5%

Prove that there are unique positive integers a, n such that

$$a^{n+1} - (a + 1)^n = 2001.$$

Solution. We prove that the unique solution is $a = 13, n = 2$.

Suppose $a^{n+1} - (a + 1)^n = 2001$. Since $a^{n+1} - [(a + 1)^n - 1]$ is a multiple of a, a divides $2002 = 2 \times 7 \times 11 \times 13$.

Since 2001 is divisible by 3, it must be that $a \equiv 1 \pmod 3$, otherwise one of a^{n+1} and $(a + 1)^n$ is a multiple of 3 and the other is not, so their difference cannot be divisible by 3. Now $a^{n+1} \equiv 1 \pmod 3$, so it must be that $(a + 1)^n \equiv 1 \pmod 3$, which can only happen if n is even, and in particular at least 2.

If a is even, then $a^{n+1} - (a + 1)^n \equiv -(a + 1)^n \pmod 4$. Since n is even, $-(a + 1)^n \equiv -1 \pmod 4$. Since $2001 \equiv 1 \pmod 4$, this is impossible. Thus a is odd, and so must divide $1001 = 7 \times 11 \times 13$. Moreover, $a^{n+1} - (a + 1)^n \equiv a \pmod 4$, so $a \equiv 1 \pmod 4$.

Of the divisors of $7 \times 11 \times 13$, those congruent to 1 modulo 3 are precisely those not divisible by 11 (since 7 and 13 are both congruent to 1 modulo 3). Thus a divides 7×13. Now $a \equiv 1 \pmod 4$ is only possible if a divides 13.

We cannot have $a = 1$, since $1 - 2^n \neq 2001$ for any n. Thus the only possibility is $a = 13$. The equality $13^3 - 14^2 = 2197 - 196 = 2001$ shows that $a = 13, n = 2$ is a solution; all that remains is to check that no other n works. In fact, if $n > 2$, then $13^{n+1} \equiv 2001 \equiv 1 \pmod 8$. But $13^{n+1} \equiv 13 \pmod 8$ since n is even, giving a contradiction. Thus $a = 13, n = 2$ is the unique solution.

Remark. Once one has that n is even, one can use that $2002 = a^{n+1} + 1 - (a + 1)^n$ is divisible by $a + 1$ to rule out cases.

A6. $(1, 0, 0, \ldots, 0, 1, 57, 141)$ 0.5%

Can an arc of a parabola inside a circle of radius 1 have a length greater than 4?

Answer. Yes, it can have length greater than 4.

Solution. Inside the circle $x^2 + (y - 1)^2 = 1$, consider the arc of the parabola $y = Ax^2$, where we initially assume that $A > 1/2$. This intersects the circle in three points, $(0, 0)$ and $(\pm\sqrt{2A - 1}/A, (2A-1)/A)$. We claim that for A sufficiently large, the length L of the parabolic arc between $(0, 0)$ and $(\sqrt{2A - 1}/A, (2A-1)/A)$ is greater than 2, which implies the desired result by symmetry. We express L

using the usual formula for arc length:

$$L = \int_{x_0}^{x_1} \sqrt{1 + \left(\frac{\partial y}{\partial x}\right)^2} \, dx$$

$$= \int_0^{\sqrt{2A-1}/A} \sqrt{1 + (2Ax)^2} \, dx.$$

Substituting $u = 2Ax$ yields $\frac{1}{2A} \int_0^{2\sqrt{2A-1}} \sqrt{1 + u^2} \, du$. Noting that

$$\frac{1}{2A} \int_0^{2\sqrt{2A-1}} u \, du = 2 - \frac{1}{A},$$

we can take u out of the integrand to obtain

$$L = 2 + \frac{1}{2A} \left(\int_0^{2\sqrt{2A-1}} (\sqrt{1 + u^2} - u) \, du - 2 \right).$$

Now, for $u \geq 0$,

$$\sqrt{1 + u^2} - u = \frac{1}{\sqrt{1 + u^2} + u} > \frac{1}{2\sqrt{1 + u^2}} \geq \frac{1}{2(u + 1)};$$

since $\int_0^\infty du/(2(u + 1))$ diverges, so does $\int_0^\infty (\sqrt{1 + u^2} - u) \, du$. Hence for sufficiently large A, $\int_0^{2\sqrt{2A-1}} (\sqrt{1 + u^2} - u) \, du > 2$ and hence $L > 2$.

Remark. A numerical computation shows that one must take $A > 34.7$ to obtain $L > 2$, and that the maximum value of L is about 4.0027, achieved for $A \approx 94.1$.

B1. (136, 25, 7, ..., 3, 3, 20, 6) 84.0%

   Let n be an even positive integer. Write the numbers $1, 2, \ldots, n^2$ in the squares of an $n \times n$ grid so that the kth row, from left to right, is

$$(k - 1)n + 1, (k - 1)n + 2, \ldots, (k - 1)n + n.$$

Color the squares of the grid so that half of the squares in each row and in each column are red and the other half are black (a checkerboard coloring is one possibility). Prove that for each coloring, the sum of the numbers on the red squares is equal to the sum of the numbers on the black squares.

Solution. Let R (resp. B) denote the set of red (resp. black) squares in such a coloring, and for $s \in R \cup B$, let $f(s)n + g(s) + 1$ denote the number written in square s, where $0 \leq f(s), g(s) \leq n - 1$. Then it is clear that the value of $f(s)$

depends only on the row of s, while the value of $g(s)$ depends only on the column of s. Since every row contains exactly $n/2$ elements of R and $n/2$ elements of B,

$$\sum_{s \in R} f(s) = \sum_{s \in B} f(s).$$

Similarly, because every column contains exactly $n/2$ elements of R and $n/2$ elements of B,

$$\sum_{s \in R} g(s) = \sum_{s \in B} g(s).$$

It follows that

$$\sum_{s \in R} f(s)n + g(s) + 1 = \sum_{s \in B} f(s)n + g(s) + 1,$$

as desired.

Remark. Richard Stanley points out a theorem of Ryser (see [**Ryser**, Theorem 3.1]) that can also be applied. Namely, if A and B are 0-1 matrices with the same row and column sums, then there is a sequence of operations on 2×2 matrices of the form

$$\begin{pmatrix} 0 & 1 \\ 1 & 0 \end{pmatrix} \to \begin{pmatrix} 1 & 0 \\ 0 & 1 \end{pmatrix}$$

or vice versa, which transforms A into B. If 0 and 1 are identified with red and black, respectively, then the given coloring and the checkerboard coloring both satisfy the sum condition. Since the desired result is clearly true for the checkerboard coloring, and performing the matrix operations does not affect this, the desired result follows in general.

B2. (38, 1, 2, ..., 2, 7, 52, 98) 20.5%
   Find all pairs of real numbers (x, y) satisfying the system of equations

$$\frac{1}{x} + \frac{1}{2y} = (x^2 + 3y^2)(3x^2 + y^2),$$

$$\frac{1}{x} - \frac{1}{2y} = 2(y^4 - x^4).$$

Answer. The unique such pair is

$$(x, y) = \left(\frac{3^{1/5} + 1}{2}, \frac{3^{1/5} - 1}{2} \right).$$

Solution. Adding and subtracting the two given equations yields the equivalent pair of equations

$$2/x = x^4 + 10x^2 y^2 + 5y^4,$$
$$1/y = 5x^4 + 10x^2 y^2 + y^4.$$

Multiplying the first equation by x and the second by y, then adding and subtracting the two resulting equations, gives another pair of equations equivalent to the given ones:

$$3 = (x + y)^5,$$
$$1 = (x - y)^5.$$

This then leads to the unique solution given above.

B3. (120, 6, 5, ..., 12, 17, 5, 35) 65.5%

For any positive integer n, let $\langle n \rangle$ denote the closest integer to $\sqrt{n}$. Evaluate

$$\sum_{n=1}^{\infty} \frac{2^{\langle n \rangle} + 2^{-\langle n \rangle}}{2^n}.$$

Answer. The sum is 3.

Solution. Let k be a positive integer. Since $(k - 1/2)^2 = k^2 - k + 1/4$ and $(k + 1/2)^2 = k^2 + k + 1/4$, a positive integer n satisfies $\langle n \rangle = k$ if and only if $k^2 - k + 1 \le n \le k^2 + k$. Hence

$$\sum_{n=1}^{\infty} \frac{2^{\langle n \rangle} + 2^{-\langle n \rangle}}{2^n} = \sum_{k=1}^{\infty} \sum_{\langle n \rangle = k} \frac{2^{\langle n \rangle} + 2^{-\langle n \rangle}}{2^n}$$

$$= \sum_{k=1}^{\infty} \sum_{n=k^2-k+1}^{k^2+k} \frac{2^k + 2^{-k}}{2^n}.$$

Summing the finite geometric series yields

$$= \sum_{k=1}^{\infty} (2^k + 2^{-k})(2^{-k^2+k} - 2^{-k^2-k})$$

$$= \sum_{k=1}^{\infty} (2^{-k(k-2)} - 2^{-k(k+2)})$$

$$= \sum_{k=1}^{\infty} 2^{-k(k-2)} - \sum_{k=3}^{\infty} 2^{-(k-2)k}$$

$$= 2^{-1(-1)} + 2^{-2(0)} = 3,$$

where the index of summation in the second term was shifted by 2.

Reinterpretation. Rewrite the sum as $\sum_{n=1}^{\infty} 2^{-(n+\langle n \rangle)} + \sum_{n=1}^{\infty} 2^{-(n-\langle n \rangle)}$. Note that $\langle n \rangle \neq \langle n+1 \rangle$ if and only if $n = m^2 + m$ for some $m \ge 1$. Thus $n + \langle n \rangle$ and

$n - \langle n \rangle$ each increase by 1 except at $n = m^2 + m$, where the former skips from $m^2 + 2m$ to $m^2 + 2m + 2$ and the latter repeats the value m^2. Thus the sums are

$$\left(\sum_{n=2}^{\infty} 2^{-n} - \sum_{m=1}^{\infty} 2^{-(m+1)^2} \right) + \left(\sum_{n=0}^{\infty} 2^{-n} + \sum_{m=1}^{\infty} 2^{-m^2} \right) = \frac{1}{2} + 2 + \frac{1}{2} = 3,$$

where the first and third summations contribute 1/2 and 2, respectively, and the terms from the second and fourth summations cancel except for one term equal to 1/2.

B4. (43, 21, 28, ..., 3, 0, 34, 71) 46.0%
Let S denote the set of rational numbers different from $-1, 0$, and 1. Define $f : S \to S$ by $f(x) = x - 1/x$. Prove or disprove:

$$\bigcap_{n=1}^{\infty} f^{(n)}(S) = \emptyset,$$

where $f^{(n)} = \underbrace{f \circ f \circ \cdots \circ f}_{n \text{ times}}$.
(Note: $f(S)$ denotes the set of all values $f(s)$ for $s \in S$.)

Answer. We prove the assertion that the intersection is empty.

Solution. For a rational number p/q expressed in lowest terms, define its *height* $H(p/q)$ to be $|p| + |q|$. Then for any $p/q \in S$ expressed in lowest terms, $H(f(p/q)) = H((p^2 - q^2)/(pq)) = |q^2 - p^2| + |pq|$. This is because any prime common divisor of $p^2 - q^2$ and pq must divide one of $p + q$ or $p - q$ and one of p or q, but by taking appropriate linear combinations of these multiples, we find that it must divide both p and q, which is impossible as p and q were assumed to be relatively prime. Since by assumption p and q are nonzero integers with $|p| \neq |q|$,

$$H(f(p/q)) - H(p/q) = |q^2 - p^2| + |pq| - |p| - |q|$$
$$\geq 3 + |pq| - |p| - |q|$$
$$= (|p| - 1)(|q| - 1) + 2 \geq 2.$$

It follows that $f^{(n)}(S)$ consists solely of numbers of height strictly larger than $2n + 2$, and hence

$$\bigcap_{n=1}^{\infty} f^{(n)}(S) = \emptyset.$$

Remark. Many choices for the height function are possible: one can take $H(p/q) = \max\{|p|, |q|\}$, or $H(p/q)$ equal to the total number of prime factors of p and q, and so on. The key properties of the height function are that on one hand, there are only finitely many rationals with height below any finite bound, and on the other hand, the height function is a sufficiently "algebraic" function of its argument that one can relate the heights of p/q and $f(p/q)$.

B5. $(2, 0, 0, \ldots, 3, 3, 82, 110)$ 1.0%

Let a and b be real numbers in the interval $(0, \frac{1}{2})$ and let g be a continuous real-valued function such that $g(g(x)) = ag(x) + bx$ for all real x. Prove that $g(x) = cx$ for some constant c.

Solution. Note that $g(x) = g(y)$ implies that $g(g(x)) = g(g(y))$ and hence $x = y$ from the given equation. That is, g is injective. Since g is also continuous, g is either strictly increasing or strictly decreasing. Moreover, g cannot tend to a finite limit L as $x \to \infty$, or else $g(g(x)) - ag(x) = bx$ with the left side bounded and the right side unbounded. Similarly, g cannot tend to a finite limit as $x \to -\infty$. Together with monotonicity and continuity, this yields that g is also surjective.

Pick x_0 arbitrary, and define x_n for all $n \in \mathbb{Z}$ recursively by $x_{n+1} = g(x_n)$ for $n > 0$, and $x_{n-1} = g^{-1}(x_n)$ for $n < 0$. Let $r_1 = (a + \sqrt{a^2 + 4b})/2$ and $r_2 = (a - \sqrt{a^2 + 4b})/2$ be the roots of $x^2 - ax - b = 0$, so that $r_1 > 0 > r_2$ and $1 > |r_1| > |r_2|$. Since $x_{n+2} = ax_{n+1} + bx_n$ for all $n \in \mathbb{Z}$, by standard facts about recurrence relations, there exist $c_1, c_2 \in \mathbb{R}$ such that $x_n = c_1 r_1^n + c_2 r_2^n$ for all $n \in \mathbb{Z}$.

Suppose g is strictly increasing. If $c_2 \neq 0$ for some choice of x_0, then x_n is dominated by r_2^n for n sufficiently negative. But taking x_n and x_{n+2} for n sufficiently negative of the right parity, we get $0 < x_n < x_{n+2}$, contradicting the fact that $g(x_n) > g(x_{n+2})$. Thus $c_2 = 0$; since $x_0 = c_1$ and $x_1 = c_1 r_1$, $g(x) = r_1 x$ for all x. Analogously, if g is strictly decreasing, then $c_2 = 0$ or else x_n is dominated by r_1^n for n sufficiently positive. But taking x_n and x_{n+2} for n sufficiently positive of the right parity, we get $0 < x_{n+2} < x_n$, contradicting the fact that $g(x_{n+2}) < g(x_n)$. Thus in that case, $g(x) = r_2 x$ for all x.

B6. $(9, 5, 2, \ldots, 2, 0, 40, 142)$ 8.0%

Assume that $(a_n)_{n \geq 1}$ is an increasing sequence of positive real numbers such that $\lim \frac{a_n}{n} = 0$. Must there exist infinitely many positive integers n such that

$$a_{n-i} + a_{n+i} < 2a_n \text{ for } i = 1, 2, \ldots, n - 1?$$

Answer. Yes, there must exist infinitely many such n.

Solution. Let S be the convex hull of the set of points (n, a_n) for $n \geq 0$. Geometrically, S is the intersection of all convex sets (or even all half-planes) containing the points (n, a_n); algebraically, S is the set of points (x, y) which can be written as $c_1(n_1, a_{n_1}) + \cdots + c_k(n_k, a_{n_k})$ for some $c_1, \ldots, c_k$ which are nonnegative of sum 1.

We prove that for infinitely many n, (n, a_n) is a vertex on the upper boundary of S, and that these n satisfy the given condition. The condition that (n, a_n) is a vertex on the upper boundary of S is equivalent to the existence of a line passing through (n, a_n) with all other points of S below it. That is, there should exist a real number $m > 0$ such that

$$a_k < a_n + m(k - n) \qquad \forall k \geq 1. \tag{1}$$

We first show that $n = 1$ satisfies (1). The condition $a_k/k \to 0$ as $k \to \infty$ implies that $(a_k - a_1)/(k - 1) \to 0$ as well. Thus the set $\{(a_k - a_1)/(k - 1)\}$ has an upper bound m, and now $a_k \leq a_1 + m(k - 1)$, as desired.

Next, we show that given one n satisfying (1), there exists a larger one also satisfying (1). Again, the condition $a_k/k \to 0$ as $k \to \infty$ implies that $(a_k - a_n)/(k - n) \to 0$ as $k \to \infty$. Thus the sequence $\{(a_k - a_n)/(k - n)\}_{k>n}$ has a maximum element. Suppose $k = r$ is the largest value that achieves this maximum, and put $m = (a_r - a_n)/(r - n)$. Then the line through (r, a_r) of slope m lies strictly above (k, a_k) for $k > r$ and passes through or lies above (k, a_k) for $k < r$. Thus (1) holds for $n = r$ with m replaced by $m - \epsilon$ for suitably small $\epsilon > 0$.

By induction, (1) holds for infinitely many n. For any such n there exists $m > 0$ such that for $i = 1, \ldots, n - 1$, the points $(n - i, a_{n-i})$ and $(n + i, a_{n+i})$ lie below the line through (n, a_n) of slope m. That means $a_{n+i} < a_n + mi$ and $a_{n-i} < a_n - mi$; adding these together gives $a_{n-i} + a_{n+i} < 2a_n$, as desired.

The Sixty-Third William Lowell Putnam
Mathematical Competition—December 7, 2002

A1. (115, 9, 41, ..., 16, 2, 20, 7) 78.6%
　　Let k **be a fixed positive integer. The nth derivative of** $\frac{1}{x^k-1}$ **has the**
form $\frac{P_n(x)}{(x^k-1)^{n+1}}$, **where** $P_n(x)$ **is a polynomial. Find** $P_n(1)$.

Answer. We have $P_n(1) = (-k)^n n!$.

Solution 1. Differentiating the given fraction $P_n(x)/(x^k-1)^{n+1}$, shows $P_{n+1}(x) = (x^k - 1)P_n'(x) - (n + 1)kx^{k-1}P_n(x)$. Substituting $x = 1$ yields $P_{n+1}(1) = -(n + 1)kP_n(1)$. Since $P_0(1) = 1$, it follows by induction that $P_n(1) = (-k)^n n!$ for all $n \geq 0$.

Solution 2. One can also argue by expanding $\frac{1}{x^k-1}$ in a Laurent series (Taylor series with negative powers allowed) around 1, giving

$$\frac{1}{x^k - 1} = \frac{1}{k(x - 1) + \cdots} = \frac{1}{k}(x - 1)^{-1} + \cdots,$$

so

$$\frac{d^n}{dx^n}\frac{1}{x^k - 1} = \frac{(-1)^n n!}{k(x - 1)^{-n-1}} + \cdots$$

and

$$P_n(x) = (x^k - 1)^{n+1}\frac{d^n}{dx^n}\frac{1}{x^k - 1}$$
$$= (k(x - 1) + \cdots)^{n+1}\left(\frac{(-1)^n n!}{k}(x - 1)^{-n-1} + \cdots\right)$$
$$= (-k)^n n! + \cdots.$$

Solution 3. Another approach is to let $f(x) = 1/(x - 1)$ and $g(x) = x^k$. Then, by the chain rule for higher order derivatives, each term of the nth derivative of $f \circ g(x)$ is a summation of terms involving $f^{(j)} \circ g(x)$ times various powers of derivatives of $g(x)$. But $(x^k - 1)^{n+1}f^{(j)} \circ g(x)$ is 0 at $x = 1$ for all $j < n$, so the only term of interest is

$$(x^k - 1)^{n+1}f^n \circ g(x)[g'(x)]^n$$
$$= (x^k - 1)^{n+1}\frac{(-1)^n n!}{(x^k - 1)^{n+1}}[kx^{k-1}]^n$$
$$= (-1)^n n![kx^{k-1}]^n,$$

which at $x = 1$ is $(-k)^n n!$.

A2. (75, 106, 14, ..., 3, 1, 1, 10) 92.9%

Given any five points on a sphere, show that some four of them must lie on a closed hemisphere.

Solution. Draw a great circle through two of the points. There are two closed hemispheres with this great circle as boundary, and each of the other three points lies in one of them. By the pigeonhole principle, two of those three points lie in the same hemisphere, and that hemisphere thus contains at least four of the five given points.

Remark. By a similar argument, one can prove that among any $n + 3$ points on an n-dimensional sphere, some $n + 2$ of them lie on a closed hemisphere. (One cannot get by with only $n + 2$ points as seen by putting them at the vertices of a regular simplex.) Namely, any n of the points lie on a great sphere, which forms the boundary of two hemispheres; of the remaining three points, some two lie in the same hemisphere.

A3. (63, 32, 8, ..., 7, 7, 26, 67) 49.0%

Let $n \geq 2$ be an integer and let T_n be the number of nonempty subsets S of $\{1, 2, 3, \ldots, n\}$ with the property that the average of the elements of S is an integer. Prove that $T_n - n$ is always even.

Solution. Each of the sets $\{1\}, \{2\}, \ldots, \{n\}$ has the desired property. Moreover, for each set S with integer average m that does not contain m, $S \cup \{m\}$ also has average m. Symmetrically, for each set T of more than one element with integer average m that contains m, $T \setminus \{m\}$ also has average m. Thus the subsets other than $\{1\}, \{2\}, \ldots, \{n\}$ can be grouped in pairs, so $T_n - n$ is even.

A4. (61, 30, 19, ..., 24, 9, 31, 36) 52.4%

In Determinant Tic-Tac-Toe, Player 1 enters a 1 in an empty 3×3 matrix. Player 0 counters with a 0 in a vacant position, and play continues in turn until the 3×3 matrix is completed with five 1's and four 0's. Player 0 wins if the determinant is 0 and Player 1 wins otherwise. Assuming both players pursue optimal strategies, who will win and how?

Answer. Player 0 wins with optimal play.

Solution. (partly due to David Savitt) We prove that Player 1 cannot prevent Player 0 from creating a row of all zeros, a column of all zeros, or a 2×2 submatrix of all zeros. Each of these forces the determinant of the matrix to be zero.

For $i, j = 1, 2, 3$, let A_{ij} denote the position in row i and column j. Without loss of generality, we may assume that Player 1's first move is at A_{11}. Player 0 then plays at A_{22}:

$$\begin{pmatrix} 1 & * & * \\ * & 0 & * \\ * & * & * \end{pmatrix}$$

After Player 1's second move, at least one of A_{23} and A_{32} remains vacant. Without loss of generality, assume A_{23} remains vacant; Player 0 then plays there.

After Player 1's third move, Player 0 wins by playing at A_{21} if that position is unoccupied. So assume instead that Player 1 has played there. Thus of Player 1's three moves so far, two are at A_{11} and A_{21}. Hence for i equal to one of 1 or 3, and for j equal to one of 2 or 3, the following are both true:

(a) The 2×2 submatrix formed by rows 2 and i and by columns 2 and 3 contains two zeros and two empty positions.

(b) Column j contains one zero and two empty positions.

Player 0 next plays at A_{ij}. To prevent a zero column, Player 1 must play in column j, upon which Player 0 completes the 2×2 submatrix in (a) for the win.

Remark. One can also solve this problem directly by making a tree of possible play sequences. This tree can be considerably collapsed using symmetries: the symmetry between rows and columns, the invariance of the outcome under re-ordering of rows or columns, and the fact that the scenario after a sequence of moves does not depend on the order of the moves (sometimes called "transposition invariance").

Remark. (Paul Cheng) One can reduce Determinant Tic-Tac-Toe to a variant of ordinary tic-tac-toe. Namely, consider a tic-tac-toe grid labeled as follows:

A_{11}	A_{22}	A_{33}
A_{23}	A_{31}	A_{12}
A_{32}	A_{13}	A_{21}

Then each term in the expansion of the determinant occurs in a row or column of the grid. Suppose Player 1 first plays in the top left. Player 0 wins by playing first in the top row, and second in the left column. Then there are only one row and column left for Player 1 to threaten, and Player 1 cannot already threaten both on the third move, so Player 0 has time to block both.

A5. (21, 32, 29, ..., 24, 3, 27, 74) 39.0%
    Define a sequence by $a_0 = 1$, together with the rules $a_{2n+1} = a_n$ and $a_{2n+2} = a_n + a_{n+1}$ for each integer $n \geq 0$. Prove that every positive rational number appears in the set

$$\left\{ \frac{a_{n-1}}{a_n} : n \geq 1 \right\} = \left\{ \frac{1}{1}, \frac{1}{2}, \frac{2}{1}, \frac{1}{3}, \frac{3}{2}, \ldots \right\}.$$

Solution. It suffices to prove that for any relatively prime positive integers r, s, there exists an integer n with $a_n = r$ and $a_{n+1} = s$. We prove this by induction on $r + s$, the case $r + s = 2$ following from the fact that $a_0 = a_1 = 1$. Given r and s not both 1 with $\gcd(r, s) = 1$, we must have $r \neq s$. If $r > s$, then by the induction hypothesis, $a_n = r - s$ and $a_{n+1} = s$ for some n; then $a_{2n+2} = r$ and $a_{2n+3} = s$. If $r < s$, then $a_n = r$ and $a_{n+1} = s - r$ for some n; then $a_{2n+1} = r$ and $a_{2n+2} = s$.

Remark. The sequence a_n appears as entry A002487 in the OEIS. With a bit more work, one can show that every positive rational number in fact appears *exactly* once in the sequence $\{a_{n-1}/a_n\}$.

A closely related construction is the following. Starting with the sequence

$$\frac{0}{1}, \frac{1}{0},$$

repeat the following operation: insert between each pair $\frac{a}{b}$ and $\frac{c}{d}$ the pair $\frac{a+c}{b+d}$. This is the formation rule for the *Stern-Brocot tree*, in which every positive rational number appears. Observe that by induction, if $\frac{a}{b}$ and $\frac{c}{d}$ are consecutive terms in the sequence, then $bc - ad = 1$. The same holds for consecutive terms of the nth *Farey sequence*, the sequence of rational numbers in $[0, 1]$ with denominator (in lowest terms) at most n (see 2014B6).

A6. (3, 4, 3, ..., 5, 5, 58, 132) 4.8%

   Fix an integer $b \geq 2$. Let $f(1) = 1$, $f(2) = 2$, and for each $n \geq 3$, define $f(n) = nf(d)$, where d is the number of base-b digits of n. For which values of b does

$$\sum_{n=1}^{\infty} \frac{1}{f(n)}$$

converge?

Answer. The sum converges for $b = 2$ and diverges for $b \geq 3$.

Solution. We first consider $b \geq 3$. Suppose the sum converges; then the fact that $f(n) = nf(d)$ whenever $b^{d-1} \leq n \leq b^d - 1$ yields

$$\sum_{n=1}^{\infty} \frac{1}{f(n)} = \sum_{d=1}^{\infty} \frac{1}{f(d)} \sum_{n=b^{d-1}}^{b^d - 1} \frac{1}{n}. \tag{1}$$

However, by comparing the integral of $1/x$ with a Riemann sum,

$$\sum_{n=b^{d-1}}^{b^d - 1} \frac{1}{n} > \int_{b^{d-1}}^{b^d} \frac{dx}{x}$$

$$= \log(b^d) - \log(b^{d-1}) = \log b,$$

where log denotes the natural logarithm. Thus (1) yields

$$\sum_{n=1}^{\infty} \frac{1}{f(n)} > (\log b) \sum_{n=1}^{\infty} \frac{1}{f(n)},$$

which is a contradiction since $\log b > 1$ for $b \geq 3$. Therefore the sum diverges.

For $b = 2$, we have a slightly different identity because $f(2) \neq 2f(2)$. Instead, for any positive integer i,

$$\sum_{n=1}^{2^i-1} \frac{1}{f(n)} = 1 + \frac{1}{2} + \frac{1}{6} + \sum_{d=3}^{i} \frac{1}{f(d)} \sum_{n=2^{d-1}}^{2^d-1} \frac{1}{n}. \tag{2}$$

By again comparing an integral to a Riemann sum, for $d \geq 3$,

$$\sum_{n=2^{d-1}}^{2^d-1} \frac{1}{n} < \frac{1}{2^{d-1}} - \frac{1}{2^d} + \int_{2^{d-1}}^{2^d} \frac{dx}{x}$$

$$= \frac{1}{2^d} + \log 2$$

$$\leq \frac{1}{8} + \log 2 < 0.125 + 0.7 < 1.$$

Put $c = \frac{1}{8} + \log 2$ and $L = 1 + \frac{1}{2} + \frac{1}{6(1-c)}$. Then we can prove that $\sum_{n=1}^{2^i-1} \frac{1}{f(n)} < L$ for all $i \geq 2$ by induction on i. The case $i = 2$ is clear. For the induction, by (2),

$$\sum_{n=1}^{2^i-1} \frac{1}{f(n)} < 1 + \frac{1}{2} + \frac{1}{6} + c \sum_{d=3}^{i} \frac{1}{f(d)}$$

$$< 1 + \frac{1}{2} + \frac{1}{6} + c \frac{1}{6(1-c)}$$

$$= 1 + \frac{1}{2} + \frac{1}{6(1-c)} = L,$$

as desired. We conclude that $\sum_{n=1}^{\infty} \frac{1}{f(n)}$ converges to a limit less than or equal to L.

Remark. The above argument proves that the sum for $b = 2$ is at most $L < 2.417$. One can also obtain a lower bound by the same technique. Letting $x = \sum_{n=3}^{\infty} \frac{1}{f(n)}$ and taking the limit of (2) as $i \to \infty$ yields

$$1 + \frac{1}{2} + x \geq 1 + \frac{1}{2} + \frac{1}{6} + x \log(2).$$

Thus $x \geq \frac{1}{6(1-\log(2))}$ and therefore $\sum_{n=1}^{\infty} \frac{1}{f(n)}$ is at least $1 + \frac{1}{2} + \frac{1}{6(1-\log(2))}$. This bound exceeds 2.043. (By contrast, summing the first 100000 terms of the series only yields a lower bound of 1.906.) Repeating the same arguments with $d \geq 4$ as the cutoff yields the upper bound 2.185 and the lower bound 2.079.

B1. (162, 17, 2, ..., 2, 2, 15, 10) 86.2%

Shanille O'Keal shoots free throws on a basketball court. She hits the first and misses the second, and thereafter the probability that she hits the next shot is equal to the proportion of shots she has hit so far. What is the probability she hits exactly 50 of her first 100 shots?

Answer. The probability is 1/99.

Solution 1. It will be shown by induction on n that, after n shots, the probability of having made any number of shots from 1 to $n-1$ is equal to $1/(n-1)$. This is evident for $n = 2$. Given the result for n and given k from 1 to $n + 1$, the probability of making k shots out of $n + 1$ attempts is equal to the sum of the probability of making k shots out of the first n attempts and missing shot $n + 1$ and the probability of making $k - 1$ shots out of the first n attempts and making shot $n + 1$. Thus the probability of making k shots out of $n + 1$ attempts is

$$\frac{i-1}{n}\frac{1}{n-1} + \left(1 - \frac{i}{n}\right)\frac{1}{n-1} = \frac{(i-1)+(n-i)}{n(n-1)} = \frac{1}{n},$$

as claimed. The requested probability for $n = 100$ is therefore 1/99.

Solution 2. The probability can also be calculated directly. There are $\binom{98}{49}$ ways for Shanille to make 49 out of 98 shots. The probability that Shanille will produce a particular sequence of 49 shots made and 49 shots missed is

$$\frac{a_3}{2} \cdot \frac{a_4}{3} \cdot \frac{a_5}{4} \cdots \frac{a_{100}}{99},$$

where, if Shanille makes her jth shot, then a_j is the number of shots she made before her jth shot, and otherwise, a_j is the number of shots she missed before her jth shot. It follows that the sequence $a_3, a_4, a_5, \ldots, a_{100}$ must include the numbers $1, 1, 2, 2, 3, 3, 4, 4, 5, 5, \ldots, 49, 49$ in some order. Thus the probability that Shanille makes a particular sequence of 98 shots is $\frac{49! \cdot 49!}{99!}$. Therefore the required probability is $\binom{98}{49}\frac{49! \cdot 49!}{99!} = \frac{98! \cdot 49! \cdot 49!}{49! \cdot 49! \cdot 99!} = \frac{1}{99}$.

B2. (107, 48, 18, ..., 18, 1, 8, 10) 82.4%

Consider a polyhedron with at least five faces such that exactly three edges emerge from each of its vertices. Two players play the following game:

> Each player, in turn, signs his or her name on a previously unsigned face. The winner is the player who first succeeds in signing three faces that share a common vertex.

Show that the player who signs first will always win by playing as well as possible.

Remark. The problem statement assumes that all polyhedra are connected and that no two edges share more than one face, so these will be assumed here. In particular, these are true for all convex polyhedra.

Solution. (based on a suggestion by Russ Mann) In fact, the first player can win on the third move. Suppose the polyhedron has a face A with at least four edges. If the first player plays there first, after the second player's first move there will be at least three consecutive faces B, C, D adjacent to A which are all unoccupied. The first player wins by playing in C. After the second player's second move, at least one of B and D remains unoccupied, and either is a winning move for the first player.

It remains to show that the polyhedron has a face with at least four edges. Suppose on the contrary that each face has only three edges. Starting with any face F_1 with vertices v_1, v_2, v_3, let v_4 be the other endpoint of the third edge out of v_1. Then the faces adjacent to F_1 must have vertices v_1, v_2, v_4; v_1, v_3, v_4; and v_2, v_3, v_4. Thus v_1, v_2, v_3, v_4 form a polyhedron by themselves, contradicting the fact that the given polyhedron is connected and has at least five vertices. One can also deduce this using Euler's formula $V - E + F = 2 - 2g$, where V, E, F are the numbers of vertices, edges, and faces, respectively, and g is the genus of the polyhedron. For a convex polyhedron, $g = 0$, giving the "usual" Euler's formula.

Remark. (Walter Stromquist) The assumption that a pair of faces may not share multiple edges is required as shown by this example. Let A be a regular tetrahedron, and let P be the midpoint of one of its edges. Let B be a contraction of A toward the point P, and let $C = A \setminus B$. Then C has two of the original triangular faces of A, two smaller triangular faces of B, and two hexagonal faces. If the game is played on C, the second player can draw by signing one of the hexagons, one of the large triangles, and one of the small triangles by always signing the other face of the same type as the one just signed by the first player.

B3. (30, 1, 0, ..., 30, 2, 78, 69) 14.8%
   Show that, for all integers $n > 1$,

$$\frac{1}{2ne} < \frac{1}{e} - \left(1 - \frac{1}{n}\right)^n < \frac{1}{ne}.$$

Solution. The desired inequalities can be rewritten as

$$1 - \frac{1}{n} < \exp\left(1 + n\log\left(1 - \frac{1}{n}\right)\right) < 1 - \frac{1}{2n}.$$

Taking logarithms gives the equivalent inequalities

$$\log\left(1 - \frac{1}{n}\right) < 1 + n\log\left(1 - \frac{1}{n}\right) < \log\left(1 - \frac{1}{2n}\right).$$

Rewrite these in terms of the Taylor expansion

$$-\log(1-x) = -\sum_{i=1}^{\infty} \frac{x^i}{i},$$

which converges for $-1 \le x < 1$. This shows that the desired result is also equivalent to

$$\sum_{i=1}^{\infty} \frac{1}{i2^i n^i} < \sum_{i=1}^{\infty} \frac{1}{(i+1)n^i} < \sum_{i=1}^{\infty} \frac{1}{in^i},$$

which is evident because the inequalities hold term by term when $i > 1$.

Remark. David Savitt points out that the upper bound can be improved from $1/(ne)$ to $2/(3ne)$ with a slightly more complicated argument. In fact, for any $c > 1/2$, one has an upper bound of $c/(ne)$, but only for n above a certain bound depending on c.

B4. (84, 13, 11, ..., 4, 6, 50, 42) 51.4%
   An integer n, **unknown to you, has been randomly chosen in the interval** $[1, 2002]$ **with uniform probability. Your objective is to select n in an odd number of guesses. After each incorrect guess, you are informed whether n is higher or lower, and you must guess an integer on your next turn among the numbers that are still feasibly correct. Show that you have a strategy so that the chance of winning is greater than** $2/3$.

Solution. Use the following strategy: guess $1, 3, 4, 6, 7, 9, \ldots$ until the target number n is revealed to be equal to or lower than one of these guesses. If $n \equiv 1$ (mod 3), it will be guessed on an odd turn. If $n \equiv 0$ (mod 3), it will be guessed on an even turn. If $n \equiv 2$ (mod 3), then $n + 1$ will be guessed on an even turn, forcing a guess of n on the next turn. Thus the probability of success with this strategy is $1335/2002 > 2/3$.

Remark. For any positive integer m, this strategy wins with probability $\frac{1}{m} \left| \frac{2m+1}{3} \right|$ when the number is being guessed from $[1, m]$. We can prove that this is best possible as follows. Let a_m denote m times the probability of winning when playing optimally. Also let b_m denote m times the corresponding probability of winning if the objective is to select the number in an even number of guesses instead. (For definiteness, extend the definitions to incorporate $a_0 = 0$ and $b_0 = 0$.)
   We first claim that for $m \ge 1$,

$$a_m = \max_{1 \le k \le m} \{b_{k-1} + b_{m-k}\} + 1 \text{ and}$$
$$b_m = \max_{1 \le k \le m} \{a_{k-1} + a_{m-k}\}.$$

To establish the first recursive identity, suppose that our first guess is some integer k. We automatically win if $n = k$, with probability $1/m$. If $n < k$, with probability $(k - 1)/m$, then we wish to guess an integer in $[1, k - 1]$ in an even number of guesses; the probability of success when playing optimally is $b_{k-1}/(k - 1)$, by assumption. Similarly, if $n < k$, with probability $(m - k)/m$, then the subsequent probability of winning is $b_{m-k}/(m-k)$. In sum, the overall probability of winning if k is our first guess is $(1 + b_{k-1} + b_{m-k})/m$. For optimal strategy, we choose k such that this quantity is maximized. (Note that this argument still holds if $k = 1$ or $k = m$, by our definitions of a_0 and b_0.) The first recursion follows, and the second recursion is established similarly.

We now prove by induction that $a_m = \lfloor(2m + 1)/3\rfloor$ and $b_m = \lfloor 2m/3\rfloor$ for $m \geq 0$. The inductive step relies on the inequality $\lfloor x\rfloor + \lfloor y\rfloor \leq \lfloor x + y\rfloor$, with equality when one of x, y is an integer. Now suppose that $a_i = \lfloor(2i + 1)/3\rfloor$ and $b_i = \lfloor 2i/3\rfloor$ for $i < m$. Then

$$1 + b_{k-1} + b_{m-k} = 1 + \left\lfloor\frac{2(k - 1)}{3}\right\rfloor + \left\lfloor\frac{2(m - k)}{3}\right\rfloor \leq \left\lfloor\frac{2m + 1}{3}\right\rfloor$$

and similarly $a_{k-1} + a_{m-k} \leq \lfloor(2m + 1)/3\rfloor$, with equality in both cases attained, for example, when $k = 1$. The inductive formula for a_m and b_m follows.

An alternative proof notes that any deterministic guessing strategy corresponds exactly to a binary tree with m vertices where each vertex corresponds to a possible answer and the root-to-node path to that vertex corresponds to the pattern of comparison clues used to find it. The probability of winning the game is then exactly the probability that a random vertex from this tree has odd depth. Other than the root node, each vertex of odd depth has a parent of even depth and this provides an at most 2-to-1 mapping between odd-depth nonroot nodes and even-depth nodes. Thus the number of nonroot odd-depth nodes is at most $2(m - 1)/3$, and thus the total probability of winning is at most $(2m + 1)/(3m)$.

B5. $(28, 0, 5, \ldots, 2, 0, 27, 148)$ 15.7%

A palindrome in base b is a positive integer whose base-b digits read the same backwards and forwards; for example, 2002 is a 4-digit palindrome in base 10. Note that 200 is not a palindrome in base 10, but it is the 3-digit palindrome 242 in base 9, and 404 in base 7. Prove that there is an integer which is a 3-digit palindrome in base b for at least 2002 different values of b.

Solution 1. (Dan Bernstein) Put $N = 2002!$. Then for $d = 1, \ldots, 2002$, the number N^2 written in base $b = N/d - 1$ has digits $d^2, 2d^2, d^2$. (These really are digits because $2(d)^2 < (2002!)^2/d - 1$ for $d \leq 2002$.)

Solution 2. One can also produce an integer N which has base-b digits $1, *, 1$ for n different values of b, as follows. Choose c with $1 < c < 2^{1/n}$. For m a large positive integer, put $N = 1 + (m+1)\cdots(m+n)\lceil cm\rceil^{n-2}$. For m sufficiently large, the bases

$$b = \frac{N-1}{(m+i)\lceil cm\rceil^{n-2}} = \prod_{j\neq i}(m+j)$$

for $i = 1,\ldots,n$ will have the properties that $N \equiv 1 \pmod b$ and $b^2 < N < 2b^2$.

Solution 3. (Russ Mann) One can also give a "nonconstructive" argument. Let N be a large positive integer. For $b \in (N^2, N^3)$, the number of 3-digit base-b palindromes in the range $[b^2, N^6 - 1]$ is at least

$$\left\lfloor \frac{N^6 - b^2}{b} \right\rfloor - 1 \geq \frac{N^6}{b} - b - 2,$$

since there is a palindrome in each interval $[kb, (k+1)b - 1]$ for $k = b, \ldots, b^2 - 1$. Thus the average number of bases for which a number in $[1, N^6 - 1]$ is a palindrome is at least

$$\frac{1}{N^6} \sum_{b=N^2+1}^{N^3-1} \left(\frac{N^6}{b} - b - 2 \right) \geq \log(N) - c$$

for some constant $c > 0$. Take N so that the right side exceeds 2002; then at least one number in $[1, N^6 - 1]$ is a base-b palindrome for at least 2002 values of b.

B6. (7, 6, 4, ..., 3, 3, 28, 159) 8.1%
Let p be a prime number. Prove that the determinant of the matrix

$$\begin{pmatrix} x & y & z \\ x^p & y^p & z^p \\ x^{p^2} & y^{p^2} & z^{p^2} \end{pmatrix}$$

is congruent modulo p to a product of polynomials of the form $ax+by+cz$, where a, b, c are integers. (We say two integer polynomials are congruent modulo p if corresponding coefficients are congruent modulo p.)

Solution 1. We show that the determinant is congruent modulo p to

$$x \prod_{i=0}^{p-1}(y + ix) \prod_{i,j=0}^{p-1}(z + ix + jy). \tag{1}$$

In the following, all computations will be taken modulo p.
For any integers a, b, c,

$$a[x, x^p, x^{p^2}] + b[y, y^p, y^{p^2}] + c[z, z^p, z^{p^2}]$$
$$= [ax + by + cz, ax^p + by^p + cz^p, ax^{p^2} + by^{p^2} + cz^{p^2}]$$
$$\equiv [ax + by + cz, (ax + by + cz)^p, (ax + by + cz)^{p^2}].$$

Thus this column vector is a linear combination of the columns of the given matrix. Therefore for a, b, c not all zero modulo p, $ax + by + cz$ divides the determinant modulo p. In particular, all of the factors of (1) divide the determinant, as then does (1) by unique factorization of polynomials; since both (1) and the determinant have degree $p^2 + p + 1$, they agree up to a scalar multiple. Moreover, they have the same coefficient of $z^{p^2} y^p x$ (since this term only appears in the expansion of (1) by taking the first term in each factor). Thus the determinant is congruent to (1), as desired.

Solution 2. We first check that

$$\prod_{i=0}^{p-1} (y + ix) \equiv y^p - x^{p-1}y \pmod{p}. \tag{2}$$

Since both sides are homogeneous as polynomials in x and y, it suffices to check (2) for $x = 1$, as a congruence between polynomials. Note that the right-hand side of (2) has $0, 1, \dots, p - 1$ as roots modulo p, as does the left-hand side. Moreover, both sides have the same leading coefficient. Since they both have degree p, they must then coincide.

We thus have

$$x \prod_{i=0}^{p-1} (y + ix) \prod_{i,j=0}^{p-1} (z + ix + jy)$$

$$\equiv x(y^p - x^{p-1}y) \prod_{j=0}^{p-1} ((z + jy)^p - x^{p-1}(z + jy))$$

$$\equiv (xy^p - x^p y) \prod_{j=0}^{p-1} (z^p - x^{p-1}z + jy^p - jx^{p-1}y)$$

$$\equiv (xy^p - x^p y)((z^p - x^{p-1}z)^p - (y^p - x^{p-1}y)^{p-1}(z^p - x^{p-1}z))$$

$$\equiv (xy^p - x^p y)(z^{p^2} - x^{p^2-p}z^p) - x(y^p - x^{p-1}y)^p(z^p - x^{p-1}z)$$

$$\equiv xy^p z^{p^2} - x^p yz^{p^2} - x^{p^2-p+1}y^p z^p + x^{p^2}yz^p - xy^{p^2}z^p$$

$$\qquad + x^{p^2-p+1}y^p z^p + x^p y^{p^2}z - x^{p^2}y^p z$$

$$\equiv xy^p z^{p^2} + yz^p x^{p^2} + zx^p y^{p^2} - xz^p y^{p^2} - yx^p z^{p^2} - zy^p x^{p^2},$$

which is precisely the desired determinant.

Remark. Either argument can be used to generalize to a corresponding $n \times n$ determinant, called a *Moore determinant*; we leave the precise formulation to the reader. Note the similarity with the classical Vandermonde determinant: if A is the $n \times n$ matrix with $A_{ij} = x_i^j$ for $i, j = 0, \ldots, n-1$, then

$$\det(A) = \prod_{1 \le i < j \le n} (x_j - x_i).$$

The Sixty-Fourth William Lowell Putnam
Mathematical Competition—December 6, 2003

A1. $(149, 3, 29, \ldots, 10, 1, 5, 4)$ 90.0%
Let n be a fixed positive integer. How many ways are there to write n as a sum of positive integers,

$$n = a_1 + a_2 + \cdots + a_k,$$

with k an arbitrary positive integer, and $a_1 \leq a_2 \leq \cdots \leq a_k \leq a_1 + 1$? For example, with $n = 4$ there are four ways: $4, 2+2, 1+1+2, 1+1+1+1$.

Answer. There are n such sums.

Solution. More precisely, there is exactly one such sum with k terms for each of $k = 1, \ldots, n$ (and clearly no others). To see this, note that if $n = a_1 + a_2 + \cdots + a_k$ with $a_1 \leq a_2 \leq \cdots \leq a_k \leq a_1 + 1$, then

$$
\begin{aligned}
ka_1 &= a_1 + a_1 + \cdots + a_1 \\
&\leq n \leq a_1 + (a_1 + 1) + \cdots + (a_1 + 1) \\
&= ka_1 + k - 1.
\end{aligned}
$$

However, there is a unique integer a_1 satisfying these inequalities, namely $a_1 = \lfloor n/k \rfloor$. Moreover, once a_1 is fixed, there are k different possibilities for the sum $a_1 + a_2 + \cdots + a_k$: if i is the last integer such that $a_i = a_1$, then the sum equals $ka_1 + (i - 1)$. The possible values of i are $1, \ldots, k$, and exactly one of these sums comes out equal to n, proving our claim.

Remark. In summary, there is a unique partition of n with k terms that is "as equally spaced as possible". One can also obtain essentially the same construction inductively: except for the all-ones sum, each partition of n is obtained by "augmenting" a unique partition of $n - 1$.

A2. $(55, 25, 8, \ldots, 15, 1, 35, 62)$ 43.8%
Let $a_1, a_2, \ldots, a_n$ and $b_1, b_2, \ldots, b_n$ be nonnegative real numbers. Show that

$$(a_1 a_2 \cdots a_n)^{1/n} + (b_1 b_2 \cdots b_n)^{1/n} \leq [(a_1 + b_1)(a_2 + b_2) \cdots (a_n + b_n)]^{1/n}.$$

Solution 1. Assume without loss of generality that $a_i + b_i > 0$ for each i (otherwise both sides of the desired inequality are zero). Then the arithmetic mean/geometric mean inequality gives

$$\left(\frac{a_1 \cdots a_n}{(a_1 + b_1) \cdots (a_n + b_n)}\right)^{1/n} \leq \frac{1}{n}\left(\frac{a_1}{a_1 + b_1} + \cdots + \frac{a_n}{a_n + b_n}\right),$$

and likewise with the roles of a and b reversed. Adding these two inequalities and clearing denominators yields the desired result.

Solution 2. Write the desired inequality in the form

$$(a_1 + b_1)\cdots(a_n + b_n) \geq [(a_1 \cdots a_n)^{1/n} + (b_1 \cdots b_n)^{1/n}]^n.$$

Expand both sides, and compare the terms on both sides in which k of the terms are among the a_i. On the left, one has the product of each k-element subset of $\{1, \ldots, n\}$; on the right, one has

$$\binom{n}{k}(a_1 \cdots a_n)^{k/n} \cdots (b_1 \ldots b_n)^{(n-k)/n},$$

which is precisely $\binom{n}{k}$ times the geometric mean of the terms on the left. Thus the arithmetic mean/geometric mean inequality shows that the terms under consideration on the left are at least as large as those on the right. Adding these inequalities over all k yields the desired result.

Solution 3. Since both sides are continuous in each a_i, it is sufficient to prove the claim with $a_1, \ldots, a_n$ all positive (the general case follows by taking limits as some of the a_i tend to zero). Put $r_i = b_i/a_i$. Then the given inequality is equivalent to

$$(1 + r_1)^{1/n} \cdots (1 + r_n)^{1/n} \geq 1 + (r_1 \cdots r_n)^{1/n}.$$

In terms of the function

$$f(x) = \log(1 + e^x)$$

and the quantities $s_i = \log r_i$, the desired inequality can be written as

$$\frac{1}{n}(f(s_1) + \cdots + f(s_n)) \geq f\left(\frac{s_1 + \cdots + s_n}{n}\right).$$

If f is a convex function, this inequality will follow from Jensen's inequality. It is enough to check that $f''(x) \geq 0$ for all x. In fact,

$$f'(x) = \frac{e^x}{1 + e^x} = 1 - \frac{1}{1 + e^x}$$

is an increasing function of x, so $f''(x) \geq 0$ as needed. (As long as the a_i are all positive, equality holds when $s_1 = \cdots = s_n$, that is, when the vectors $(a_1, \ldots, a_n)$ and $(b_1, \ldots, b_n)$ are parallel. Of course other equality cases crop up if some of the a_i vanish, for example, if $a_1 = b_1 = 0$.)

Solution 4. The result follows by an induction on n. The case $n = 1$ is evident. Consider the auxiliary inequality

$$(a^n + b^n)(c^n + d^n)^{n-1} \geq (ac^{n-1} + bd^{n-1})^n$$

for $a, b, c, d \geq 0$. The left side can be written as

$$a^n c^{n(n-1)} + b^n d^{n(n-1)} + \sum_{i=1}^{n-1} \binom{n-1}{i} b^n c^{ni} d^{n(n-1-i)} + \sum_{i=1}^{n-1} \binom{n-1}{i-1} a^n c^{n(i-1)} d^{n(n-i)}.$$

Applying the weighted arithmetic mean/geometric mean inequality between matching terms in the two sums yields

$$(a^n + b^n)(c^n + d^n)^{n-1} \geq a^n c^{n(n-1)} + b^n d^{n(n-1)} + \sum_{i=1}^{n-1} \binom{n}{i} a^i b^{n-i} c^{(n-1)i} d^{(n-1)(n-i)},$$

proving the auxiliary inequality.

Now given the auxiliary inequality and the $n-1$ case of the desired inequality, apply the auxiliary inequality with $a = a_1^{1/n}$, $b = b_1^{1/n}$, $c = (a_2 \cdots a_n)^{1/n(n-1)}$, $d = (b_2 \dots b_n)^{1/n(n-1)}$. The right side will be the nth power of the desired inequality. The left side comes out to

$$(a_1 + b_1)((a_2 \cdots a_n)^{1/(n-1)} + (b_2 \cdots b_n)^{1/(n-1)})^{n-1},$$

and by the induction hypothesis, the second factor is less than $(a_2 + b_2) \cdots (a_n + b_n)$. This yields the desired result.

Remark. Equality holds if and only if $a_i = b_i = 0$ for some i or if the vectors $(a_1, \dots, a_n)$ and $(b_1, \dots, b_n)$ are proportional. As pointed out by Naoki Sato, the problem also appeared on the 1992 Irish Mathematical Olympiad. It is also a special case of a classical inequality, known as *Hölder's inequality*, which generalizes the Cauchy-Schwarz inequality (this is visible from the $n = 2$ case). The first solution above is adapted from the standard proof of Hölder's inequality. Conceivably, the declaration "Apply Hölder's inequality" by itself might have been considered an acceptable solution to this problem.

A3. $(10, 1, 7, \dots, 2, 4, 100, 77)$ 9.0%

Find the minimum value of

$$|\sin x + \cos x + \tan x + \cot x + \sec x + \csc x|$$

for real numbers x.

Answer. The minimum value is $2\sqrt{2} - 1$.

Solution 1. Write

$$f = f(x) = \sin x + \cos x + \tan x + \cot x + \sec x + \csc x$$

$$= \sin x + \cos x + \frac{1}{\sin x \cos x} + \frac{\sin x + \cos x}{\sin x \cos x}.$$

The identity $\sin x + \cos x = \sqrt{2} \cos(\pi/4 - x)$ suggests making the substitution $y = \pi/4 - x$. In this new coordinate,

$$\sin x \cos x = \frac{1}{2} \sin 2x = \frac{1}{2} \cos 2y,$$

and writing $c = \sqrt{2}\cos y$ yields

$$f = (1 + c)\left(1 + \frac{2}{c^2 - 1}\right) - 1$$

$$= c + \frac{2}{c - 1}.$$

The answer is the maximum of f for c in the range $[-\sqrt{2}, \sqrt{2}]$. Its value at $c = -\sqrt{2}$ is $2 - 3\sqrt{2} < -2.24$, and at $c = \sqrt{2}$ is $2 + 3\sqrt{2} > 6.24$. Its derivative is $1 - 2/(c - 1)^2$, which vanishes when $(c - 1)^2 = 2$, that is, where $c = 1 \pm \sqrt{2}$. Only the value $c = 1 - \sqrt{2}$ is in bounds, at which the value of f is $1 - 2\sqrt{2} > -1.83$. As for the pole at $c = 1$, observe that f decreases as c approaches 1 from below and, thus it takes negative values for all $c < 1$. It increases as c approaches 1 from above, and, thus it takes positive values for all $c > 1$. Therefore f has no sign changes, so the minimum of $|f|$ is achieved at a critical point of f. Conclude that the minimum value of $|f|$ is $2\sqrt{2} - 1$.

Remark. (Zuming Feng) The function $|c + 2/(c - 1)|$ can be maximized without calculus or worrying about boundary conditions. For $c > 1$,

$$1 + (c - 1) + \frac{2}{c - 1} \geq 1 + 2\sqrt{2}$$

by the arithmetic mean/geometric mean inequality applied to the last two terms, with equality for $c - 1 = \sqrt{2}$, which is outside of range for c. Similarly, for $c < 1$,

$$-1 + 1 - c + \frac{2}{1 - c} \geq -1 + 2\sqrt{2},$$

with equality for $1 - c = \sqrt{2}$.

Solution 2. Write

$$f = f(a, b) = a + b + \frac{1}{ab} + \frac{a + b}{ab}.$$

Then the problem is to minimize $|f(a, b)|$ subject to the constraint $a^2 + b^2 - 1 = 0$. Since the constraint region has no boundary, it is enough to check the value at each critical point and each potential discontinuity (that is, where $ab = 0$) and select the smallest value after checking that f has no sign crossings.

The critical points can be located using the Lagrange multiplier condition: the gradient of f should be parallel to that of the constraint, which is to say, to the vector (a, b). Since

$$\frac{\partial f}{\partial a} = 1 - \frac{1}{a^2 b} - \frac{1}{a^2}$$

and similarly for b, the proportionality yields

$$a^2 b^3 - a^3 b^2 + a^3 - b^3 + a^2 - b^2 = 0.$$

The irreducible factors of the left side are $1 + a$, $1 + b$, $a - b$, $ab - a - b$. So one must check what happens when any of those factors, or a or b, vanishes.

As (a, b) approaches $(-1, 0)$ along the circle $a^2 + b^2 = 1$,

$$f = a + b + \frac{1 + a + b}{ab} = a + b + \frac{b(1 + a) + b^2}{ab^2} = a + b + \frac{b + 1 - a}{a(1 - a)}.$$

Thus when $1 + a = 0$ and $b = 0$, the singularity of f becomes removable and f is -2. The same occurs when $1 + b = 0$.

If $a - b = 0$, then $a = b = \pm\sqrt{2}/2$, and either $f = 2 + 3\sqrt{2} > 6.24$, or $f = 2 - 3\sqrt{2} < -2.24$.

If $a = 0$, then either $b = -1$ as discussed above, or $b = 1$. In the latter case, $|f|$ blows up as one approaches this point, so there cannot be a global minimum there.

Finally, if $ab - a - b = 0$, then

$$a^2 b^2 = (a + b)^2 = 2ab + 1,$$

and so $ab = 1 \pm \sqrt{2}$. The plus sign is impossible since $|ab| \leq 1$, so $ab = 1 - \sqrt{2}$ and

$$f(a, b) = ab + \frac{1}{ab} + 1$$
$$= 1 - 2\sqrt{2} > -1.83.$$

This yields the smallest value of $|f|$ in the list, and, since no sign crossings are possible, $2\sqrt{2} - 1$ is the desired minimum of $|f|$.

Remark. Instead of using the geometry of the graph of f to rule out sign crossings, one can verify explicitly that f cannot take the value 0. In the first solution, note that $c + 2/(c - 1) = 0$ implies $c^2 - c + 2 = 0$, which has no real roots. In the second solution, a sign crossing implies

$$a^2 b + ab^2 + a + b = -1.$$

Squaring both sides and simplifying yields

$$2a^3 b^3 + 5a^2 b^2 + 4ab = 0,$$

whose only real root is $ab = 0$. But the cases with $ab = 0$ do not yield $f = 0$, as verified above.

A4. (15, 4, 5, ..., 71, 18, 27, 61) 11.9%
   Suppose that a, b, c, A, B, C are real numbers, $a \neq 0$ and $A \neq 0$, such that

$$|ax^2 + bx + c| \leq |Ax^2 + Bx + C|$$

for all real numbers x. Show that

$$|b^2 - 4ac| \leq |B^2 - 4AC|.$$

Solution. We split into three cases. Note first that $|A| \geq |a|$, by applying the condition for large x.

Suppose $B^2 - 4AC > 0$. In this case $Ax^2 + Bx + C$ has two distinct real roots r_1 and r_2. The condition implies that $ax^2 + bx + c$ also vanishes at r_1 and r_2, so $b^2 - 4ac > 0$. Now

$$B^2 - 4AC = A^2(r_1 - r_2)^2$$
$$\geq a^2(r_1 - r_2)^2$$
$$= b^2 - 4ac.$$

Suppose $B^2 - 4AC \leq 0$ and $b^2 - 4ac \leq 0$. Assume without loss of generality that $A \geq a > 0$, and that $B = 0$ (because shifting x doesn't change the discriminant). Then $Ax^2 + Bx + C \geq ax^2 + bx + c \geq 0$ for all x; in particular, $C \geq c \geq 0$. Thus

$$4AC - B^2 = 4AC$$
$$\geq 4ac$$
$$\geq 4ac - b^2.$$

Robin Chapman points out an alternate derivation in this case: the ellipse $Ax^2 + Bxy + Cy^2 = 1$ is contained within the ellipse $ax^2 + bxy + cy^2 = 1$, and their respective enclosed areas are $\pi/(4AC - B^2)$ and $\pi/(4ac - b^2)$.

Suppose $B^2 - 4AC \leq 0$ and $b^2 - 4ac > 0$. Here $Ax^2 + Bx + C$ has a graph not crossing the x-axis, so without loss of generality it is nonnegative for all x. Therefore the given inequality of quadratics is equivalent to $Ax^2 + Bx + C \geq \pm(ax^2 + bx + c)$ for all x. Hence $(Ax^2 + Bx + C) \pm (ax^2 + bx + c) \geq 0$ for all x, and in particular, these quadratics don't cross the x-axis. Thus

$$(B - b)^2 - 4(A - a)(C - c) \leq 0,$$
$$(B + b)^2 - 4(A + a)(C + c) \leq 0$$

and adding these together yields

$$2(B^2 - 4AC) + 2(b^2 - 4ac) \leq 0.$$

Hence $b^2 - 4ac \leq 4AC - B^2$, as desired.

A5. $(27, 0, 1, \ldots, 6, 2, 33, 132)$ 13.9%

A **Dyck** n-**path** is a lattice path of n **upsteps** $(1, 1)$ **and** n **downsteps** $(1, -1)$ **that starts at the origin** O **and never dips below the** x-**axis. A return is a maximal sequence of contiguous downsteps that terminates on the** x-**axis. For example, the Dyck 5-path illustrated has two returns, of length 3 and 1 respectively.**

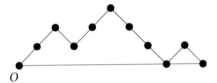

Show that there is a one-to-one correspondence between the Dyck n-paths with no return of even length and the Dyck $(n-1)$-paths.

Solution 1. We represent a Dyck n-path by a sequence $a_1 \cdots a_{2n}$, where each a_i is either $(1, 1)$ or $(1, -1)$.

Given an $(n-1)$-path $P = a_1 \cdots a_{2n-2}$, we distinguish two cases. If P has no returns of even length, then let $f(P)$ denote the n-path $(1, 1)(1, -1)P$. Otherwise, let $a_i a_{i+1} \cdots a_j$ denote the rightmost even-length return in P, and let $f(P) = (1, 1)a_1 a_2 \cdots a_j (1, -1)a_{j+1} \cdots a_{2n-2}$. In both cases, $f(P)$ has no even returns. In the first case, this is because $f(P)$ has only returns that P had and a return of length 1. In the second case, it is because $f(P)$ has a return of length one more than the last even return of P, and of lengths equal to the lengths of the subsequent odd returns of P. Thus f clearly maps the set of Dyck $(n-1)$-paths to the set of Dyck n-paths having no even return.

We claim that f is bijective; to see this, we simply construct the inverse mapping. Given an n-path P (with no even returns), let $R = a_i a_{i+1} \cdots a_j$ denote the leftmost return in P, and let $g(P)$ denote the path obtained by removing a_1 and a_j from P. This is a Dyck path because all of the points after a_j remain (shifted left two spaces), and all the points before (other than the start and the end of the first return) are shifted down and left one, but will remain on or above the axis. Then evidently $g \circ f$ is the identity map. We also have $f \circ g$ is the identity because $a_i a_{i+1} \cdots a_{j-1}$ will be the last even return of $g(P)$. This proves the claim.

Solution 2. (Dan Bernstein) Let C_n be the number of Dyck paths of length n, let O_n be the number of Dyck paths whose final return has odd length, and let X_n be the number of Dyck paths with no return of even length.

We first exhibit a recursion for O_n; note that $O_0 = 0$. Given a Dyck n-path whose final return has odd length, split it just after its next-to-last return. For some k (possibly zero), this yields a Dyck k-path, an upstep, a Dyck $(n-k-1)$-path whose final return has even length, and a downstep. Thus for $n \geq 1$,

$$O_n = \sum_{k=0}^{n-1} C_k(C_{n-k-1} - O_{n-k-1}).$$

We next exhibit a similar recursion for X_n, noting that $X_0 = 1$. Given a Dyck n-path with no even return, splitting as above yields for some k a Dyck k-path with no even return, an upstep, a Dyck $(n-k-1)$-path whose final return has even length, then a downstep. Thus for $n \geq 1$,

$$X_n = \sum_{k=0}^{n-1} X_k(C_{n-k-1} - O_{n-k-1}).$$

To conclude, we verify that $X_n = C_{n-1}$ for $n \geq 1$, by induction on n. This is clear for $n = 1$ since $X_1 = C_0 = 1$. Given $X_k = C_{k-1}$ for $k < n$, we have

$$X_n = \sum_{k=0}^{n-1} X_k(C_{n-k-1} - O_{n-k-1})$$

$$= C_{n-1} - O_{n-1} + \sum_{k=1}^{n-1} C_{k-1}(C_{n-k-1} - O_{n-k-1})$$

$$= C_{n-1} - O_{n-1} + O_{n-1}$$

$$= C_{n-1},$$

as desired.

Remark. Since the problem only asked about the *existence* of a one-to-one correspondence, we believe that any proof, bijective or not, that the two sets have the same cardinality is an acceptable solution. (Indeed, it would be highly unusual to insist on using or not using a specific proof technique!) The second solution above can also be phrased in terms of generating functions. Also the C_n are well-known to equal the Catalan numbers $\frac{1}{n+1}\binom{2n}{n}$; the problem at hand is part of a famous exercise in [**Stanley**] giving 66 combinatorial interpretations of the Catalan numbers.

A6. (18, 6, 4, ..., 7, 4, 45, 117) 13.9%

For a set S of nonnegative integers, let $r_S(n)$ denote the number of ordered pairs (s_1, s_2) such that $s_1 \in S$, $s_2 \in S$, $s_1 \neq s_2$, and $s_1 + s_2 = n$. Is it possible to partition the nonnegative integers into two sets A and B in such a way that $r_A(n) = r_B(n)$ for all n?

Answer. Yes, such a partition is possible.

Solution 1. We will establish the desired property for the partition constructed by the following procedure: place each integer into A if it has an even number of 1's in its binary representation, and into B if it has an odd number. (One discovers this by simply attempting to place the first few numbers by hand and noticing the resulting pattern.)

To show that $r_A(n) = r_B(n)$, we exhibit a bijection between the pairs (a_1, a_2) of distinct elements of A with $a_1 + a_2 = n$ and the pairs (b_1, b_2) of distinct elements of B with $b_1 + b_2 = n$. Namely, given a pair (a_1, a_2) with $a_1 + a_2 = n$, write both numbers in binary and find the lowest-order place in which they differ (such a place exists because $a_1 \neq a_2$). Change both numbers in that place and call the resulting numbers b_1, b_2. Then $a_1 + a_2 = b_1 + b_2 = n$, but the parity of the number of 1's in b_1 is opposite that of a_1, and likewise between b_2 and a_2. This yields the desired bijection.

Solution 2. (Micah Smukler) Write $b(n)$ for the number of 1's in the base-2 expansion of n, and $f(n) = (-1)^{b(n)}$. Then the desired partition can be described as $A = f^{-1}(1)$ and $B = f^{-1}(-1)$. Since $f(2n) + f(2n + 1) = 0$,

$$\sum_{i=0}^{n} f(n) = \begin{cases} 0 & n \text{ odd}, \\ f(n) & n \text{ even}. \end{cases}$$

If p, q are both in A, then $f(p) + f(q) = 2$; if p, q are both in B, then $f(p) + f(q) = -2$; if p, q are in different sets, then $f(p) + f(q) = 0$. In other words,

$$2(r_A(n) - r_B(n)) = \sum_{p+q=n, p<q} (f(p) + f(q))$$

and it suffices to show that the sum on the right is always zero. If n is odd, that sum is visibly $\sum_{i=0}^{n} f(i) = 0$. If n is even, the sum equals

$$\left(\sum_{i=0}^{n} f(i) \right) - f(n/2) = f(n) - f(n/2) = 0.$$

This yields the desired result.

Solution 3. (Dan Bernstein) With A and B as in the previous two solutions, put $f(x) = \sum_{n \in A} x^n$ and $g(x) = \sum_{n \in B} x^n$; then the value of $r_A(n)$ (resp. $r_B(n)$) is the coefficient of x^n in $f(x)^2 - f(x^2)$ (resp. $g(x)^2 - g(x^2)$). From the evident identities

$$\frac{1}{1-x} = f(x) + g(x),$$
$$f(x) = f(x^2) + xg(x^2),$$
$$g(x) = g(x^2) + xf(x^2),$$

we have

$$f(x) - g(x) = f(x^2) - g(x^2) + xg(x^2) - xf(x^2)$$
$$= (1-x)(f(x^2) - g(x^2))$$
$$= \frac{f(x^2) - g(x^2)}{f(x) + g(x)}.$$

We deduce that $f(x)^2 - g(x)^2 = f(x^2) - g(x^2)$, yielding the desired equality.

Remark. This partition is actually unique, up to interchanging A and B. More precisely, the condition that $0 \in A$ and $r_A(n) = r_B(n)$ for $n = 1, \ldots, m$ uniquely determines the positions of $0, \ldots, m$. We see this by induction on m: given the result for $m - 1$, switching the location of m changes $r_A(m)$ by one and does not change $r_B(m)$, so it is not possible for both positions to work. Robin Chapman points out this problem is solved in [**Newman**]; in that solution, one uses generating functions to find the partition and establish its uniqueness, not just verify it.

B1. (62, 6, 4, ..., 14, 6, 83, 26) 35.8%
   Do there exist polynomials $a(x), b(x), c(y), d(y)$ **such that**
$$1 + xy + x^2 y^2 = a(x)c(y) + b(x)d(y)$$
holds identically?

Answer. No, there do not.

Solution 1. Suppose the contrary. By setting $y = -1, 0, 1$ in succession, it is seen that the polynomials $1 - x + x^2, 1, 1 + x + x^2$ are linear combinations of $a(x)$ and $b(x)$. But these three polynomials are linearly independent, so they cannot all be written as linear combinations of two other polynomials. This contradicts the assumption and shows that the representation is not possible.

Reinterpretation. Let $n = \max\{1, \deg a, \deg b, \deg c, \deg d\}$. The polynomials $1 + xy + x^2 y^2$, $a(x)c(y)$, $b(x)d(y)$ can each be represented by an $(n + 1) \times (n + 1)$ matrix of coefficients, where the i, j entry in the matrix gives the coefficient of the $x^{i-1} y^{j-1}$ term of the polynomial. The matrix for $1 + xy + x^2 y^2$ is a diagonal matrix with diagonal entries $1, 1, 1, 0, \ldots, 0$, so it has rank 3. Each of the matrices for $a(x)c(y)$ and $b(x)d(y)$ have the property that all nonzero rows are proportional, so each of these matrices have rank 1. The sum of two matrices of rank 1 cannot be a matrix of rank 3, and this shows that $1 + xy + x^2 y^2$ cannot be written as $a(x)c(y) + b(x)d(y)$.

Solution 2. Write $a(x) = \sum a_i x^i$, $b(x) = \sum b_i x^i$, $c(y) = \sum c_j y^j$, $d(y) = \sum d_j y^j$. By comparing coefficients of $1 + xy + x^2 y^2$ and $a(x)c(y) + b(x)d(y)$, it is seen that
$$1 = a_i c_i + b_i d_i \qquad (i = 0, 1, 2),$$
$$0 = a_i c_j + b_i d_j \qquad (i \neq j).$$
These equations show that if $a_0 = 0$, it follows that $a_0 c_0 = 0$, so $b_0 d_0 \neq 0$. But $a_0 c_1 = a_0 c_2 = 0$ implies $b_0 d_1 = b_0 d_2 = 0$, so $d_1 = d_2 = 0$. Thus $b_1 d_1 = b_2 d_2 = 0$, so $a_1 c_1 \neq 0$ and $a_2 c_2 \neq 0$. But $a_1 c_2 \neq 0$ implies $b_1 d_2 \neq 0$ which contradicts $d_2 = 0$. By symmetry, none of the variables a_i, b_i, c_i, d_i can equal zero for $i = 0, 1, 2$. The second equation says that $a_i / b_i = -d_j / c_j$ when $i \neq j$ and $i, j \in \{0, 1, 2\}$. But then
$$a_0 / b_0 = -d_1 / c_1 = a_2 / b_2 = -d_0 / c_0,$$

contradicting the equation $a_0 c_0 + b_0 d_0 = 1$.

Solution 3. Let ω be a primitive cube root of 1. This solution will use the fact that there is unique factorization of polynomials in two variables over a field.

Suppose the proposed representation in the problem is possible. Since $1 + xy + x^2 y^2 = (1 - xy/\omega)(1 - xy/\omega^2)$, the rational function $a(\omega/y)c(y) + b(\omega/y)d(y)$ must vanish identically (that is, coefficient by coefficient). If one of the polynomials, say a, vanished identically, then one of b or d would also, and the desired inequality could not hold. So none of them vanish identically, and one can write

$$\frac{c(y)}{d(y)} = -\frac{b(\omega/y)}{a(\omega/y)}.$$

Likewise,

$$\frac{c(y)}{d(y)} = -\frac{b(\omega^2/y)}{a(\omega^2/y)}.$$

Put $f(x) = a(x)/b(x)$. Then $f(\omega x) = f(x)$ identically. That is, $a(x)b(\omega x) = b(x)a(\omega x)$. Since a and b have no common factor (otherwise $1 + xy + x^2 y^2$ would have a factor divisible only by x, which it does not since it does not vanish identically for any particular x), $a(x)$ divides $a(\omega x)$. Since they have the same degree, they are equal up to scalars. It follows that one of $a(x), xa(x), x^2 a(x)$ is a polynomial in x^3 alone, and likewise for b (with the same power of x).

If $xa(x)$ and $xb(x)$, or $x^2 a(x)$ and $x^2 b(x)$, are polynomials in x^3, then a and b are divisible by x, but a and b have no common factor. Hence $a(x)$ and $b(x)$ are polynomials in x^3. Likewise, $c(y)$ and $d(y)$ are polynomials in y^3. But then $1 + xy + x^2 y^2 = a(x)c(y) + b(x)d(y)$ is a polynomial in x^3 and y^3, which is a contradiction.

Remark. The third solution only works over fields of characteristic not equal to 3, whereas the other two work over arbitrary fields. In the first solution, one must replace -1 by another value if working in characteristic 2.

B2. (119, 13, 4, ..., 30, 6, 12, 17) 67.7%
Let n be a positive integer. **Starting with the sequence** $1, \frac{1}{2}, \frac{1}{3}, \dots, \frac{1}{n}$, **form a new sequence of** $n - 1$ **entries** $\frac{3}{4}, \frac{5}{12}, \dots, \frac{2n-1}{2n(n-1)}$ **by taking the averages of two consecutive entries in the first sequence. Repeat the averaging of neighbors on the second sequence to obtain a third sequence of** $n - 2$ **entries and continue until the final sequence produced consists of a single number** x_n. **Show that** $x_n < 2/n$.

Solution. Induction shows that the jth entry of the kth sequence (where the original sequence is $k = 1$) is

$$\sum_{i=1}^{k} \frac{\binom{k-1}{i-1}}{2^{k-1}(i+j-1)}.$$

Indeed, when $k = 1$, the expression is the given sequence, and if it is true for some $k = m$, then the jth term of the $(m+1)$st sequence is

$$\frac{1}{2}\left(\sum_{i=1}^{m} \frac{\binom{m-1}{i-1}}{2^{m-1}(i+j-1)} + \sum_{i=1}^{m} \frac{\binom{m-1}{i-1}}{2^{m-1}(i+j)}\right) =$$

$$\frac{1}{2}\left(\sum_{i=1}^{m} \frac{\binom{m-1}{i-1}}{2^{m-1}(i+j-1)} + \sum_{i=2}^{m+1} \frac{\binom{m-1}{i}}{2^{m-1}(i+j-1)}\right) = \sum_{i=1}^{m+1} \frac{\binom{m}{i-1}}{2^{m}(i+j-1)},$$

completing the induction argument. From this $x_n = \frac{\sum_{i=1}^{n} \binom{n-1}{i-1}}{i 2^{n-1}}$. Then using $\binom{n-1}{i-1}/i = \binom{n}{i}/n$ gives

$$x_n = \frac{1}{n 2^{n-1}} \sum_{i=1}^{n} \binom{n}{i} = \frac{2^n - 1}{n 2^{n-1}} < 2/n,$$

as desired.

B3. (97, 35, 20, ..., 10, 5, 12, 22) 75.6%
Show that for each positive integer n,

$$n! = \prod_{i=1}^{n} \mathrm{lcm}\{1, 2, \ldots, \lfloor n/i \rfloor\}.$$

(Here lcm denotes the least common multiple, and $\lfloor x \rfloor$ denotes the greatest integer $\leq x$.)

Solution 1. It is enough to show that for each prime p, the exponent of p in the prime factorization of each side of the equation is the same. For any prime p, because $\lfloor \frac{n}{p^i} \rfloor$ counts the number of factors of $n!$ divisible by p^i, it follows that the exponent of p in the prime factorization of $n!$ is

$$\sum_{i=1}^{n} \left\lfloor \frac{n}{p^i} \right\rfloor.$$

This number can be reinterpreted as the cardinality of the set S of points in the plane with positive integer coordinates lying on or under the curve $y = np^{-x}$. In particular, for each i, the value of $\lfloor \frac{n}{p^i} \rfloor$ gives the number of points of S with $x = i$.

On the right side of the equation, the power of p in the prime factorization of $\mathrm{lcm}(1, \ldots, \lfloor n/i \rfloor)$ is the largest power of p that divides n/i, so its exponent is

$\lfloor \log_p \lfloor n/i \rfloor \rfloor = \lfloor \log_p(n/i) \rfloor$. However, this is precisely the number of points of S with $y = i$. Thus

$$\sum_{i=1}^{n} \left\lfloor \log_p \left\lfloor \frac{n}{i} \right\rfloor \right\rfloor = \sum_{i=1}^{n} \left\lfloor \frac{n}{p^i} \right\rfloor,$$

and the desired result follows.

Solution 2. The result can be proved by induction on n. The case for $n = 1$ is the trivial equality $1 = 1$. Assume that the given equation holds for $n - 1$ where $n > 1$. Changing the equation from the $(n-1)$st case to the nth case multiplies the left-hand side of the equation by n and the right-hand side of the equation by

$$\prod_{i=1}^{n-1} \frac{\mathrm{lcm}\{1, 2, \ldots, \lfloor n/i \rfloor\}}{\mathrm{lcm}\{1, 2, \ldots, \lfloor (n-1)/i \rfloor\}}.$$

The ith factor in this product is equal to 1 if n/i is not an integer, that is, if n/i is not a divisor of n. It is also equal to 1 if n/i is a divisor of n but not a prime power, since any composite number divides the lcm of all smaller numbers. However, if n/i is a power of p, then the ith factor is equal to p.

Since n/i runs over all proper divisors of n, the product includes one factor of the prime p for each factor of p in the prime factorization of n. Thus the whole product is indeed equal to n, which is the same as the factor from the left side of the equation. This completes the proof by induction.

B4. (120, 12, 11, ..., 5, 2, 16, 35) 71.1%
    Let $f(z) = az^4 + bz^3 + cz^2 + dz + e = a(z - r_1)(z - r_2)(z - r_3)(z - r_4)$ where a, b, c, d, e are integers, $a \neq 0$. Show that if $r_1 + r_2$ is a rational number and $r_1 + r_2 \neq r_3 + r_4$, then $r_1 r_2$ is a rational number.

Solution 1. Put $g = r_1 + r_2$, $h = r_3 + r_4$, $u = r_1 r_2$, $v = r_3 r_4$. We are given that g is rational. The following are also rational:

$$\frac{-b}{a} = g + h,$$

$$\frac{c}{a} = gh + u + v,$$

$$\frac{-d}{a} = gv + hu.$$

From the first line, h is rational. From the second line, $u + v$ is rational. From the third line, $g(u + v) - (gv + hu) = (g - h)u$ is rational. Since $g \neq h$, u is rational, as desired.

Solution 2. This solution uses some basic Galois theory. We may assume $r_1 \neq r_2$, since otherwise they are both rational and so then is $r_1 r_2$.

Let τ be an automorphism of the field of algebraic numbers; then τ maps each r_i to another one, and fixes the rational number $r_1 + r_2$. If $\tau(r_1)$ equals one of r_1 or r_2, then $\tau(r_2)$ must equal the other one, and vice versa. Thus τ either fixes the set $\{r_1, r_2\}$ or moves it to $\{r_3, r_4\}$. But if the latter happened, we would have $r_1 + r_2 = r_3 + r_4$, contrary to hypothesis. Thus τ fixes the set $\{r_1, r_2\}$ and in particular the number $r_1 r_2$. Since this is true for any τ, $r_1 r_2$ must be rational.

Remark. The conclusion fails if we allow $r_1 + r_2 = r_3 + r_4$. For instance, take the polynomial $x^4 - 2$ and label its roots so that $(x - r_1)(x - r_2) = x^2 - \sqrt{2}$ and $(x - r_3)(x - r_4) = x^2 + \sqrt{2}$.

B5. (31, 6, 19, ..., 15, 0, 36, 94) 27.9%

Let A, B, and C be equidistant points on the circumference of a circle of unit radius centered at O, and let P be any point in the circle's interior. Let a, b, c be the distance from P to A, B, C, respectively. Show that there is a triangle with side lengths a, b, c, and that the area of this triangle depends only on the distance from P to O.

Solution 1. Place the unit circle on the complex plane so that A, B, C correspond to the complex numbers $1, \omega, \omega^2$, where $\omega = e^{2\pi i/3}$, and let P correspond to the complex number x. The distances a, b, c are then $|x - 1|, |x - \omega|, |x - \omega^2|$. Now the identity

$$(x - 1) + \omega(x - \omega) + \omega^2(x - \omega^2) = 0$$

implies that there is a triangle whose sides, as vectors, correspond to the complex numbers $x - 1, \omega(x - \omega), \omega^2(x - \omega^2)$; this triangle has sides of length a, b, c.

To calculate the area of this triangle, we first note a more general formula: if a triangle in the plane has vertices at $0, v_1 = s_1 + it_1, v_2 = s_2 + it_2$, then the area of the triangle is $|s_1 t_2 - s_2 t_1|/2 = |v_1 \overline{v_2} - v_2 \overline{v_1}|/4$. In the case at hand, $v_1 = x - 1$ and $v_2 = \omega(x - \omega)$; then

$$v_1 \overline{v_2} - v_2 \overline{v_1} = (\omega^2 - \omega)(x\overline{x} - 1) = i\sqrt{3}(1 - |x|^2).$$

Hence the area of the triangle is $\sqrt{3}(1 - |x|^2)/4$, which depends only on the distance $|x|$ from P to O.

Solution 2. (Florian Herzig) Let A', B', C' be the points obtained by intersecting the lines $\overleftrightarrow{AP}, \overleftrightarrow{BP}, \overleftrightarrow{CP}$ with the unit circle. Let d denote OP. Then $A'P = (1 - d^2)/a$, etc., by using the power of the point P. As triangles $\triangle A'B'P$ and $\triangle BAP$ are similar, we get that $A'B' = AB \cdot A'P/b = \sqrt{3}(1 - d^2)/(ab)$. It follows that triangle $\triangle A'B'C'$ has sides proportional to a, b, c, by a factor of $\sqrt{3}(1 - d^2)/(abc)$. In particular, there is a triangle with sides a, b, c, and it has circumradius $R = (abc)/(\sqrt{3}(1 - d^2))$. Its area is $abc/(4R) = \sqrt{3}(1 - d^2)/4$.

B6. (10, 0, 0, ..., 1, 9, 49, 132) 5.0%

Let $f(x)$ be a continuous real-valued function defined on the interval $[0, 1]$. Show that

$$\int_0^1 \int_0^1 |f(x) + f(y)|\, dx\, dy \geq \int_0^1 |f(x)|\, dx.$$

Solution 1. (composite of solutions by Feng Xie and David Pritchard) Let μ denote Lebesgue measure on $[0, 1]$. Define

$$E_+ = \{x \in [0, 1] : f(x) \geq 0\},$$
$$E_- = \{x \in [0, 1] : f(x) < 0\};$$

then E_+ and E_- are measurable and $\mu(E_+) + \mu(E_-) = 1$. Write μ_+ and μ_- for $\mu(E_+)$ and $\mu(E_-)$. Also define

$$I_+ = \int_{E_+} |f(x)|\, dx,$$

$$I_- = \int_{E_-} |f(x)|\, dx,$$

so that $\int_0^1 |f(x)|\, dx = I_+ + I_-$.

By the triangle inequality,

$$\iint_{E_+ \times E_-} |f(x) + f(y)|\, dx\, dy$$

$$\geq \pm \iint_{E_+ \times E_-} (|f(x)| - |f(y)|)\, dx\, dy$$

$$= \pm(\mu_- I_+ - \mu_+ I_-),$$

and likewise with E_+ and E_- switched. Adding these inequalities together and allowing all possible choices of the signs, we get

$$\iint_{(E_+ \times E_-) \cup (E_- \times E_+)} |f(x) + f(y)|\, dx\, dy$$

$$\geq \max\{0, 2(\mu_- I_+ - \mu_+ I_-), 2(\mu_+ I_- - \mu_- I_+)\}.$$

To this inequality, we add the equalities

$$\iint_{E_+ \times E_+} |f(x) + f(y)|\, dx\, dy = 2\mu_+ I_+,$$

$$\iint_{E_- \times E_-} |f(x) + f(y)|\, dx\, dy = 2\mu_- I_-$$

$$- \int_0^1 |f(x)|\, dx = -(\mu_+ + \mu_-)(I_+ + I_-)$$

to obtain

$$\int_0^1 \int_0^1 |f(x) + f(y)| \, dx \, dy - \int_0^1 |f(x)| \, dx$$
$$\geq \max\{(\mu_+ - \mu_-)(I_+ + I_-) + 2\mu_-(I_- - I_+), (\mu_+ - \mu_-)(I_+ - I_-),$$
$$(\mu_- - \mu_+)(I_+ + I_-) + 2\mu_+(I_+ - I_-)\}.$$

For each of the possible comparisons between μ_+ and μ_-, and between I_+ and I_-, one of the three terms in the maximum is manifestly nonnegative. This yields the desired result.

Solution 2. We will show at the end that it is enough to prove a discrete analogue: if $x_1, \ldots, x_n$ are real numbers, then

$$\frac{1}{n^2} \sum_{i,j=1}^n |x_i + x_j| \geq \frac{1}{n} \sum_{i=1}^n |x_i|.$$

In the meantime, we concentrate on this assertion.

Let $f(x_1, \ldots, x_n)$ denote the difference between the two sides. We induct on the number of nonzero values of $|x_i|$. We leave for later the base case, where there is at most one such value. Suppose instead for now that there are two or more nonzero values. Let s be the smallest nonzero value of $|x_i|$, and suppose without loss of generality that $x_1 = \cdots = x_a = s$, $x_{a+1} = \cdots = x_{a+b} = -s$, and for $i > a + b$, either $x_i = 0$ or $|x_i| > s$. (One of a, b might be zero.)

Now consider

$$f(\overbrace{t, \ldots, t}^{a \text{ terms}}, \overbrace{-t, \ldots, -t}^{b \text{ terms}}, x_{a+b+1}, \ldots, x_n)$$

as a function of t. It is piecewise linear near s; in fact, it is linear between 0 and the smallest nonzero value among $|x_{a+b+1}|, \ldots, |x_n|$ (which exists by hypothesis). Thus its minimum is achieved by one (or both) of those two endpoints. In other words, we can reduce the number of distinct nonzero absolute values among the x_i without increasing f. This yields the induction, pending verification of the base case.

As for the base case, suppose that $x_1 = \cdots = x_a = s > 0$, $x_{a+1} = \cdots = x_{a+b} = -s$, and $x_{a+b+1} = \cdots = x_n = 0$. (Here one or even both of a, b could be zero, though the latter case is trivial.) Then

$$f(x_1, \ldots, x_n) = \frac{s}{n^2}(2a^2 + 2b^2 + (a+b)(n-a-b))$$
$$- \frac{s}{n}(a+b) = \frac{s}{n^2}(a^2 - 2ab + b^2) \geq 0.$$

This proves the base case of the induction, completing the solution of the discrete analogue.

To deduce the original statement from the discrete analogue, approximate both integrals by equally spaced Riemann sums and take limits. This works because given a continuous function on a product of closed intervals, any sequence of Riemann sums with mesh size tending to zero converges to the integral. (The domain is compact, so the function is uniformly continuous. Hence for any $\epsilon > 0$ there is a cutoff below which any mesh size forces the discrepancy between the Riemann sum and the integral to be less than ϵ.)

Remark. (based on a solution by Dan Bernstein) From the discrete analogue, we may also argue that

$$\sum_{1 \leq i < j \leq n} |f(x_i) + f(x_j)| \geq \frac{n-2}{2} \sum_{i=1}^{n} |f(x_i)|,$$

for all $x_1, \ldots, x_n \in [0,1]$. Integrating both sides as $(x_1, \ldots, x_n)$ runs over $[0,1]^n$ yields

$$\frac{n(n-1)}{2} \int_0^1 \int_0^1 |f(x) + f(y)| \, dy \, dx \geq \frac{n(n-2)}{2} \int_0^1 |f(x)| \, dx,$$

or

$$\int_0^1 \int_0^1 |f(x) + f(y)| \, dy \, dx \geq \frac{n-2}{n-1} \int_0^1 |f(x)| \, dx.$$

Taking the limit as $n \to \infty$ now yields the desired result.

Solution 3. (David Savitt) We give an argument which yields the following improved result. Let μ_p and μ_n be the measure of the sets $\{x : f(x) > 0\}$ and $\{x : f(x) < 0\}$, respectively, and let $\mu \leq 1/2$ be $\min\{\mu_p, \mu_n\}$. Then

$$\int_0^1 \int_0^1 |f(x) + f(y)| \, dx \, dy \geq (1 + (1 - 2\mu)^2) \int_0^1 |f(x)| \, dx.$$

The constant can be seen to be best possible by considering a sequence of functions tending towards the step function which is 1 on $[0, \mu]$ and -1 on $(\mu, 1]$.

Suppose without loss of generality that $\mu = \mu_p$. As in the second solution, it suffices to prove a strengthened discrete analogue, namely

$$\frac{1}{n^2} \sum_{i,j} |x_i + x_j| \geq \left(1 + \left(1 - \frac{2p}{n}\right)^2\right) \left(\frac{1}{n} \sum_{i=1}^{n} |x_i|\right),$$

where $p \leq n/2$ is the number of $x_1, \ldots, x_n$ which are positive. (We need only make sure to choose meshes so that $p/n \to \mu$ as $n \to \infty$.) An equivalent inequality is

$$\sum_{1 \leq i < j \leq n} |x_i + x_j| \geq \left(n - 1 - 2p + \frac{2p^2}{n}\right) \sum_{i=1}^{n} |x_i|.$$

Write $r_i = |x_i|$, and assume without loss of generality that $r_i \geq r_{i+1}$ for each i. Then for $i < j$, $|x_i + x_j| = r_i + r_j$ if x_i and x_j have the same sign, and is $r_i - r_j$ if they have opposite signs. The left-hand side is therefore equal to

$$\sum_{i=1}^{n}(n-i)r_i + \sum_{j=1}^{n} r_j C_j,$$

where

$$C_j = \#\{i < j \ : \ \text{sgn}(x_i) = \text{sgn}(x_j)\} - \#\{i < j \ : \ \text{sgn}(x_i) \neq \text{sgn}(x_j)\}.$$

Consider the partial sum $P_k = \sum_{j=1}^{k} C_j$. If exactly p_k of $x_1, \ldots, x_k$ are positive, then this sum is equal to

$$\binom{p_k}{2} + \binom{k-p_k}{2} - \left[\binom{k}{2} - \binom{p_k}{2} - \binom{k-p_k}{2}\right],$$

which expands and simplifies to

$$-2p_k(k-p_k) + \binom{k}{2}.$$

For $k \leq 2p$ even, this partial sum would be minimized with $p_k = \frac{k}{2}$, and would then equal $-\frac{k}{2}$; for $k < 2p$ odd, this partial sum would be minimized with $p_k = \frac{k\pm 1}{2}$, and would then equal $-\frac{k-1}{2}$. Either way, $P_k \geq -\lfloor\frac{k}{2}\rfloor$. On the other hand, if $k > 2p$, then

$$-2p_k(k-p_k) + \binom{k}{2} \geq -2p(k-p) + \binom{k}{2}$$

since p_k is at most p. Define Q_k to be $-\lfloor\frac{k}{2}\rfloor$ if $k \leq 2p$ and $-2p(k-p) + \binom{k}{2}$ if $k \geq 2p$, so that $P_k \geq Q_k$. Note that $Q_1 = 0$.

Partial summation gives

$$\sum_{j=1}^{n} r_j C_j = r_n P_n + \sum_{j=2}^{n}(r_{j-1} - r_j)P_{j-1}$$

$$\geq r_n Q_n + \sum_{j=2}^{n}(r_{j-1} - r_j)Q_{j-1}$$

$$= \sum_{j=2}^{n} r_j(Q_j - Q_{j-1})$$

$$= -r_2 - r_4 - \cdots - r_{2p} + \sum_{j=2p+1}^{n}(j-1-2p)r_j.$$

It follows that

$$\sum_{1 \le i < j \le n} |a_i + a_j| = \sum_{i=1}^{n} (n-i) r_i + \sum_{j=1}^{n} r_j C_j$$

$$\ge \sum_{i=1}^{2p} (n - i - [i \text{ even}]) r_i$$

$$+ \sum_{i=2p+1}^{n} (n - 1 - 2p) r_i$$

$$= (n - 1 - 2p) \sum_{i=1}^{n} r_i$$

$$+ \sum_{i=1}^{2p} (2p + 1 - i - [i \text{ even}]) r_i$$

$$\ge (n - 1 - 2p) \sum_{i=1}^{n} r_i + p \sum_{i=1}^{2p} r_i$$

$$\ge (n - 1 - 2p) \sum_{i=1}^{n} r_i + p \frac{2p}{n} \sum_{i=1}^{n} r_i,$$

as desired. The next-to-last and last inequalities each follow from the monotonicity of the r_i's, the former by pairing the ith term with the $(2p + 1 - i)$th.

Related question. Compare the closely related Problem 6 from the 2000 USA Mathematical Olympiad [**AF01**]: prove that for any nonnegative real numbers $a_1, \ldots, a_n, b_1, \ldots, b_n$, one has

$$\sum_{i,j=1}^{n} \min\{a_i a_j, b_i b_j\} \le \sum_{i,j=1}^{n} \min\{a_i b_j, a_j b_i\}.$$

The Sixty-Fifth William Lowell Putnam
Mathematical Competition—December 4, 2004

A1. (139, 3, 26, ..., 7, 0, 20, 1) 85.7%

Basketball star Shanille O'Keal's team statistician keeps track of the number, $S(N)$, of successful free throws she has made in her first N attempts of the season. Early in the season, $S(N)$ was less than 80% of N, but by the end of the season, $S(N)$ was more than 80% of N. Was there necessarily a moment in between when $S(N)$ was exactly 80% of N?

Answer. Yes, there necessarily was such a moment.

Solution. Suppose otherwise. Then there would be an N such that $S(N) < .8N$ and $S(N+1) > .8(N+1)$. That is, O'Keal's free throw percentage is under 80% at some point, and after one subsequent free throw (necessarily made), her percentage is over 80%. If she makes m of her first N free throws, then $m/N < 4/5$ and $(m+1)/(N+1) > 4/5$. This means that $5m < 4N < 5m+1$, which is impossible since then $4N$ is an integer between the consecutive integers $5m$ and $5m+1$.

Remark. This same argument works for any fraction of the form $(n-1)/n$ for some integer $n > 1$, but not for any other real number between 0 and 1.

Remark. Peter Winkler, who claims to prefer mathematical puzzles to problems because puzzles are more likely to teach new mathematical insights, says about this problem: "the Shanille O'Keal problem has the delightful property that solving it awakens you to something that might never have occurred to you—in this case, that even with discrete steps, there are fractions that 'can't be skipped on the way up' (and, as well, some that can't be skipped going down). Problems with this property, whether easy or hard, are to be treasured!"

A2. (64, 10, 11, ..., 7, 1, 83, 20) 43.4%

For $i = 1, 2$ let T_i be a triangle with side lengths a_i, b_i, c_i, and area A_i. Suppose that $a_1 \leq a_2, b_1 \leq b_2, c_1 \leq c_2$, and that T_2 is an acute triangle. Does it follow that $A_1 \leq A_2$?

Answer. Yes, it does follow.

Solution 1. For $i = 1, 2$, let P_i, Q_i, R_i be the vertices of T_i opposite the sides of length a_i, b_i, c_i, respectively. Since the angle measures in any triangle add up to π, some angle of T_1 must have measure less than or equal to its counterpart in T_2. Without loss of generality assume that $\angle P_1 \leq \angle P_2$. Since the latter is acute (because T_2 is acute), it follows that $\sin \angle P_1 \leq \sin \angle P_2$. Then

$$A_1 = \frac{1}{2}b_1 c_1 \sin \angle P_1 \leq \frac{1}{2}b_2 c_2 \sin \angle P_2 = A_2.$$

Solution 2. (partly due to Ravi Vakil) Retain notation as in the first paragraph of the first solution. Start with the case where $a_1 = a_2$ (or $b_1 = b_2$ or $c_1 = c_2$, by the same argument after relabeling). Imagine T_2 as being drawn with the base $\overline{Q_2R_2}$ horizontal and the point P_2 above the line $\overleftrightarrow{Q_2R_2}$. Position T_1 so that $Q_1 = Q_2$, $R_1 = R_2$, and P_1 lies above the line $\overleftrightarrow{Q_1R_1} = \overleftrightarrow{Q_2R_2}$. Then P_1 also lies inside the region bounded by the circles through P_2 centered at Q_2 and R_2. Since $\angle Q_2$ and $\angle R_2$ are acute, the part of this region above $\overleftrightarrow{Q_2R_2}$ lies within T_2. In particular, the distance from P_1 to $\overleftrightarrow{Q_2R_2}$ is less than or equal to the distance from P_2 to $\overleftrightarrow{Q_2R_2}$. Hence $A_1 \le A_2$.

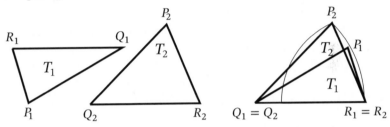

To deduce the general case, put

$$r = \max\{a_1/a_2, b_1/b_2, c_1/c_2\}.$$

Let T_3 be the triangle with sides ra_2, rb_2, rc_2, which has area r^2A_2. Apply the special case to T_1 and T_3 to deduce that $A_1 \le r^2A_2$. Since $r \le 1$ by hypothesis, it follows that $A_1 \le A_2$ as desired.

Remark. As seen in the diagram, T_1 need not fit inside T_2.

Solution 3. As in Solution 2, it is enough to consider the case where $a_1 = a_2$. Use the same labeling as above, and let $\overline{Q_1R_1} = \overline{Q_2R_2}$ be horizontal with P_1 and P_2 above the horizontal as shown below. Because the angles $\angle Q_2$ and $\angle R_2$ are acute, the perpendicular to $\overleftrightarrow{Q_2R_2}$ through P_2 separates Q_2 from R_2. If $A_1 > A_2$, then P_1 lies above the parallel to $\overleftrightarrow{Q_2R_2}$ through P_2. Then, if P_1 lies on or to the left of the vertical line through P_2, it follows that $b_1 > b_2$ because the inequality holds for both horizontal and vertical components, with equality possible for one, but not both. Similarly, if P_1 lies to the right of the vertical, then $c_1 > c_2$.

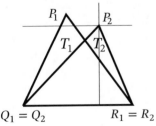

Remark. Many other solutions are possible. For instance, one solution uses Heron's formula for the area of a triangle in terms of its side lengths.

A3. (148, 13, 4, ..., 2, 9, 8, 12) 84.2%

   Define a sequence $\{u_n\}_{n=0}^{\infty}$ by $u_0 = u_1 = u_2 = 1$, and thereafter by the condition that

$$\det\begin{pmatrix} u_n & u_{n+1} \\ u_{n+2} & u_{n+3} \end{pmatrix} = n!$$

for all $n \geq 0$. Show that u_n is an integer for all n. (By convention, $0! = 1$.)

Solution. Define a sequence v_n by $v_n = (n-1)(n-3)\cdots(4)(2)$ if n is odd and $v_n = (n-1)(n-3)\cdots(3)(1)$ if n is even. It suffices to prove that $u_n = v_n$ for all $n \geq 2$. Given this, $v_{n+3}v_n = (n+2)(n)(n-1)!$ and $v_{n+2}v_{n+1} = (n+1)!$, and so $v_{n+3}v_n - v_{n+2}v_{n+1} = n!$. By direct calculation $u_2 = v_2 = 1$, $u_3 = v_3 = 2$, and $u_4 = v_4 = 3$. Because u_n and v_n satisfy the same recurrence, it follows by induction that $u_n = v_n$ for all $n \geq 2$, as desired.

Remark. The common double factorial notation $n!! = n(n-2)(n-4)\cdots$ could be used here to represent $v_n = (n-1)!!$. The sequence $n!!$ appears as entry A006882 in the OEIS.

A4. (23, 6, 8, ..., 15, 13, 69, 62) 18.9%

   Show that for any positive integer n there is an integer N such that the product $x_1 x_2 \cdots x_n$ can be expressed identically in the form

$$x_1 x_2 \cdots x_n = \sum_{i=1}^{N} c_i (a_{i1}x_1 + a_{i2}x_2 + \cdots + a_{in}x_n)^n$$

where the c_i are rational numbers and each a_{ij} is one of the numbers $-1, 0, 1$.

Solution. It suffices to verify that

$$x_1 \cdots x_n = \frac{1}{2^n n!} \sum_{e_i \in \{-1,1\}} (e_1 \cdots e_n)(e_1 x_1 + \cdots + e_n x_n)^n.$$

In this equation, the right side vanishes identically for $x_1 = 0$, because each term cancels the corresponding term with e_1 negated. Hence the right side, as a polynomial, is divisible by x_1, and similarly by $x_2, \ldots, x_n$. Thus as it is a polynomial of degree n, the right side is equal to $x_1 \cdots x_n$ times a scalar. (Another way to see this: the right side is clearly odd as a polynomial in each individual variable, but the only degree-n monomial in $x_1, \ldots, x_n$ with that property is $x_1 \cdots x_n$.) Since each summand contributes $\frac{1}{2^n}x_1 \cdots x_n$ to the sum, the scalar factor is 1 and we are done.

Remark. Several variants on the above construction are possible. For instance,

$$x_1 \cdots x_n = \frac{1}{n!} \sum_{e_i \in \{0,1\}} (-1)^{n - e_1 - \cdots - e_n} (e_1 x_1 + \cdots + e_n x_n)^n$$

by the same argument as above.

Remark. These constructions work over any field of characteristic greater than n (at least for $n > 1$). On the other hand, no construction is possible over a field of characteristic $p \leq n$, since the coefficient of $x_1 \cdots x_n$ in the expansion of $(e_1 x_1 + \cdots + e_n x_n)^n$ is zero for any e_i.

Remark. Richard Stanley asks whether one can use fewer than 2^n terms, and what the smallest possible number is.

A5. $(14, 0, 2, \ldots, 0, 0, 55, 125)$ 8.2%
  An $m \times n$ **checkerboard is colored randomly: each square is independently assigned red or black with probability** $1/2$. **We say that two squares, p and q, are in the same connected monochromatic region if there is a sequence of squares, all of the same color, starting at p and ending at q, in which successive squares in the sequence share a common side. Show that the expected number of connected monochromatic regions is greater than** $mn/8$.

Solution 1. First recall that any graph with n vertices and e edges has at least $n - e$ connected components (add each edge one at a time, and note that it reduces the number of components by at most 1). Now imagine the squares of the checkerboard as a graph, whose vertices are connected if the corresponding squares share a side and are the same color. Let A be the number of edges in the graph, and let B be the number of 4-cycles (formed by monochromatic 2×2 squares). If we remove the bottom edge of each 4-cycle, the resulting graph has the same number of connected components as the original one; hence this number is at least

$$mn - A + B.$$

By the linearity of expectation, the expected number of connected components is at least

$$mn - E(A) + E(B).$$

Moreover, we may compute $E(A)$ by summing over the individual pairs of adjacent squares, and we may compute $E(B)$ by summing over the individual 2×2 squares. Thus

$$E(A) = \frac{1}{2}(m(n-1) + (m-1)n),$$

$$E(B) = \frac{1}{8}(m-1)(n-1),$$

and so the expected number of components is at least

$$mn - \frac{1}{2}(m(n-1) + (m-1)n) + \frac{1}{8}(m-1)(n-1)$$
$$= \frac{mn + 3m + 3n + 1}{8} > \frac{mn}{8}.$$

Remark. A "dual" approach is to consider the graph whose vertices are the corners of the squares of the checkerboard, with two vertices joined if they are adjacent and the edge between then does not separate two squares of the same color. In this approach, the 4-cycles become isolated vertices, and the bound on components is replaced by a call to Euler's formula relating the vertices, edges and faces of a planar figure. (One must be careful, however, to correctly handle faces which are not simply connected.)

Solution 2. (Noam Elkies) Number the squares of the checkerboard $1, \ldots, mn$ by numbering the first row from left to right, then the second row, and so on. We prove by induction on i that if we just consider the figure formed by the first i squares, its expected number of monochromatic components is at least $i/8$. For $i = 1$, this is clear.

Suppose the ith square does not abut the left edge or the top row of the board. Then we may divide into three cases.

With probability $1/4$, the ith square is opposite in color from the adjacent squares directly above and to the left of it. In this case adding the ith square adds one component.

With probability $1/8$, the ith square is the same in color as the adjacent squares directly above and to the left of it, but opposite in color from its diagonal neighbor above and to the left. In this case, adding the ith square either removes a component or leaves the number unchanged.

In all other cases, the number of components remains unchanged upon adding the ith square.

Hence adding the ith square increases the expected number of components by at least $1/4 - 1/8 = 1/8$.

If the ith square does abut the left edge of the board, the situation is even simpler: if the ith square differs in color from the square above it, one component is added, otherwise the number does not change. Hence adding the ith square increases the expected number of components by $1/2$. Likewise if the ith square abuts the top edge of the board. Thus the expected number of components is at least $i/8$ by induction, as desired.

Remark. Some solvers attempted to consider adding one row at a time, rather than one square. This must be handled with great care, as it is possible that the number of components can drop rather precipitously upon adding an entire row.

A6. $(7, 3, 4, \ldots, 1, 0, 49, 132)$ 7.1%

Suppose that $f(x, y)$ is a continuous real-valued function on the unit square $0 \le x \le 1, 0 \le y \le 1$. Show that

$$\int_0^1 \left(\int_0^1 f(x, y) dx \right)^2 dy + \int_0^1 \left(\int_0^1 f(x, y) dy \right)^2 dx$$
$$\le \left(\int_0^1 \int_0^1 f(x, y) dx \, dy \right)^2 + \int_0^1 \int_0^1 [f(x, y)]^2 dx \, dy.$$

Solution. By approximating each integral with a Riemann sum, we may reduce to proving the discrete analogue: for $x_{ij} \in \mathbb{R}$ for $i, j = 1, \ldots, n$,

$$n \sum_{i=1}^n \left(\sum_{j=1}^n x_{ij} \right)^2 + n \sum_{j=1}^n \left(\sum_{i=1}^n x_{ij} \right)^2 \le \left(\sum_{i=1}^n \sum_{j=1}^n x_{ij} \right)^2 + n^2 \sum_{i=1}^n \sum_{j=1}^n x_{ij}^2.$$

To show this, note that by expanding out

$$\frac{1}{4} \sum_{i,j,k,l=1}^n (x_{ij} + x_{kl} - x_{il} - x_{kj})^2,$$

and reindexing the sums, we get the difference of the right-hand and left-hand sides. However, this is evidently nonnegative.

As an alternative to discretizing, one may rewrite the original inequality as

$$\int_0^1 \int_0^1 \int_0^1 \int_0^1 F(x, y, z, w)^2 \, dx \, dy \, dz \, dw \ge 0$$

for

$$F(x, y, z, w) = f(x, y) + f(z, w) - f(x, w) - f(z, y)$$

by similar reasoning.

Remark. (Po-Ning Chen) The discrete inequality can be arrived at more systematically by repeatedly applying the following identity: for any real $x_1, \ldots, x_n$,

$$\sum_{1 \le i < j \le n} (x_i - x_j)^2 = n \sum_{i=1}^n x_i^2 - \left(\sum_{i=1}^n x_i \right)^2.$$

Remark. (David Savitt) The discrete inequality can also be interpreted as follows. For $c, d \in \{1, \ldots, n-1\}$ and $\zeta_n = e^{2\pi i/n}$, put

$$z_{c,d} = \sum_{i,j} \zeta_n^{ci+dj} x_{ij}.$$

Then the given inequality is equivalent to

$$\sum_{c,d=1}^{n-1} |z_{c,d}|^2 \geq 0.$$

B1. (156, 3, 2, ..., 2, 3, 27, 3) 82.1%

   Let $P(x) = c_n x^n + c_{n-1} x^{n-1} + \cdots + c_0$ be a polynomial with integer coefficients. Suppose that r is a rational number such that $P(r) = 0$. Show that the n numbers

$$c_n r, \ c_n r^2 + c_{n-1} r, \ c_n r^3 + c_{n-1} r^2 + c_{n-2} r,$$
$$\ldots, \ c_n r^n + c_{n-1} r^{n-1} + \cdots + c_1 r$$

are integers.

Solution. The case where $r = 0$ is trivial, so assume that $r \neq 0$. Let k be an integer, $0 \leq k \leq n - 1$. Since $P(r)/r^k = 0$,

$$c_n r^{n-k} + c_{n-1} r^{n-k-1} + \cdots + c_{k+1} r = -(c_k + c_{k-1} r^{-1} + \cdots + c_0 r^{-k}).$$

Write $r = p/q$, where p and q are relatively prime integers. Then the left-hand side of the above equation can be written as a fraction with denominator q^{n-k}, while the right-hand side is a fraction with denominator p^k. Since p and q are relatively prime, both sides of the equation must be an integer, and the result follows.

Remark. If r is written as a/b in lowest terms, then the polynomial $P(x)$ factors as $(bx - a)Q(x)$, where the polynomial Q has integer coefficients because one can either do the long division from the left and get denominators divisible only by primes dividing b, or do it from the right and get denominators divisible only by primes dividing a. The numbers given in the problem are none other than a times the coefficients of Q. More generally, if $P(x)$ is divisible, as a polynomial over the rationals, by a polynomial $R(x)$ with integer coefficients, then P/R also has integer coefficients. This is known as *Gauss's lemma* and holds in any unique factorization domain.

Remark. More generally, for any root r of P, the n given sums are algebraic integers. This comes up in the work of Birch and Merriman on rings associated to binary forms [**BM**].

B2. (56, 41, 39, ..., 22, 0, 28, 10) 69.4%

   Let m and n be positive integers. Show that

$$\frac{(m+n)!}{(m+n)^{m+n}} < \frac{m! \ n!}{m^m \ n^n}.$$

Solution 1. It follows from the binomial theorem that

$$(m + n)^{m+n} > \binom{m + n}{m} m^m n^n$$

because the expansion of $(m + n)^{m+n}$ includes the term on the right as well as some other positive terms. Rearranging this inequality yields the claim.

Reinterpretation. One can also interpret this argument combinatorially. Suppose $m + n$ random and independent selections are made with replacement from a set consisting of m red balls and n blue balls. Then the probability of picking each ball exactly once is $(m+n)!\,/(m+n)^{m+n}$. On the other hand, if p is the probability of picking exactly m red balls, then $p < 1$ and the probability of picking each ball exactly once is $p\frac{m!}{m^m}\frac{n!}{n^n}$.

Solution 2. (David Savitt) Define

$$S_k = \{i/k : i = 1, \ldots, k\}$$

and rewrite the desired inequality as

$$\prod_{x \in S_m} x \prod_{y \in S_n} y > \prod_{z \in S_{m+n}} z.$$

To prove this, it suffices to check that if the multiplicands on both sides are sorted into increasing order, the ith factor on the left side is greater than or equal to the ith factor on the right side. The inequality is strict already for $i = 1$ because $\min(1/m, 1/n) > 1/(m + n)$, so the total inequality is strict.

Another way to say this is that for any i, the number of factors on the left side which are less than $i/(m + n)$ is less than i. But since $j/m < i/(m + n)$ is equivalent to $j < im/(m + n)$, that number is

$$\left\lceil \frac{im}{m + n} \right\rceil - 1 + \left\lceil \frac{in}{m + n} \right\rceil - 1$$
$$\leq \frac{im}{m + n} + \frac{in}{m + n} - 1 = i - 1.$$

Solution 3. Put $f(x) = x(\log(x + 1) - \log x)$. For $x > 0$,

$$f'(x) = \log(1 + 1/x) - \frac{1}{x + 1},$$

$$f''(x) = -\frac{1}{x(x + 1)^2}.$$

Hence $f''(x) < 0$ for all x. Since $f'(x) \to 0$ as $x \to \infty$, it follows that $f'(x) > 0$ for $x > 0$, so f is strictly increasing.

Put $g(m) = m \log m - \log(m!\,)$. Then $g(m + 1) - g(m) = f(m)$, so $g(m + 1) - g(m)$ increases with m. By induction, $g(m + n) - g(m)$ increases with n for any positive integer n, so in particular

$$g(m+n) - g(m) > g(n) - g(1) + f(m)$$
$$\geq g(n)$$

since $g(1) = 0$. Exponentiating yields the desired inequality.

Solution 4. (W.G. Boskoff and Bogdan Suceavă) This can be proved by induction on $m+n$. The base case is $m = n = 1$, in which case the desired inequality is true because $2!/2^2 = 1/2 < 1 = (1!/1^1)(1!/1^1)$. To prove the induction step, suppose that for some k the inequality holds for all m and n with $m+n < k$. Then suppose $m + n = k > 2$, so either $m > 1$ or $n > 1$ or both. Because the desired result is symmetric in m and n, assume that $n > 1$. By the induction hypothesis,

$$\frac{(m+n-1)!}{(m+n-1)^{m+n-1}} < \frac{m!}{m^m}\frac{(n-1)!}{(n-1)^{n-1}}.$$

To obtain the desired inequality, it will suffice to check that

$$\frac{(m+n-1)^{m+n-1}}{(m+n-1)!}\frac{(m+n)!}{(m+n)^{m+n}} < \frac{(n-1)^{n-1}}{(n-1)!}\frac{n!}{(n)^n},$$

or in other words

$$\left(1 - \frac{1}{m+n}\right)^{m+n-1} < \left(1 - \frac{1}{n}\right)^{n-1}.$$

To show this, check that the function $f(x) = (1-1/x)^{x-1}$ is strictly decreasing for $x > 1$. While this can be achieved using the weighted arithmetic mean/geometric mean inequality, here is a simple calculus proof instead. The derivative of $\log f(x)$ is $\log(1 - 1/x) + 1/x$, so it is enough to check that this is negative for $x > 1$. An equivalent statement is that $\log(1 - x) + x < 0$ for $0 < x < 1$. This in turn holds because the function $g(x) = \log(1-x)+x$ tends to 0 as $x \to 0^+$ and has derivative $1 - \frac{1}{1-x} < 0$ for $0 < x < 1$.

B3. (79, 10, 1, ..., 3, 44, 35, 24) 45.9%
　　Determine all real numbers $a > 0$ for which there exists a nonnegative continuous function $f(x)$ defined on $[0, a]$ with the property that the region

$$R = \{(x,y) : 0 \leq x \leq a, 0 \leq y \leq f(x)\}$$

has perimeter k units and area k square units for some real number k.

Answer. The set of such a consists of all $a > 2$.

Solution. If $a > 2$, then the function $f(x) = 2a/(a-2)$ has the desired property: both the perimeter and area of R in this case are $2a^2/(a-2)$.
　　Now suppose that $a \leq 2$, and let $f(x)$ be a nonnegative continuous function on $[0, a]$. Let $P = (x_0, y_0)$ be a point on the graph of $f(x)$ with maximal

y-coordinate. Then the area of R is at most ay_0 since it lies below the line $y = y_0$. On the other hand, the points $(0,0)$, $(a,0)$, and P divide the boundary of R into three sections. The length of the section between $(0,0)$ and P is at least the distance between $(0,0)$ and P, which is at least y_0; the length of the section between P and $(a,0)$ is similarly at least y_0; and the length of the section between $(0,0)$ and $(a,0)$ is a. Since $a \le 2$, it follows that $2y_0 + a > ay_0$ and hence the perimeter of R is strictly greater than the area of R.

B4. (92, 42, 10, ..., 8, 9, 19, 16) 73.5%
    Let n be a positive integer, $n \ge 2$, and put $\theta = 2\pi/n$. Define points $P_k = (k,0)$ in the xy-plane, for $k = 1, 2, \ldots, n$. Let R_k be the map that rotates the plane counterclockwise by the angle θ about the point P_k. Let R denote the map obtained by applying, in order, R_1, then $R_2, \ldots$, then R_n. For an arbitrary point (x, y), find, and simplify, the coordinates of $R(x, y)$.

Answer. We prove that $R(x, y) = (x + n, y)$.

Solution 1. Identify the xy-plane with the complex plane $\mathbb{C}$, so that P_k is the real number k. If z is sent to z' by a counterclockwise rotation by θ about P_k, then $z' - k = e^{i\theta}(z - k)$; hence the rotation R_k sends z to $\zeta z + k(1 - \zeta)$, where $\zeta = e^{2\pi i/n}$. It follows that R_1 followed by R_2 sends z to $\zeta(\zeta z + (1-\zeta)) + 2(1-\zeta) = \zeta^2 z + (1 - \zeta)(\zeta + 2)$, and so forth. By induction on k, R sends z to

$$\zeta^n z + (1 - \zeta)(\zeta^{n-1} + 2\zeta^{n-2} + \cdots + (n-1)\zeta + n).$$

Expanding the product $(1 - \zeta)(\zeta^{n-1} + 2\zeta^{n-2} + \cdots + (n-1)\zeta + n)$ yields $-\zeta^n - \zeta^{n-1} - \cdots - \zeta + n = n$. Thus R sends z to $z + n$; in Cartesian coordinates, $R(x, y) = (x + n, y)$.

Solution 2. (Andy Lutomirski, via Ravi Vakil) Imagine a regular n-gon of side length 1 placed with its top edge on the x-axis and the left endpoint of that edge at the origin. Then the rotations correspond to rolling this n-gon along the x-axis; after the n rotations, it ends up in its original orientation and translated n units to the right. Hence the whole plane must do so as well.

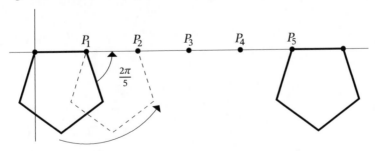

Solution 3. Viewing each R_k as a function of a complex number z as in the first solution, the function $R_n \circ R_{n-1} \circ \cdots \circ R_1(z)$ is a composition of linear functions each with slope ζ, and this is itself linear in z with slope $\zeta^n = 1$. It thus equals $z + T$ for some $T \in \mathbb{C}$. Since $f_1(1) = 1$, we can write $1 + T = R_n \circ \cdots \circ R_2(1)$. However, we also have

$$R_n \circ \cdots \circ R_2(1) = R_{n-1} \circ \cdots \circ R_1(0) + 1$$

by the symmetry in how the R_i are defined. Hence

$$R_n(1 + T) = R_n \circ \cdots \circ R_1(0) + \zeta = T + \zeta;$$

that is, $R_n(T) = T$. Hence $T = n$, as desired.

B5. (16, 3, 1, ..., 3, 12, 62, 99) 10.2%

Evaluate

$$\lim_{x \to 1^-} \prod_{n=0}^{\infty} \left(\frac{1 + x^{n+1}}{1 + x^n} \right)^{x^n}.$$

Answer. The limit is $2/e$.

Solution 1. The desired limit equals $\exp(L)$ for

$$L = \lim_{x \to 1^-} \sum_{n=0}^{\infty} x^n \left(\log(1 + x^{n+1}) - \log(1 + x^n) \right).$$

Now

$$\sum_{n=0}^{N} x^n \left(\log(1 + x^{n+1}) - \log(1 + x^n) \right)$$

$$= 1/x \sum_{n=0}^{N} x^{n+1} \log(1 + x^{n+1}) - \sum_{n=0}^{N} x^n \log(1 + x^n)$$

$$= x^N \log(1 + x^{N+1}) - \log 2 + (1/x - 1) \sum_{n=1}^{N} x^n \log(1 + x^n).$$

Since $\lim_{N \to \infty} (x^N \log(1 + x^{N+1})) = 0$ for $0 < x < 1$, we conclude that $L = -\log 2 + \lim_{x \to 1^-} f(x)$, where

$$f(x) = (1/x - 1) \sum_{n=1}^{\infty} x^n \log(1 + x^n)$$

$$= (1/x - 1) \sum_{n=1}^{\infty} \sum_{m=1}^{\infty} (-1)^{m+1} x^{n+mn}/m.$$

This final double sum converges absolutely when $0 < x < 1$, since

$$\sum_{n=1}^{\infty}\sum_{m=1}^{\infty} x^{n+mn}/m = \sum_{n=1}^{\infty} x^n(-\log(1-x^n))$$

$$< \sum_{n=1}^{\infty} x^n(-\log(1-x)),$$

which converges. (Note that $-\log(1-x)$ and $-\log(1-x^n)$ are positive.) Hence we may interchange the summations in $f(x)$ to obtain

$$f(x) = (1/x - 1)\sum_{m=1}^{\infty}\sum_{n=1}^{\infty}\frac{(-1)^{m+1}x^{(m+1)n}}{m}$$

$$= \sum_{m=1}^{\infty}\frac{(-1)^{m+1}}{m}\left(\frac{x^m(1-x)}{1-x^{m+1}}\right).$$

This last sum converges absolutely uniformly in x as the mth term is at most $1/m^2$, so it is legitimate to take limits term by term. Since $\lim_{x\to1^-}\frac{x^m(1-x)}{1-x^{m+1}} = \frac{1}{m+1}$ for fixed m,

$$\lim_{x\to1^-} f(x) = \sum_{m=1}^{\infty}\frac{(-1)^{m+1}}{m(m+1)}$$

$$= \sum_{m=1}^{\infty}(-1)^{m+1}\left(\frac{1}{m} - \frac{1}{m+1}\right)$$

$$= 2\left(\sum_{m=1}^{\infty}\frac{(-1)^{m+1}}{m}\right) - 1$$

$$= 2\log 2 - 1,$$

and hence $L = \log 2 - 1$ and the desired limit is $2/e$.

Remark. The last series is not absolutely convergent, so the recombination must be done without rearranging terms.

Solution 2. (Greg Price, via Tony Zhang and Anders Kaseorg) Put $t_n(x) = \log(1+x^n)$. We can then write $x^n = \exp(t_n(x)) - 1$, and

$$L = \lim_{x\to1^-}\sum_{n=0}^{\infty}(t_n(x) - t_{n+1}(x))(1 - \exp(t_n(x))).$$

The expression on the right is a Riemann sum approximating the integral $\int_0^{\log 2}(1-e^t)\,dt$, over the subdivision of $[0,\log 2]$ given by the $t_n(x)$. As $x\to1^-$, the maximum difference between consecutive $t_n(x)$ tends to 0, so the Riemann sum tends to the value of the integral. Hence $L = \int_0^{\log 2}(1-e^t)\,dt = \log 2 - 1$, as desired.

B6. $(4, 1, 0, \ldots, 1, 1, 58, 131)$ 2.6%

Let A be a nonempty set of positive integers, and let $N(x)$ denote the number of elements of A not exceeding x. Let $\mathcal{B}$ denote the set of positive integers b that can be written in the form $b = a - a'$ with $a \in A$ and $a' \in A$. Let $b_1 < b_2 < \cdots$ be the members of $\mathcal{B}$, listed in increasing order. Show that if the sequence $b_{i+1} - b_i$ is unbounded, then

$$\lim_{x \to \infty} N(x)/x = 0.$$

Solution 1. Assume by way of contradiction that $\limsup N(x)/x > 0$. (In what follows, all limits are taken as $x \to \infty$ and we omit the subscript.) For an integer n, let $A + n = \{a + n : a \in A\}$ denote the translate of A by n. Call a set of integers $S = \{n_1, n_2, \ldots, n_k\}$ good if the translates $A + n_j$ are disjoint. We claim that no good set can have size larger than $1/(\limsup N(x)/x)$. Namely, for any good set $S = \{n_1, n_2, \ldots, n_k\}$,

$$\left| \bigcup_{j=1}^{k} (A + n_j) \cap [0, x] \right| = \sum_{j=1}^{k} |(A + n_j) \cap [0, x]| = \sum_{j=1}^{k} N(x - n_j) \geq kN(x) - \sum_{j=1}^{k} n_j.$$

However, this sum is also evidently at most x, and therefore $N(x) \leq (x + \sum_{j=1}^{k} n_j)/k$, implying that $\limsup N(x)/x \leq 1/k$.

This means that good sets have bounded size and therefore that there must be a good set of maximal size, say $S = \{n_1, n_2, \ldots, n_k\}$. By the maximality, $S \cup \{n\}$ cannot be a good set for any $n \notin S$. In particular, for any such n, $A + n$ will not be disjoint from some $A + n_j$. This means that there are some $a, a' \in A$ so that $a + n = a' + n_j$, or equivalently $n - n_j = a' - a$. Thus for any such n, there exists a j for which $n - n_j \in \mathcal{B}$. However this contradicts the fact that $b_{i+1} - b_i$ is unbounded, as $b_{i+1} - n_j$ will be in $\mathcal{B}$ for some j and thus $b_{i+1} - b_i$ will be at least $\max_j\{n_j\}$. This completes our proof.

Solution 2. (based on a solution of Dan Bernstein) For any b, the condition that $b \notin \mathcal{B}$ already forces $\limsup N(x)/x$ to be at most $1/2$: pair off $2mb + n$ with $(2m + 1)b + n$ for $n = 1, \ldots, b$, and at most one member of each pair may belong to A. The idea of the proof is to do something similar with pairs replaced by larger clumps, using long runs of excluded elements of B.

Suppose we have positive integers $b_0 = 1, b_1, \ldots, b_n$ with the following properties:

(a) For $i = 1, \ldots, n$, $c_i = b_i/(2b_{i-1})$ is an integer.

(b) For $e_i \in \{-1, 0, 1\}$, $|e_1 b_1 + \cdots + e_n b_n| \notin \mathcal{B}$.

Each nonnegative integer a has a unique "base expansion"

$$a = a_0 b_0 + \cdots + a_{n-1} b_{n-1} + m b_n \qquad (0 \leq a_i < 2c_i).$$

If two integers have expansions with the same value of m, and values of a_i differing by at most 1 for $i = 0, \ldots, n-1$, then their difference is not in $\mathcal{B}$, so at most one of them lies in $\mathcal{A}$. In particular, for any $d_i \in \{0, \ldots, c_i - 1\}$, any $m_0 \in \{0, 2c_0 - 1\}$, and any m_n, the set

$$\{m_0 b_0 + (2d_1 + e_1)b_0 + \cdots + (2d_{n-1} + e_{n-1})b_{n-1} + (2m_n + e_n)b_n\},$$

where each e_i runs over $\{0, 1\}$, contains at most one element of $\mathcal{A}$; consequently, $\limsup N(x)/x \leq 1/2^n$.

We now produce such b_i recursively, starting with $b_0 = 1$ (and both (a) and (b) holding vacuously). Given $b_0, \ldots, b_n$ satisfying (a) and (b), $b_0 + \cdots + b_{n-1} < b_n$ by induction on n. By the hypotheses of the problem, we can find a set S_n of $6b_n$ consecutive integers, none of which belongs to $\mathcal{B}$. Let b_{n+1} be the second-smallest multiple of $2b_n$ in S_n. Then $b_{n+1} + x \in S_n$ for $-2b_n \leq x \leq 0$, and also for $0 \leq x \leq 2b_n$ because there are at most $4b_n - 1$ elements of S_n preceding b_{n+1}. In particular, the analogue of (b) with n replaced by $n + 1$ holds for $e_{n+1} \neq 0$; of course it holds for $e_{n+1} = 0$ because (b) was already known. Since the analogue of (a) holds by construction, we have completed this step of the construction and the recursion may continue.

Since we can construct $b_0, \ldots, b_n$ satisfying (a) and (b) for any n, we have $\limsup N(x)/x \leq 1/2^n$ for any n, yielding $\lim N(x)/x = 0$ as desired.

Solution 3. (Paul Pollack) Let S be the set of all possible values of $\limsup N(x)/x$; since $S \subseteq [0, 1]$ is bounded, it has a least upper bound L. Suppose by way of contradiction that $L > 0$; we can then choose $\mathcal{A}, \mathcal{B}$ satisfying the conditions of the problem such that $\limsup N(x)/x > 3L/4$.

To begin with, we can find some positive integer $m \notin \mathcal{B}$, so that $\mathcal{A}$ is disjoint from $\mathcal{A} + m = \{a + m : a \in \mathcal{A}\}$. Put $\mathcal{A}' = \mathcal{A} \cup (\mathcal{A} + m)$ and let $N'(x)$ be the size of $\mathcal{A}' \cap \{1, \ldots, x\}$; then $\limsup N'(x)/x = 3L/2 > L$, so $\mathcal{A}'$ cannot obey the conditions of the problem statement. That is, if we let $\mathcal{B}'$ be the set of positive integers that occur as differences between elements of $\mathcal{A}'$, then there exists an integer n such that among any n consecutive integers, at least one lies in $\mathcal{B}'$. But

$$\mathcal{B}' \subseteq \{b + em : b \in \mathcal{B}, e \in \{-1, 0, 1\}\},$$

so among any $n + 2m$ consecutive integers, at least one lies in $\mathcal{B}$. This contradicts the condition of the problem statement.

We conclude that it is impossible to have $L > 0$. Hence $L = 0$ and $\lim N(x)/x = 0$ as desired.

The Sixty-Sixth William Lowell Putnam
Mathematical Competition—December 3, 2005

A1. (132, 17, 6, ..., 10, 4, 16, 11) 79.1%

Show that every positive integer is a sum of one or more numbers of the form $2^r 3^s$, where r and s are nonnegative integers and no summand divides another. (For example, $23 = 9 + 8 + 6$.)

Solution. We proceed by induction, with base case $1 = 2^0 3^0$. Suppose all integers less than n can be represented. If n is even, then take a representation of $n/2$ and multiply each term by 2 to obtain a representation of n. If n is odd, put $m = \lfloor \log_3 n \rfloor$, so that $3^m \leq n < 3^{m+1}$. If $3^m = n$, then 3^m is the needed representation. Otherwise, choose a representation $(n - 3^m)/2 = s_1 + \cdots + s_k$ in the desired form. Then

$$n = 3^m + 2s_1 + \cdots + 2s_k,$$

and clearly none of the $2s_i$ divide each other or 3^m. Moreover, since $2s_i \leq n - 3^m < 3^{m+1} - 3^m$, it follows that $s_i < 3^m$, so 3^m cannot divide $2s_i$ either. Thus n has a representation of the desired form in all cases, completing the induction.

Remark. This problem is originally due to Paul Erdős. The representations need not be unique: for instance,

$$11 = 2 + 9 = 3 + 8.$$

A2. (85, 44, 13, ..., 24, 5, 12, 13) 72.4%

Let $S = \{(a, b) : a = 1, 2, \ldots, n, b = 1, 2, 3\}$. A *rook tour* of S is a polygonal path made up of line segments connecting points $p_1, p_2, \ldots, p_{3n}$ in sequence such that

(i) $p_i \in S$,

(ii) p_i and p_{i+1} are a unit distance apart, for $1 \leq i < 3n$,

(iii) for each $p \in S$ there is a unique i such that $p_i = p$.

How many rook tours are there that begin at $(1, 1)$ and end at $(n, 1)$? (An example of such a rook tour for $n = 5$ is depicted.)

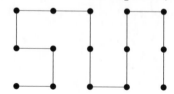

Answer. There are 0 rook tours for $n = 1$ and 2^{n-2} rook tours for $n \geq 2$.

Solution 1. It is not possible for a rook tour to begin and end at $(1,1)$ without repeating points on the path, so the answer is 0 for $n = 1$. Assume hereafter than $n \geq 2$. We will show that there is a bijection between the set of rook tours from $(1,1)$ to $(n,1)$ and the set of subsets of $\{1, 2, \ldots, n\}$ that include n and contain an even number of elements in total. Because half of the subsets of $\{1, 2, \ldots, n-1\}$ have an odd number of elements, it will follow that the number of rook tours will equal $2^{n-1}/2 = 2^{n-2}$.

The map from subsets to rook tours is defined as follows. Given a subset $T = \{a_1, a_2, \ldots, a_{2r} = n\} \subset \{1, 2, \ldots, n\}$ with $a_1 < a_2 < \cdots < a_{2r}$, form a rook tour by performing the following steps for $j = 1, \ldots, r$ (where $a_{-1} = a_0 = 0$).

- Starting from $(a_{2j-3}+1, 1)$, take rightward horizontal steps to $(a_{2j-1}, 1)$, then a vertical step to $(a_{2j-1}, 2)$.

- Take leftward horizontal steps to $(a_{2j-2} + 1, 2)$, then a vertical step to $(a_{2j-2} + 1, 3)$.

- Take rightward horizontal steps to $(a_{2j}, 3)$, then a vertical step to $(a_{2j}, 2)$.

- Take leftward horizontal steps to $(a_{2j-1} + 1, 2)$, then a vertical step to $(a_{2j-1} + 1, 1)$.

It is clear that this defines a rook tour, and that the resulting map from subsets to rook tours is injective.

It remains to check that the map from subsets to rook tours is surjective. To facilitate this, consider the following lemma.

Lemma. For $i = 1, \ldots, n-1$, no rook tour includes any of the following directed segments:

$$(i+1, 1) \text{ to } (i, 1); \quad (i, 2) \text{ to } (i+1, 2); \quad (i+1, 3) \text{ to } (i, 3).$$

Proof. Let L be the vertical line $x = i + 1/2$. Any rook tour starts to the left of L and ends to the right of L, so must cross L either once (from left to right) or three times (twice from left to right, once from right to left). It will suffice to show that in both of these cases, the possible crossings of L do not include any of the forbidden segments.

Suppose first that the rook tour crosses L once, and that this crossing goes from $(i, 2)$ to $(i + 1, 2)$. Then $(i, 1)$ would have to be adjacent to both $(i - 1, 1)$ (if $i > 1$) and $(i, 2)$ in the rook tour. Similarly, $(i, 3)$ would have to be adjacent to both $(i - 1, 3)$ (if $i > 1$) and $(i, 2)$ in the rook tour. But then $(i, 2)$ would be adjacent to three different points in the rook tour, a contradiction.

Suppose next that the rook tour crosses L three times. These must consist of a left-to-right crossing, then a right-to-left crossing, then a left-to-right crossings.

There are four cases to rule out, one of which is the case where the crossings are (in order)

$$(i, 2) \text{ to } (i + 1, 2); \quad (i + 1, 1) \text{ to } (i, 1); \quad (i, 3) \text{ to } (i + 1, 3).$$

In this case, the points $(1, 1)$, $(i, 1)$, $(i + 1, 2)$, $(i, 3)$ lie in that order on the boundary of a convex polygon, but there are disjoint segments of the rook tour joining opposite pairs of points, a contradiction. The other three cases are similar. □

It remains to show that an arbitrary rook tour P from $(1, 1)$ to $(n, 1)$ arises from some subset T via the previous construction. For $i = 1, 2, \ldots, n$, let U_i represent a directed segment from $(i, 1)$ to $(i, 2)$, and let D_i represent a directed segment from $(i, 3)$ to $(i, 2)$. By the lemma (applied to rows 1 and 3), the segment U_i occurs in P if and only if $i < n$ and the directed segment from $(i, 1)$ to $(i + 1, 1)$ does not occur. Similarly, the segment D_i occurs in P if and only if the directed segment from $(i, 1)$ to $(i + 1, 1)$ does not occur (and always occurs if $i = n$). At the point where some U_i occurs, the points $(1, 1), \ldots, (i, 1)$ have already appeared, and the subsequent points are all of the form $(j, 2)$ with $j \leq i$, so the next vertical step must be to row 3. Similarly, after some D_i occurs, the next vertical step must be to row 1. It follows that steps of the form U_i alternate with steps of the form D_i, with the former type occurring first (because P starts in row 1) and the latter type occurring last (because D_n always occurs and no U_i or D_i can occur thereafter). Let T be the set of $i \in \{1, 2, \ldots, n\}$ of indices for which either U_i or D_i occurs in P. It is now clear that T contains n, T has an even number of elements, and the rook path corresponding to T equals P. This establishes the desired bijection.

Remark. The proof of the lemma is similar to the reasoning used in a genre of logic puzzles known variously as *Fences* or *Slitherlink*. The latter name is used by Nikoli, a Japanese publisher that specializes in language-free puzzles of the sort used in the World Puzzle Championship.

Solution 2. As above, assume $n \geq 2$. Let A_n denote the set of rook tours beginning at $(1, 1)$ and ending at $(n, 1)$, and let B_n denote the set of rook tours beginning at $(1, 1)$ and ending at $(n, 3)$.

For $n \geq 2$, construct a bijection between A_n and $A_{n-1} \cup B_{n-1}$ as follows. Any path P in A_n contains either the line segment P_1 between $(n-1, 1)$ and $(n, 1)$ or the line segment P_2 between $(n, 2)$ and $(n, 1)$. In the former case, P must also contain the subpath P_1' which joins $(n - 1, 3)$ to $(n, 3)$ to $(n, 2)$ to $(n - 1, 2)$. Deleting P_1 and P_1' from P and adding the line segment joining $(n - 1, 3)$ to $(n - 1, 1)$ results in a path in A_{n-1}. This construction can be made reversible by showing that any path in A_{n-1} can be extended to a path in A_n. In the latter case, P contains the subpath P_2' which joins $(n - 1, 3)$ to $(n, 3)$ to $(n, 2)$ to $(n, 1)$. Deleting P_2' results in a path in B_{n-1}, and this construction is also reversible. The desired bijection follows.

Similarly, there is a bijection between B_n and $A_{n-1} \cup B_{n-1}$ for $n \geq 2$. Thus for any $n \geq 2$, $|A_n| = |B_n| = |A_{n-1}| + |B_{n-1}|$. Because $|A_1| = 0$ and $|B_1| = 1$, it follows that

$$|A_2| = |B_2| = |A_1| + |B_1| = 1,$$
$$|A_3| = |B_3| = 2|A_2| = 2,$$
$$|A_4| = |B_4| = 2|A_3| = 2^2,$$

and induction shows that for $n \geq 2$, $|A_n| = 2^{n-2}$.

Remark. Other bijective arguments are possible: for instance, Noam Elkies points out that each element of $A_n \cup B_n$ contains a different one of the possible sets of segments of the form $(i, 2), (i + 1, 2)$ for $i = 1, \ldots, n-1$. Richard Stanley provides the reference [CK97]; this problem is Theorem 1 of that paper, but the cases of $4 \times n$ and $5 \times n$ grids are also treated.

A3. $(14, 2, 5, \ldots, 6, 4, 86, 79)$ 10.7%

Let $p(z)$ be a polynomial of degree n all of whose zeros have absolute value 1 in the complex plane. Put $g(z) = p(z)/z^{n/2}$. Show that all zeros of $g'(z) = 0$ have absolute value 1.

Remark. It is implicit in the problem that p is nonconstant, one may take any branch of the square root, and that $z = 0$ should be ignored.

Solution 1. Write $p(z) = c \prod_{j=1}^{n}(z - r_j)$, so that

$$\frac{g'(z)}{g(z)} = \frac{1}{2z} \sum_{j=1}^{n} \frac{z + r_j}{z - r_j}.$$

Now if z is a zero of $g'(z)$ with $z \neq r_j$ for all j, then

$$\frac{z + r_j}{z - r_j} = \frac{(z + r_j)(\bar{z} - \bar{r}_j)}{|z - r_j|^2} = \frac{|z|^2 - 1 + 2i\,\mathrm{Im}(\bar{z}r_j)}{|z - r_j|^2},$$

and so

$$\mathrm{Re}\,\frac{zg'(z)}{g(z)} = \frac{|z|^2 - 1}{2}\left(\sum_j \frac{1}{|z - r_j|^2}\right).$$

Since the quantity in parentheses is positive, $g'(z)/g(z)$ can be 0 only if $|z| = 1$. If on the other hand z is a zero of $g'(z)$ with $z = r_j$ for some j, then $|z| = |r_j| = 1$.

Solution 2. Write $p(z) = c \prod_{j=1}^{n}(z - r_j)$, so that

$$\frac{g'(z)}{g(z)} = \sum_{j=1}^{n}\left(\frac{1}{z - r_j} - \frac{1}{2z}\right).$$

We first check that $g'(z) \neq 0$ whenever z is real and $z > 1$. In this case, for $r_j = e^{i\theta_j}$, so $z - r_j = (z - \cos(\theta_j)) - \sin(\theta_j)i$. The real part of $\frac{1}{z-r_j} - \frac{1}{2z}$ is

$$\frac{z - \cos(\theta_j)}{z^2 - 2z\cos(\theta_j) + 1} - \frac{1}{2z} = \frac{z^2 - 1}{2z(z^2 - 2z\cos(\theta_j) + 1)} > 0.$$

Hence $g'(z)/g(z)$ has positive real part, so $g'(z)/g(z)$ and hence $g(z)$ are nonzero.

For any real value of θ, the polynomial $p(e^{i\theta}z)$ satisfies the same hypothesis as $p(z)$ does. So, if $g_\theta(z) = p(e^{i\theta}z)/z^{n/2}$, the above argument shows that no zero of $g'_\theta(z)$ can have real part greater than 1, and thus $g'(z)$ cannot have a zero outside the unit circle. The same reasoning applied to the polynomial $z^n p(1/z)$, which also satisfies the same hypothesis, implies that g' cannot have any roots inside the unit circle. Hence all roots of g' have absolute value 1, as desired.

Solution 3. Write $p(z) = c \prod_{j=1}^n (z - r_j)$ and put $r_j = e^{2i\theta_j}$. Note that $g(e^{2i\theta})$ is equal to the nonzero constant $c \cdot (2i)^n \prod_{i=1}^n e^{i\theta_j}$ times

$$h(\theta) = \prod_{j=1}^n \frac{e^{i(\theta-\theta_j)} - e^{-i(\theta-\theta_j)}}{2i} = \prod_{j=1}^n \sin(\theta - \theta_j).$$

Since h has at least $2n$ roots (counting multiplicity) in the interval $[0, 2\pi)$, h' does also by repeated application of Rolle's theorem. Since $g'(e^{2i\theta})$ is a constant times $2ie^{2i\theta}h'(\theta)$, $g'(z^2)$ has at least $2n$ roots on the unit circle. This follows from the fact that $g(z^2)$ is holomorphic in a neighborhood of the unit circle, so a zero derivative of $g(e^{2i\theta})$ can only occur at a zero derivative of $g(z^2)$. Because $g'(z^2)$ is equal to z^{-n-1} times a polynomial of degree $2n$, it can have at most $2n$ zeros, so all the roots of $g'(z^2)$ lie on the unit circle, as they then do for $g'(z)$.

Remark. The second solution imitates the proof of the *Gauss-Lucas theorem*: the roots of the derivative of a complex polynomial lie in the convex hull of the roots of the original polynomial. The second solution is close to that of Putnam problem 2000B3 [**PutnamIII**]. A hybrid between the first and third solutions is to check that on the unit circle, $\operatorname{Re}(zg'(z)/g(z)) = 0$ while between any two roots of p, $\operatorname{Im}(zg'(z)/g(z))$ runs from ∞ to $-\infty$ and so must have a zero crossing. (This only works when p has distinct roots, but the general case follows by the continuity of the roots of a polynomial as functions of the coefficients.) One can also construct a solution using Rouché's theorem.

A4. $(20, 0, 7, \ldots, 3, 0, 55, 111)$ 13.8%

Let H be an $n \times n$ matrix all of whose entries are ± 1 and whose rows are mutually orthogonal. Suppose H has an $a \times b$ submatrix whose entries are all 1. Show that $ab \leq n$.

Solution 1. Choose a set of a rows $r_1, \ldots, r_a$ containing an $a \times b$ submatrix whose entries are all 1. Then for $i, j \in \{1, \ldots, a\}$, $r_i \cdot r_j = n$ if $i = j$ and $r_i \cdot r_j = 0$ otherwise. Hence

$$\sum_{i,j=1}^{a} r_i \cdot r_j = an.$$

On the other hand, the term on the left is the dot product of $r_1 + \cdots + r_a$ with itself, that is, its squared length. Since this vector has a in each of b of its coordinates, the dot product is at least $a^2 b$. Hence $an \geq a^2 b$, whence $n \geq ab$ as desired.

Solution 2. (Richard Stanley) Suppose without loss of generality that the $a \times b$ submatrix occupies the first a rows and the first b columns. Let M be the submatrix occupying the first a rows and the last $n - b$ columns. Then the hypothesis implies that the matrix MM^T has $n - b$'s on the main diagonal and $-b$'s elsewhere. Hence the column vector v of length a consisting of all 1's satisfies $MM^T v = (n - ab)v$, so $n - ab$ is an eigenvalue of MM^T. But MM^T is semidefinite, so its eigenvalues are all nonnegative real numbers. Hence $n - ab \geq 0$.

Remark. A matrix as in the problem is called a *Hadamard matrix*, because it meets the equality condition of Hadamard's inequality: any $n \times n$ matrix with ± 1 entries has determinant of absolute value at most $n^{n/2}$, with equality if and only if the rows are mutually orthogonal (from the interpretation of the determinant as the volume of a parallelepiped whose edges are parallel to the row vectors). This implies that the columns are also mutually orthogonal. A generalization of this problem, with a similar proof, is known as *Lindsey's lemma*: the sum of the entries in any $a \times b$ submatrix of a Hadamard matrix is at most $\sqrt{abn}$. Stanley notes that Ryser asked for the smallest size of a Hadamard matrix containing an $r \times s$ submatrix of all 1's; see [**Michael**] for more information.

A5. (10, 10, 0, ..., 2, 2, 40, 132) 10.2%
   Evaluate $\int_0^1 \frac{\ln(x+1)}{x^2+1} dx$.

Answer. The integral is $\pi \log(2)/8$.

Solution 1. (Steven Sivek) Define the function

$$f(t) = \int_0^1 \frac{\log(xt + 1)}{x^2 + 1} dx$$

so that $f(0) = 0$ and the desired integral is $f(1)$. Then by differentiation under the integral,

$$f'(t) = \int_0^1 \frac{x}{(xt + 1)(x^2 + 1)} dx.$$

By partial fractions,

$$f'(t) = \frac{2t \arctan(x) - 2\log(tx+1) + \log(x^2+1)}{2(t^2+1)} \Bigg|_{x=0}^{x=1}$$

$$= \frac{\pi t + 2\log(2) - 4\log(t+1)}{4(t^2+1)},$$

whence

$$f(t) = \frac{\log(2)\arctan(t)}{2} + \frac{\pi \log(t^2+1)}{8} - \int_0^t \frac{\log(s+1)}{s^2+1} ds$$

and hence

$$f(1) = \frac{\pi \log(2)}{4} - \int_0^1 \frac{\log(s+1)}{s^2+1} ds.$$

But the integral on the right is again the desired integral $f(1)$, so we may move it to the left to obtain

$$2f(1) = \frac{\pi \log(2)}{4}$$

and hence $f(1) = \pi \log(2)/8$ as desired.

Solution 2. We make the substitution $x = \tan\theta$, rewriting the desired integral as

$$\int_0^{\pi/4} \log(\tan(\theta)+1)\, d\theta.$$

Write

$$\log(\tan(\theta)+1) = \log(\sin(\theta)+\cos(\theta)) - \log(\cos(\theta))$$

and note that $\sin(\theta) + \cos(\theta) = \sqrt{2}\cos(\pi/4 - \theta)$. We may thus rewrite the integrand as

$$\frac{1}{2}\log(2) + \log(\cos(\pi/4 - \theta)) - \log(\cos(\theta)).$$

But over the interval $[0, \pi/4]$, the integrals of $\log(\cos(\theta))$ and $\log(\cos(\pi/4 - \theta))$ are equal, so their contributions cancel out. The desired integral is then just the integral of $\frac{1}{2}\log(2)$ over the interval $[0, \pi/4]$, which is $\pi \log(2)/8$.

Solution 3. (Roger Nelsen) Let I denote the desired integral. We make the substitution $x = (1-u)/(1+u)$ to obtain

$$I = \int_0^1 \frac{(1+u)^2 \log(2/(1+u))}{2(1+u^2)} \frac{2\,du}{(1+u)^2}$$

$$= \int_0^1 \frac{\log(2) - \log(1+u)}{1+u^2}\, du$$

$$= \log(2) \int_0^1 \frac{du}{1+u^2} - I,$$

yielding

$$I = \frac{1}{2}\log(2)\int_0^1 \frac{du}{1+u^2} = \frac{\pi\log(2)}{8}.$$

Solution 4. (David Rusin) Using the power series for logarithm,

$$\int_0^1 \frac{\log(x+1)}{x^2+1}\,dx = \int_0^1 \left(\sum_{n=1}^{\infty} \frac{(-1)^{n-1}x^n}{n(x^2+1)}\right) dx.$$

To justify interchanging the sum and the integral sign, note that

$$\sum_{n=1}^{\infty} \int_0^1 \frac{(-1)^{n-1}x^n\,dx}{n(x^2+1)}$$

is an alternating series whose terms strictly decrease to zero, so it converges. Moreover its partial sums alternately bound the previous integral above and below, so the sum of the series coincides with the integral.

Let

$$J_n = \int_0^1 \frac{x^n\,dx}{x^2+1};$$

then $J_0 = \arctan(1) = \frac{\pi}{4}$ and $J_1 = \frac{1}{2}\log(2)$. Moreover

$$J_n + J_{n+2} = \int_0^1 x^n\,dx = \frac{1}{n+1}.$$

Setting

$$A_m = \sum_{i=1}^{m} \frac{(-1)^{i-1}}{2i-1},$$

$$B_m = \sum_{i=1}^{m} \frac{(-1)^{i-1}}{2i}$$

gives

$$J_{2n} = (-1)^n(J_0 - A_n),$$
$$J_{2n+1} = (-1)^n(J_1 - B_n).$$

Now the $2N$th partial sum of our series equals

$$\sum_{n=1}^{N}\left[\frac{J_{2n-1}}{2n-1} - \frac{J_{2n}}{2n}\right] = \sum_{n=1}^{N} \frac{(-1)^{n-1}}{2n-1}(J_1 - B_{n-1}) - \frac{(-1)^n}{2n}(J_0 - A_n)$$
$$= A_N(J_1 - B_{N-1}) + B_N(J_0 - A_N) + A_N B_N.$$

As $N \to \infty$, $A_N \to J_0$ and $B_N \to J_1$, so the sum tends to $J_0 J_1 = \pi\log(2)/8$.

Solution 5. (Alin Bostan) Note that

$$\log(1 + x) = \int_0^1 \frac{x \, dy}{1 + xy},$$

so the desired integral I may be written as

$$I = \int_0^1 \int_0^1 \frac{x \, dy \, dx}{(1 + xy)(1 + x^2)}.$$

We may interchange x and y in this expression, then use Fubini's theorem to interchange the order of summation, to obtain

$$I = \int_0^1 \int_0^1 \frac{y \, dy \, dx}{(1 + xy)(1 + y^2)}.$$

We then add these expressions to obtain

$$2I = \int_0^1 \int_0^1 \left(\frac{x}{1 + x^2} + \frac{y}{1 + y^2} \right) \frac{dy \, dx}{1 + xy}$$

$$= \int_0^1 \int_0^1 \frac{x + y + xy^2 + x^2 y}{(1 + x^2)(1 + y^2)} \frac{dy \, dx}{1 + xy}$$

$$= \int_0^1 \int_0^1 \frac{(x + y) \, dy \, dx}{(1 + x^2)(1 + y^2)}.$$

By another symmetry argument,

$$2I = 2 \int_0^1 \int_0^1 \frac{x \, dy \, dx}{(1 + x^2)(1 + y^2)},$$

so

$$I = \left(\int_0^1 \frac{x \, dx}{1 + x^2} \right) \left(\int_0^1 \frac{1}{1 + y^2} \right) = \log(2) \cdot \frac{\pi}{8}.$$

Remark. Solutions 2 and 3 are related by the fact that if $x = \tan(\theta)$, then $(1 - x)/(1 + x) = \tan(\pi/4 - \theta)$. The strategy of the first solution (introducing a parameter then differentiating it) was a favorite of physics Nobelist (and Putnam Fellow) Richard Feynman. The fifth solution resembles Gauss's evaluation of $\int_{-\infty}^{\infty} \exp(-x^2) \, dx$. Noam Elkies notes that this integral is number 2.491#8 in [**GR15**]. The *Mathematica* computer algebra system (version 5.2) successfully computes this integral, as does *Wolfram Alpha*, but neither gives a derivation of the result.

A6. (5, 0, 2, ..., 3, 0, 65, 121) 3.6%

Let n be given, $n \geq 4$, and suppose that $P_1, P_2, \ldots, P_n$ are n **randomly, independently and uniformly, chosen points on a circle. Consider the** convex n-gon whose vertices are the P_i. **What is the probability that at least one of the vertex angles of this polygon is acute?**

Answer. The probability is $n(n-2)2^{-n+1}$.

Solution 1. The angle at a vertex P is acute if and only if all of the other points lie on an open semicircle. We first deduce from this that if there are any two acute angles at all, they must occur consecutively. Suppose the contrary. Label the vertices $Q_1, \dots, Q_n$ in counterclockwise order (starting anywhere), and suppose that the angles at Q_1 and Q_i are acute for some i with $3 \le i \le n-1$. Then the open semicircle starting at Q_2 and proceeding counterclockwise must contain all of $Q_3, \dots, Q_n$, while the open semicircle starting at Q_i and proceeding counterclockwise must contain $Q_{i+1}, \dots, Q_n, Q_1, \dots, Q_{i-1}$. Thus two open semicircles cover the entire circle, a contradiction.

It follows that if the polygon has at least one acute angle, then it has either one acute angle or two acute angles occurring consecutively. In particular, there is a unique pair of consecutive vertices Q_1, Q_2 in counterclockwise order for which $\angle Q_2$ is acute and $\angle Q_1$ is not acute. Then the remaining points all lie in the arc from the antipode of Q_1 to Q_1, but Q_2 cannot lie in the arc, and the remaining points cannot all lie in the arc from the antipode of Q_1 to the antipode of Q_2. Given the choice of Q_1, Q_2, let x be the fraction of the circle covered by the counterclockwise arc from Q_1 to Q_2; then the probability that the other points fall into position is $2^{-n+2} - x^{n-2}$ if $x \le 1/2$ and 0 otherwise.

Hence the probability that the polygon has at least one acute angle with a *given* choice of which two points will act as Q_1 and Q_2 is

$$\int_0^{1/2} (2^{-n+2} - x^{n-2})\, dx = \frac{n-2}{n-1} 2^{-n+1}.$$

Since there are $n(n-1)$ choices for which two points act as Q_1 and Q_2, the probability of at least one acute angle is $n(n-2)2^{-n+1}$.

Solution 2. (Calvin Lin) As in the first solution, we may compute the probability that for a particular one of the points Q_1, the angle at Q_1 is not acute but the following angle is, and then multiply by n. Imagine picking the points by first choosing Q_1, then picking $n-1$ *pairs* of antipodal points and then picking one member of each pair. Let $R_2, \dots, R_n$ be the points of the pairs which lie in the semicircle, taken in order away from Q_1, and let $S_2, \dots, S_n$ be the antipodes of these. Then to get the desired situation, we must choose from the pairs to end up with all but one of the S_i, and we cannot take R_n and the other S_i or else $\angle Q_1$ will be acute. That gives us $(n-2)$ good choices out of 2^{n-1}; since we could have chosen Q_1 to be any of the n points, the probability is again $n(n-2)2^{-n+1}$.

B1. (155, 9, 22, ..., 7, 0, 3, 0) 94.9%

Find a nonzero polynomial $P(x,y)$ such that $P(\lfloor a\rfloor, \lfloor 2a\rfloor) = 0$ for all real numbers a. (Note: $\lfloor v\rfloor$ is the greatest integer less than or equal to v.)

Answer. The polynomial $P(x,y) = (y-2x)(y-2x-1)$ works.

Solution. If $a - \lfloor a\rfloor < 1/2$, then $2a - 2\lfloor a\rfloor < 1$ and $\lfloor 2a\rfloor = 2\lfloor a\rfloor$, ensuring that $\lfloor 2a\rfloor - 2\lfloor a\rfloor = 0$. If, on the other hand, $a - \lfloor a\rfloor \geq 1/2$, then $2a - 2\lfloor a\rfloor \geq 1$. But it is always the case that $2a - 2\lfloor 2a\rfloor < 2(\lfloor a\rfloor + 1) - 2\lfloor a\rfloor = 2$, so $\lfloor 2a\rfloor = 2\lfloor a\rfloor + 1$ and $\lfloor 2a\rfloor - 2\lfloor a\rfloor - 1 = 0$. In either case $P(\lfloor a\rfloor, \lfloor 2a\rfloor) = 0$, as needed.

B2. (148, 11, 4, ..., 9, 1, 13, 10) 83.2%

Find all positive integers $n, k_1, \ldots, k_n$ such that $k_1 + \cdots + k_n = 5n - 4$ and

$$\frac{1}{k_1} + \cdots + \frac{1}{k_n} = 1.$$

Answer. The solutions are:

- $n = 1$ and $k_1 = 1$,

- $n = 3$ and (k_1, k_2, k_3) is a permutation of $(2, 3, 6)$, and

- $n = 4$ and $(k_1, k_2, k_3, k_4) = (4, 4, 4, 4)$.

Solution. By the arithmetic mean/harmonic mean inequality or the Cauchy-Schwarz inequality,

$$(k_1 + \cdots + k_n)\left(\frac{1}{k_1} + \cdots + \frac{1}{k_n}\right) \geq n^2.$$

Thus it must be that $5n - 4 \geq n^2$, so $n \leq 4$. Without loss of generality, suppose that $k_1 \leq \cdots \leq k_n$.

If $n = 1$, the only possibility is $k_1 = 1$, which gives a sum equal to 1. We may assume hereafter that $k_1 > 1$.

If $n = 2$, then $5n - 4 = 6$, and the only possibilities for (k_1, k_2) are $(2, 4)$ and $(3, 3)$, neither of which give a sum equal to 1.

If $n = 3$, then $5n - 4 = 11$, so $k_1 + k_2 + k_3 = 11$ and therefore $2 \leq k_1 \leq 3$. Hence the only possibilities for (k_1, k_2, k_3) are

$$(2, 2, 7), (2, 3, 6), (2, 4, 5), (3, 3, 5), (3, 4, 4),$$

and only $(2, 3, 6)$ gives a sum equal to 1.

If $n = 4$, then $5n - 4 = 16$, and equality occurs in the arithmetic mean/harmonic mean inequality, which only happens when $k_1 = k_2 = k_3 = k_4 = 4$.

Hence the conditions are only satisfied in the claimed cases.

B3. (23, 34, 8, ..., 2, 8, 75, 46) 33.2%

    Find all differentiable functions $f : (0, \infty) \to (0, \infty)$ **for which there is a positive real number** a **such that**

$$f'\left(\frac{a}{x}\right) = \frac{x}{f(x)}$$

for all $x > 0$.

Answer. The functions are precisely $f(x) = cx^d$ for $c, d > 0$ arbitrary except that c must be 1 when $d = 1$.

Solution 1. To see that these solutions work, note that $f'(a/x) = dc(a/x)^{d-1}$ and $x/f(x) = 1/(cx^{d-1})$, so the given equation holds if and only if $dc^2 a^{d-1} = 1$. If $d \neq 1$, one can find an a no matter what c is, but if $d = 1$, the value of c must be 1. (Thanks to Brad Rodgers for pointing out the $d = 1$ restriction.)

    To check that these are all the solutions, put $b = \log(a)$ and $y = \log(a/x)$, so the given equation becomes

$$f(e^{b-y})f'(e^y) = e^{b-y}.$$

Put

$$g(y) = \log f(e^y).$$

Then the given equation becomes

$$g(b - y) + \log g'(y) + g(y) - y = b - y,$$

or

$$\log g'(y) = b - g(y) - g(b - y).$$

By the symmetry of the right side, it follows that $g'(b - y) = g'(y)$. Hence the function $g(y) + g(b-y)$ has zero derivative, so it is constant, as then is $g'(y)$. From this, deduce that $f(x) = cx^d$ for some c and d, where both c and d are necessarily positive since $f'(x) > 0$ for all x.

Solution 2. Substitute a/x for x in the given equation to get

$$f'(x) = \frac{a}{xf(a/x)}.$$

Differentiating this shows that

$$f''(x) = -\frac{a}{x^2 f(a/x)} + \frac{a^2 f'(a/x)}{x^3 f(a/x)^2}.$$

Now substitute $\frac{a}{xf'(x)}$ for $f(a/x)$ and obtain

$$f''(x) = -\frac{f'(x)}{x} + \frac{f'(x)^2}{f(x)}.$$

Clearing the denominators gives

$$xf(x)f''(x) + f(x)f'(x) = xf'(x)^2.$$

Divide through by $f(x)^2$ and rearrange to get

$$0 = \frac{f'(x)}{f(x)} + \frac{xf''(x)}{f(x)} - \frac{xf'(x)^2}{f(x)^2}.$$

The right side is the derivative of $xf'(x)/f(x)$, so that quantity is constant. That is, for some d,

$$\frac{f'(x)}{f(x)} = \frac{d}{x}.$$

Integrating yields $f(x) = cx^d$, as desired.

B4. (97, 15, 12, ..., 13, 12, 27, 20) 63.3%
  For positive integers m and n, let $f(m, n)$ denote the number of n-tuples $(x_1, x_2, \ldots, x_n)$ of integers such that $|x_1| + |x_2| + \cdots + |x_n| \le m$. Show that $f(m, n) = f(n, m)$.

Solution 1. Define $f(m, n, k)$ as the number of n-tuples $(x_1, x_2, \ldots, x_n)$ of integers such that $|x_1| + \cdots + |x_n| \le m$ and exactly k of $x_1, \ldots, x_n$ are nonzero. To choose such a tuple, we may choose the k nonzero positions, the signs of those k numbers, and then an ordered k-tuple of positive integers with sum $\le m$. There are $\binom{n}{k}$ options for the first choice, and 2^k for the second. As for the third, the following "sticks and stones" argument shows that there are $\binom{m}{k}$ options. Given an m-tuple $(y_1, \ldots, y_m)$ of positive integers with sum m, draw a row of symbols consisting of, for $i = 1, \ldots, m$, a single stick (represented by |) followed by y_i stones (represented by ∘). For example, the tuple $(2, 3, 3)$ would be represented as

$$|\circ\circ|\circ\circ\circ|\circ\circ\circ$$

in this fashion. Since each pile is nonempty, each | is immediately followed by a ∘; the resulting row is thus a permutation of k copies of the string |∘ and $m - k$ copies of the singleton string ∘. Conversely, each permutation of these m strings is a row corresponding to one of the tuples to be counted. We thus conclude that there are $\binom{m}{k}$ such tuples. From the previous calculations, we conclude that

$$f(m, n, k) = 2^k \binom{m}{k}\binom{n}{k} = f(n, m, k);$$

summing over k gives $f(m, n) = f(n, m)$. (One may also extract a bijective interpretation of the equality.)

Solution 2. (Greg Kuperberg) It will be convenient to extend the definition of $f(m, n)$ to $m, n \geq 0$, in which case $f(0, m) = f(n, 0) = 1$.

Let $S_{m,n}$ be the set of n-tuples $(x_1, \ldots, x_n)$ of integers such that $|x_1| + \cdots + |x_n| \leq m$. Then elements of $S_{m,n}$ can be classified into three types. Tuples with $|x_1| + \cdots + |x_n| < m$ also belong to $S_{m-1,n}$. Tuples with $|x_1| + \cdots + |x_n| = m$ and $x_n \geq 0$ correspond to elements of $S_{m,n-1}$ by dropping x_n. Tuples with $|x_1| + \cdots + |x_n| = m$ and $x_n < 0$ correspond to elements of $S_{m-1,n-1}$ by dropping x_n. It follows that

$$f(m, n) = f(m-1, n) + f(m, n-1) + f(m-1, n-1),$$

so f satisfies a symmetric recurrence with symmetric boundary conditions $f(0, m) = f(n, 0) = 1$. Hence f is symmetric.

Solution 3. (Greg Martin) As in the second solution, it is convenient to allow $f(m, 0) = f(0, n) = 1$. Define the generating function

$$G(x, y) = \sum_{m=0}^{\infty} \sum_{n=0}^{\infty} f(m, n) x^m y^n.$$

As equalities of formal power series (or convergent series on some region, such as $|x|, |y| < \frac{1}{3}$),

$$G(x, y) = \sum_{m \geq 0} \sum_{n \geq 0} x^m y^n \sum_{\substack{k_1, \ldots, k_n \in \mathbb{Z} \\ |k_1| + \cdots + |k_n| \leq m}} 1$$

$$= \sum_{n \geq 0} y^n \sum_{k_1, \ldots, k_n \in \mathbb{Z}} \sum_{m \geq |k_1| + \cdots + |k_n|} x^m$$

$$= \sum_{n \geq 0} y^n \sum_{k_1, \ldots, k_n \in \mathbb{Z}} \frac{x^{|k_1| + \cdots + |k_n|}}{1 - x}$$

$$= \frac{1}{1-x} \sum_{n \geq 0} y^n \left(\sum_{k \in \mathbb{Z}} x^{|k|} \right)^n$$

$$= \frac{1}{1-x} \sum_{n \geq 0} y^n \left(\frac{1+x}{1-x} \right)^n$$

$$= \frac{1}{1-x} \cdot \frac{1}{1 - y(1+x)/(1-x)} = \frac{1}{1 - x - y - xy}.$$

(The fourth line comes from separating the variables k_i in the inner sum.) Since $G(x, y) = G(y, x)$, it follows that $f(m, n) = f(n, m)$ for all $m, n \geq 0$.

B5. (4, 0, 1, ..., 0, 0, 54, 137) 2.6%

Let $P(x_1, \ldots, x_n)$ **denote a polynomial with real coefficients in the variables** $x_1, \ldots, x_n$, **and suppose that**

$$\left(\frac{\partial^2}{\partial x_1^2} + \cdots + \frac{\partial^2}{\partial x_n^2} \right) P(x_1, \ldots, x_n) = 0 \quad \text{(identically)}$$

and that

$$x_1^2 + \cdots + x_n^2 \text{ divides } P(x_1, \ldots, x_n).$$

Show that $P = 0$ **identically.**

Solution 1. Put $Q = x_1^2 + \cdots + x_n^2$. Since Q is homogeneous, P is divisible by Q if and only if each of the homogeneous components of P is divisible by Q. It is thus sufficient to solve the problem in case P itself is homogeneous, say of degree d.

Suppose that there is a factorization $P = Q^m R$ for some $m > 0$, where R is homogeneous of degree d and not divisible by Q; the homogeneity implies that

$$\sum_{i=1}^{n} x_i \frac{\partial R}{\partial x_i} = d \cdot R.$$

Write ∇^2 as shorthand for $\frac{\partial^2}{\partial x_1^2} + \cdots + \frac{\partial^2}{\partial x_n^2}$; then

$$0 = \nabla^2 P$$

$$= \sum_{i=1}^{n} \left(2mQ^{m-1}R + 4m(m-1)x_i^2 Q^{m-2}R + 4mx_i q^{m-1} \frac{\partial R}{\partial x_i} + Q^m \frac{\partial^2 R}{\partial^2 x_i} \right)$$

$$= (2mn + 4m(m-1) + 4md)Q^{m-1}R + Q^m \nabla^2 R.$$

Since $m > 0$, and both sides are divisible by Q^m, R must be divisible by Q, which is a contradiction.

Solution 2. (Noam Elkies) Retain notation as in the first solution. Let P_d be the set of homogeneous polynomials of degree d, and let H_d be the subset of P_d of polynomials killed by ∇^2, which has dimension $\geq \dim(P_d) - \dim(P_{d-2})$; the given problem amounts to showing that this inequality is actually an equality.

Consider the operator $Q\nabla^2$ (that is, apply ∇^2 then multiply by Q) on P_d; its zero eigenspace is precisely H_d. By the calculation from the first solution, if $R \in P_d$, then

$$\nabla^2(QR) - Q\nabla^2 R = (2n + 4d)R.$$

Consequently, $Q^j H_{d-2j}$ is contained in the eigenspace of $Q\nabla^2$ on P_d of eigenvalue

$$(2n + 4(d - 2j)) + \cdots + (2n + 4(d - 2)).$$

In particular, the $Q^j H^{d-2j}$ lie in distinct eigenspaces, so are linearly independent within P_d. But by dimension counting, their total dimension is at least that of P_d. Hence they exhaust P_d, and the zero eigenspace cannot have dimension greater than $\dim(P_d) - \dim(P_{d-2})$, as desired.

Solution 3. (Richard Stanley) Write x and ∇ as shorthand for $(x_1, \dots, x_n)$ and $(\frac{\partial}{\partial x_1}, \dots, \frac{\partial}{\partial x_n})$. Suppose that $P(x) = Q(x)(x_1^2 + \cdots + x_n^2)$. Then

$$P(\nabla)P(x) = Q(\nabla)(\nabla^2)P(x) = 0.$$

On the other hand, if $P(x) = \sum_\alpha c_\alpha x^\alpha$ (where $\alpha = (\alpha_1, \dots, \alpha_n)$ and $x^\alpha = x_1^{\alpha_1} \cdots x_n^{\alpha_n}$), then the constant term of $P(\nabla)P(x)$ is seen to be $\sum_\alpha c_\alpha^2$. Hence $c_\alpha = 0$ for all α.

Remark. The first two solutions apply directly over any field of characteristic zero. (The result fails in characteristic $p > 0$ because we may take $P = (x_1^2 + \cdots + x_n^2)^p = x_1^{2p} + \cdots + x_n^{2p}$.) The third solution can be extended to complex coefficients by replacing $P(\nabla)$ by its complex conjugate, and again the result may be deduced for any field of characteristic zero. Stanley also suggests [**PS09**, §5] for some algebraic background for this problem.

B6. $(18, 0, 1, \dots, 2, 1, 41, 133)$ 9.7%
   Let S_n denote the set of all permutations of the numbers $1, 2, \dots, n$. For $\pi \in S_n$, let $\sigma(\pi) = 1$ if π is an even permutation and $\sigma(\pi) = -1$ if π is an odd permutation. Also, let $\nu(\pi)$ denote the number of fixed points of π. Show that

$$\sum_{\pi \in S_n} \frac{\sigma(\pi)}{\nu(\pi) + 1} = (-1)^{n+1} \frac{n}{n+1}.$$

Solution 1. Start by recalling a form of the inclusion/exclusion principle: if f is a function on the power set of $\{1, \dots, n\}$, then

$$f(S) = \sum_{T \supseteq S} (-1)^{|T|-|S|} \sum_{U \supseteq T} f(U).$$

In this case take $f(S)$ to be the sum of $\sigma(\pi)$ over all permutations π whose fixed points are exactly S. Then $\sum_{U \supseteq T} f(U) = 1$ if $|T| \geq n - 1$ and 0 otherwise (since a permutation group on 2 or more symbols has as many even and odd permutations), so

$$f(S) = (-1)^{n-|S|}(1 - n + |S|).$$

The desired sum can thus be written, by grouping over fixed point sets, as

$$\sum_{i=0}^{n}\binom{n}{i}(-1)^{n-i}\frac{1-n+i}{i+1} = \sum_{i=0}^{n}(-1)^{n-i}\binom{n}{i} - \sum_{i=0}^{n}(-1)^{n-i}\frac{n}{i+1}\binom{n}{i}$$

$$= 0 - \sum_{i=0}^{n}(-1)^{n-i}\frac{n}{n+1}\binom{n+1}{i+1}$$

$$= (-1)^{n+1}\frac{n}{n+1}.$$

Solution 2. Let I be the identity matrix, and let J_x be the matrix with x's on the diagonal and 1's elsewhere. Note that $J_x - (x-1)I$, being the all 1's matrix, has rank 1 and trace n, so has $n-1$ eigenvalues equal to 0 and one equal to n. Hence J_x has $n-1$ eigenvalues equal to $x-1$ and one equal to $x+n-1$, implying

$$\det J_x = (x+n-1)(x-1)^{n-1}.$$

On the other hand, we may expand the determinant as a sum indexed by permutations, in which case

$$\det J_x = \sum_{\pi\in S_n} \operatorname{sgn}(\pi)x^{\nu(\pi)}.$$

Integrating both sides from 0 to 1 (and substituting $y = 1-x$) yields

$$\sum_{\pi\in S_n}\frac{\operatorname{sgn}(\pi)}{\nu(\pi)+1} = \int_0^1 (x+n-1)(x-1)^{n-1}\,dx$$

$$= \int_0^1 (-1)^{n+1}(n-y)y^{n-1}\,dy$$

$$= (-1)^{n+1}\frac{n}{n+1},$$

as desired.

Solution 3. (Richard Stanley) The *cycle indicator* of the symmetric group S_n is defined by

$$Z_n(x_1,\ldots,x_n) = \sum_{\pi\in S_n} x_1^{c_1(\pi)}\cdots x_n^{c_n(\pi)},$$

where $c_i(\pi)$ is the number of cycles of π of length i. Put

$$F_n = \sum_{\pi\in S_n}\sigma(\pi)x^{\nu(\pi)} = Z_n(x,-1,1,-1,1,\ldots)$$

and

$$f(n) = \sum_{\pi\in S_n}\frac{\sigma(\pi)}{\nu(\pi)+1} = \int_0^1 F_n(x)\,dx.$$

A standard argument in enumerative combinatorics (the *exponential formula*) gives

$$\sum_{n=0}^{\infty} Z_n(x_1,\ldots,x_n)\frac{t^n}{n!} = \exp\sum_{k=1}^{\infty} x_k\frac{t^k}{k},$$

yielding

$$\sum_{n=0}^{\infty} f(n)\frac{t^n}{n!} = \int_0^1 \exp\left(xt - \frac{t^2}{2} + \frac{t^3}{3} - \cdots\right)dx$$

$$= \int_0^1 e^{(x-1)t+\log(1+t)}\,dx$$

$$= \int_0^1 (1+t)e^{(x-1)t}\,dx$$

$$= \frac{1}{t}(1 - e^{-t})(1 + t).$$

Expanding the right side as a Taylor series and comparing coefficients yields the desired result.

Solution 4. (David Savitt) The identity of rational functions

$$\sum_{\pi \in S_n} \frac{\sigma(\pi)}{\nu(\pi) + x} = \frac{(-1)^{n+1}n!\,(x + n - 1)}{x(x+1)\cdots(x+n)}$$

can be proved by induction on n, which for $x = 1$ implies the desired result. (This can also be deduced as in the other solutions, but in this argument it is necessary to formulate the strong induction hypothesis.)

Let $R(n, x)$ be the right-hand side of the above equation. Then

$$R(x, n) = R(x + 1, n - 1) + (n - 1)!\,\frac{(-1)^{n+1}}{x}$$

$$+ \sum_{l=2}^{n-1}(-1)^{l-1}\frac{(n-1)!}{(n-l)!}R(x, n - l),$$

since the sum telescopes. To prove the desired equality, it suffices to show that the left-hand side satisfies the same recurrence. This follows because we can classify each $\pi \in S_n$ as either fixing n, being an n-cycle, or having n in an l-cycle for one of $l = 2,\ldots,n-1$; writing the sum over these classes gives the desired recurrence.

The Sixty-Seventh William Lowell Putnam
Mathematical Competition—December 2, 2006

A1. $(129, 3, 11, \ldots, 6, 2, 47, 0)$ 72.2%
  Find the volume of the region of points (x, y, z) such that
$$(x^2 + y^2 + z^2 + 8)^2 \le 36(x^2 + y^2).$$

Answer. The volume is $6\pi^2$.

Solution. In cylindrical coordinates with $r = \sqrt{x^2 + y^2}$, the given inequality is
$$r^2 + z^2 + 8 \le 6r,$$
or
$$(r - 3)^2 + z^2 \le 1.$$
This defines a solid of revolution (a solid torus): the area being rotated is the disc $(x-3)^2 + z^2 \le 1$ in the xz-plane. By Pappus's theorem, the volume of this equals the area of this disc, which is π, times the distance through which the center of mass is being rotated, which is $(2\pi)3$. That is, the total volume is $6\pi^2$.

A2. $(96, 37, 30, \ldots, 4, 4, 27, 0)$ 82.3%
  Alice and Bob play a game in which they take turns removing stones from a heap that initially has n stones. The number of stones removed at each turn must be one less than a prime number. The winner is the player who takes the last stone. Alice plays first. Prove that there are infinitely many n such that Bob has a winning strategy. (For example, if $n = 17$, then Alice might take 6 leaving 11; then Bob might take 1 leaving 10; then Alice can take the remaining stones to win.)

Solution 1. Suppose on the contrary that the set B of values of n for which Bob has a winning strategy is finite. For convenience, include $n = 0$ in B, and write $B = \{b_1, \ldots, b_m\}$. Then for every nonnegative integer n not in B, Alice must have some move on a heap of n stones leading to a position in which the second player wins. That is, every nonnegative integer not in B can be written as $b + p - 1$ for some $b \in B$ and some prime p.

Let t be any integer bigger than all of the $b \in B$. Then one can write down t consecutive composite integers by taking $(t + 1)! + 2, \ldots, (t + 1)! + t + 1$. Take $n = (t + 1)! + t$. Then for each $b \in B$, $n - b + 1$ is one of the composite integers just listed. This contradicts B being finite.

Solution 2. As in the first solution, every nonnegative integer not in B can be written as $b + p - 1$ for some $b \in B$ and some prime p. Let $\{p_1, \ldots, p_{2m}\}$ be any set of $2m$ prime numbers. Then by the Chinese remainder theorem, there exists a positive integer x such that

$$x - b_1 \equiv -1 \quad (\text{mod } p_1 p_{m+1})$$

$$\cdots$$

$$x - b_m \equiv -1 \quad (\text{mod } p_m p_{2m}).$$

For each $b \in B$, the unique integer p such that $x = b + p - 1$ is divisible by at least two primes, so p cannot be prime. Again, this contradicts B being finite.

Solution 3. (Catalin Zara) Again, as in the first solution, every nonnegative integer not in B can be written as $b + p - 1$ for some $b \in B$ and some prime p. Put $b_1 = 0$, and take $n = (b_2 - 1) \cdots (b_m - 1)$. Then n is composite because $3, 8 \in B$, and for any nonzero $b \in B$, $n - b_i + 1$ is divisible by but not equal to $b_i - 1$. (One could also take $n = b_2 \cdots b_m - 1$, so that $n - b_i + 1$ is divisible by b_i.) Again, this contradicts B being finite.

A3. (63, 17, 13, ..., 6, 0, 39, 60) 47.0%
    Let $1, 2, 3, \ldots, 2005, 2006, 2007, 2009, 2012, 2016, \ldots$ **be a sequence defined by** $x_k = k$ **for** $k = 1, 2, \ldots, 2006$ **and** $x_{k+1} = x_k + x_{k-2005}$ **for** $k \geq 2006$. **Show that the sequence has 2005 consecutive terms each divisible by 2006.**

Solution. First observe that given any sequence of integers $x_1, x_2, \ldots$ satisfying a recursion

$$x_k = f(x_{k-1}, \ldots, x_{k-n}) \qquad (k > n),$$

where n is fixed and f is a fixed polynomial of n variables with integer coefficients, for any positive integer N, the sequence modulo N is eventually periodic. This is simply because there are only finitely many possible sequences of n consecutive values modulo N, and once such a sequence is repeated, every subsequent value is repeated as well.
    Next observe that if one can rewrite the same recursion as

$$x_{k-n} = g(x_{k-n+1}, \ldots, x_k) \qquad (k > n),$$

where g is also a polynomial with integer coefficients, then the sequence extends uniquely to a doubly infinite sequence $\ldots, x_{-1}, x_0, x_1, \ldots$ which is fully periodic modulo any N. That is the case in the situation at hand, because we can rewrite the given recursion as

$$x_{k-2005} = x_{k+1} - x_k.$$

It thus suffices to find 2005 consecutive terms divisible by N in the doubly infinite sequence, for any fixed N (so in particular for $N = 2006$). Running the recursion backwards,

$$x_1 = x_0 = \cdots = x_{-2004} = 1,$$
$$x_{-2005} = \cdots = x_{-4009} = 0,$$

yielding the desired result.

A4. (112, 17, 0, ..., 3, 6, 32, 28) 65.2%
   Let $S = \{1, 2, \ldots, n\}$ **for some integer** $n > 1$. **Say a permutation** π **of** S **has a** *local maximum* **at** $k \in S$ **if**

(i) $\pi(k) > \pi(k + 1)$ **for** $k = 1$;

(ii) $\pi(k - 1) < \pi(k)$ **and** $\pi(k) > \pi(k + 1)$ **for** $1 < k < n$;

(iii) $\pi(k - 1) < \pi(k)$ **for** $k = n$.

(For example, if $n = 5$ **and** π **takes values at** $1, 2, 3, 4, 5$ **of** $2, 1, 4, 5, 3$, **then** π **has a local maximum of 2 at** $k = 1$, **and a local maximum of 5 at** $k = 4$.**) What is the average number of local maxima of a permutation of** S, **averaging over all permutations of** S?

Answer. The average number of local maxima is $\frac{n+1}{3}$.

Solution 1. By the linearity of expectation, the average number of local maxima is equal to the sum of the probability of having a local maximum at k over $k = 1, \ldots, n$. For $k = 1$, this probability is $1/2$: given the pair $\{\pi(1), \pi(2)\}$, it is equally likely that $\pi(1)$ or $\pi(2)$ is greater. Similarly, for $k = n$, the probability is $1/2$. For $1 < k < n$, the probability is $1/3$: given the triple $\{\pi(k - 1), \pi(k), \pi(k + 1)\}$, it is equally likely that any of the three is the greatest. Thus the average number of local maxima is

$$2 \cdot \frac{1}{2} + (n - 2) \cdot \frac{1}{3} = \frac{n + 1}{3}.$$

Solution 2. Another way to apply the linearity of expectation is to compute the probability that $i \in \{1, \ldots, n\}$ occurs as a local maximum. The most efficient way to do this is to imagine the permutation as consisting of the symbols $1, \ldots, n, *$ written in a circle in some order. The number i occurs as a local maximum if the two symbols it is adjacent to both belong to the set $\{*, 1, \ldots, i - 1\}$. There are $i(i - 1)$ pairs of such symbols and $n(n - 1)$ pairs in total, so the probability of i occurring as a local maximum is $i(i - 1)/(n(n - 1))$, and the average number of local maxima is

$$\sum_{i=1}^{n} \frac{i(i-1)}{n(n-1)} = \frac{2}{n(n-1)} \sum_{i=1}^{n} \binom{i}{2}$$

$$= \frac{2}{n(n-1)} \binom{n+1}{3}$$

$$= \frac{n+1}{3}.$$

One can obtain a similar (if slightly more intricate) solution inductively, by removing the known local maximum n and splitting into two shorter sequences.

Remark. The usual term for a local maximum in this sense is a *peak*. The complete distribution for the number of peaks is known; Richard Stanley suggests the reference [**DB62**] (see page 162 and subsequent).

A5. (16, 3, 3, ..., 5, 5, 46, 120) 11.1%
      Let n be a positive odd integer and let θ be a real number such that θ/π is irrational. Set $a_k = \tan(\theta + k\pi/n)$, $k = 1, 2, \ldots, n$. Prove that
$$\frac{a_1 + a_2 + \cdots + a_n}{a_1 a_2 \cdots a_n}$$
is an integer, and determine its value.

Answer. The value is n if $n \equiv 1 \pmod 4$ and $-n$ if $n \equiv 3 \pmod 4$.

Solution. Since the given expression is symmetric in $a_1, \ldots, a_n$, we start by finding a polynomial with $a_1, \ldots, a_n$ as roots. Note that
$$1 \pm i \tan \theta = e^{\pm i\theta} \sec \theta$$
so that
$$1 + i \tan \theta = e^{2i\theta}(1 - i \tan \theta).$$
Consequently, if we put $\omega = e^{2in\theta}$, then the polynomial
$$Q_n(x) = (1 + ix)^n - \omega(1 - ix)^n$$
has among its roots $a_1, \ldots, a_n$. Since these are distinct and Q_n has degree n, these must be exactly the roots.
      If we write
$$Q_n(x) = c_n x^n + \cdots + c_1 x + c_0,$$
then $a_1 + \cdots + a_n = -c_{n-1}/c_n$ and $a_1 \cdots a_n = -c_0/c_n$, so the ratio we are seeking is c_{n-1}/c_0. By inspection,
$$c_{n-1} = ni^{n-1} - \omega n(-i)^{n-1} = ni^{n-1}(1 - \omega),$$
$$c_0 = 1 - \omega$$

so

$$\frac{a_1 + \cdots + a_n}{a_1 \cdots a_n} i = \begin{cases} n & n \equiv 1 \pmod 4, \\ -n & n \equiv 3 \pmod 4. \end{cases}$$

Remark. The same argument shows that the ratio between any two *odd* (that is, odd as functions of each individual variable) elementary symmetric functions of $a_1, \ldots, a_n$ is independent of θ.

A6. $(1, 0, 0, \ldots, 0, 2, 58, 137)$ 0.5%
Four points are chosen uniformly and independently at random in the interior of a given circle. Find the probability that they are the vertices of a convex quadrilateral.

Answer. The probability is $1 - \frac{35}{12\pi^2}$.

Solution 1. We start with some notation and simplifications. For simplicity, we assume without loss of generality that the circle has radius 1. Let E denote the expected value of a random variable over all choices of P, Q, R. Write $[XYZ]$ for the area of triangle XYZ.

If P, Q, R, S are the four points, we may ignore the case where three of them are collinear, as this occurs with probability zero. Then the only way they can fail to form the vertices of a convex quadrilateral is if one of them lies inside the triangle formed by the other three. There are four such configurations, depending on which point lies inside the triangle, and they are mutually exclusive. Hence the desired probability is 1 minus four times the probability that S lies inside triangle PQR. That latter probability is simply $E([PQR])$ divided by the area of the disc.

Let O denote the center of the circle, and let P', Q', R' be the projections of P, Q, R onto the circle from O. We can write

$$[PQR] = \pm[OPQ] \pm [OQR] \pm [ORP]$$

for a suitable choice of signs, determined as follows. If the points P', Q', R' lie on no semicircle, then all of the signs are positive. If P', Q', R' lie on a semicircle in that order and Q lies inside the triangle OPR, then the sign on $[OPR]$ is positive and the others are negative. If P', Q', R' lie on a semicircle in that order and Q lies outside the triangle OPR, then the sign on $[OPR]$ is negative and the others are positive.

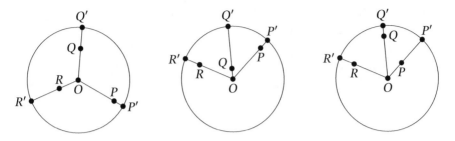

We first calculate

$$E([OPQ] + [OQR] + [ORP]) = 3E([OPQ]).$$

Write $r_1 = OP, r_2 = OQ, \theta = \angle POQ$, so that

$$[OPQ] = \frac{1}{2} r_1 r_2 (\sin \theta).$$

The distribution of r_1 is given by $2r_1$ on $[0, 1]$ (for example, by the change of variable formula to polar coordinates), and similarly for r_2. The distribution of θ is uniform on $[0, \pi]$. These three distributions are independent; hence

$$E([OPQ]) = \frac{1}{2} \left(\int_0^1 2r^2 \, dr \right)^2 \left(\frac{1}{\pi} \int_0^\pi \sin(\theta) \, d\theta \right) = \frac{4}{9\pi},$$

and by the linearity of expectation,

$$E([OPQ] + [OQR] + [ORP]) = \frac{4}{3\pi}.$$

We now treat the case where P', Q', R' lie on a semicircle in that order. Put $\theta_1 = \angle POQ$ and $\theta_2 = \angle QOR$; then the distribution of θ_1, θ_2 is uniform on the region

$$0 \le \theta_1, \quad 0 \le \theta_2, \quad \theta_1 + \theta_2 \le \pi.$$

In particular, the distribution on $\theta = \theta_1 + \theta_2$ is $\frac{2\theta}{\pi^2}$ on $[0, \pi]$. Put $r_P = OP, r_Q = OQ, r_R = OR$. Again, the distribution on r_P is given by $2r_P$ on $[0, 1]$, and similarly for r_Q, r_R; these are independent from each other and from the joint distribution of θ_1, θ_2. Write $E'(X)$ for the expectation of a random variable X restricted to this part of the domain.

Let χ be the random variable with value 1 if Q is inside triangle OPR and 0 otherwise. We now compute

$$E'([OPR]) = \frac{1}{2}\left(\int_0^1 2r^2\, dr\right)^2 \left(\int_0^\pi \frac{2\theta}{\pi^2}\sin(\theta)\, d\theta\right)$$

$$= \frac{4}{9\pi},$$

$$E'(\chi[OPR]) = E'(2[OPR]^2/\theta)$$

$$= \frac{1}{2}\left(\int_0^1 2r^3\, dr\right)^2 \left(\int_0^\pi \frac{2\theta}{\pi^2}\theta^{-1}\sin^2(\theta)\, d\theta\right)$$

$$= \frac{1}{8\pi}.$$

Also recall that given any triangle XYZ, if T is chosen uniformly at random inside XYZ, the expectation of $[TXY]$ is the area of the triangle bounded by XY and the centroid of XYZ, namely $\frac{1}{3}[XYZ]$.

Let χ be the random variable with value 1 if Q is inside triangle OPR and 0 otherwise. Then

$$E'([OPQ] + [OQR] + [ORP] - [PQR])$$

$$= 2E'(\chi([OPQ] + [OQR]) + 2E'((1-\chi)[OPR])$$

$$= 2E'(\frac{2}{3}\chi[OPR]) + 2E'([OPR]) - 2E'(\chi[OPR])$$

$$= 2E'([OPR]) - \frac{2}{3}E'(\chi[OPR]) = \frac{29}{36\pi}.$$

Finally, the case when P', Q', R' lie on a semicircle in some order occurs with probability 3/4. (The case where they lie on a semicircle proceeding clockwise from P' to its antipode has probability 1/4; this case and its two analogues are exclusive and exhaustive.) Hence

$$E([PQR]) = E([OPQ] + [OQR] + [ORP])$$

$$- \frac{3}{4}E'([OPQ] + [OQR] + [ORP] - [PQR])$$

$$= \frac{4}{3\pi} - \frac{29}{48\pi} = \frac{35}{48\pi},$$

so the original probability is

$$1 - \frac{4E([PQR])}{\pi} = 1 - \frac{35}{12\pi^2}.$$

Solution 2. (David Savitt) As in the first solution, it suffices to check that for P, Q, R chosen uniformly at random in the disc, $E([PQR]) = \frac{35}{48\pi}$. Draw the lines $\overleftrightarrow{PQ}, \overleftrightarrow{QR}, \overleftrightarrow{RP}$, which with probability 1 divide the interior of the circle into seven regions. Put $a = [PQR]$, let b_1, b_2, b_3 denote the areas of the three other regions sharing a side with the triangle, and let c_1, c_2, c_3 denote the areas of the other three regions. Put $A = E(a), B = E(b_1), C = E(c_1)$, so that $A + 3B + 3C = \pi$.

Note that $c_1 + c_2 + c_3 + a$ is the area of the region in which we can choose a fourth point S so that the quadrilateral $PQRS$ fails to be convex. By comparing expectations, $3C + A = 4A$, so $A = C$ and $4A + 3B = \pi$.

We will compute $B + 2A = B + 2C$, which is the expected area of the part of the circle cut off by a chord through two random points D, E, on the side of the chord not containing a third random point F. Let h be the distance from the center O of the circle to the line $\overleftrightarrow{DE}$. We now determine the distribution of h.

Put $r = OD$; the distribution of r is $2r$ on $[0, 1]$. Without loss of generality, suppose O is the origin and D lies on the positive x-axis. For fixed r, the distribution of h runs over $[0, r]$, and can be computed as the area of the infinitesimal region in which E can be chosen so the chord through DE has distance to O between h and $h + dh$, divided by π. This region splits into two symmetric pieces, one of which lies between chords making angles of $\arcsin(h/r)$ and $\arcsin((h+dh)/r)$ with the x-axis. The angle between these is $d\theta = dh/(r^2 - h^2)$. Draw the chord through D at distance h to O, and let L_1, L_2 be the lengths of the parts on opposite sides of D; then the area we are looking for is $\frac{1}{2}(L_1^2 + L_2^2)d\theta$. Since

$$\{L_1, L_2\} = \sqrt{1 - h^2} \pm \sqrt{r^2 - h^2},$$

the area we are seeking (after doubling) is

$$2\frac{1 + r^2 - 2h^2}{\sqrt{r^2 - h^2}}.$$

Dividing by π, then integrating over r, we compute the distribution of h to be

$$\frac{1}{\pi}\int_h^1 2\frac{1 + r^2 - 2h^2}{\sqrt{r^2 - h^2}}2r\, dr = \frac{16}{3\pi}(1 - h^2)^{3/2}.$$

We now return to computing $B + 2A$. Let $A(h)$ denote the smaller of the two areas of the disc cut off by a chord at distance h. The chance that the third point is in the smaller (resp. larger) portion is $A(h)/\pi$ (resp. $1 - A(h)/\pi$), and then the area we are trying to compute is $\pi - A(h)$ (resp. $A(h)$). Using the distribution on h, and the fact that

$$A(h) = 2\int_h^1 \sqrt{1 - h^2}\, dh = \frac{\pi}{2} - \arcsin(h) - h\sqrt{1 - h^2},$$

we find

$$B + 2A = \frac{2}{\pi}\int_0^1 A(h)(\pi - A(h))\frac{16}{3\pi}(1 - h^2)^{3/2}\, dh = \frac{35 + 24\pi^2}{72\pi}.$$

Since $4A + 3B = \pi$, we solve to obtain $A = \frac{35}{48\pi}$ as in the first solution.

Solution 3. (Noam Elkies) Again, we reduce to computing the average area of a triangle formed by three random points A, B, C inside a unit circle. Let O be the center of the circle, and put $c = \max\{OA, OB, OC\}$; then the probability that $c \le r$ is $(r^2)^3$, so the distribution of c is $6c^5 \, dc$ on $[0, 1]$.

Given c, the expectation of $[ABC]$ is equal to c^2 times X, the expected area of a triangle formed by two random points P, Q in a circle and a fixed point R on the boundary. We introduce polar coordinates centered at R, in which the circle is given by $r = 2\sin\theta$ for $\theta \in [0, \pi]$. The distribution of a random point in that circle is $\frac{1}{\pi} r \, dr \, d\theta$ over $\theta \in [0, \pi]$ and $r \in [0, 2\sin\theta]$. If (r, θ) and (r', θ') are the two random points, then the area is $\frac{1}{2} rr' \sin|\theta - \theta'|$.

Performing the integrals over r and r' first,

$$X = \frac{32}{9\pi^2} \int_0^\pi \int_0^\pi \sin^3\theta \sin^3\theta' \sin|\theta - \theta'| \, d\theta' \, d\theta$$

$$= \frac{64}{9\pi^2} \int_0^\pi \int_0^\theta \sin^3\theta \sin^3\theta' \sin(\theta - \theta') \, d\theta' \, d\theta.$$

This integral is unpleasant but straightforward; it yields $X = 35/(36\pi)$, and $E([PQR]) = \int_0^1 6c^7 X \, dc = 35/(48\pi)$, giving the desired result.

Remark. This is one of the oldest problems in geometric probability; it is an instance of *Sylvester's four-point problem*, which nowadays is usually solved using a device known as *Crofton's formula*. We defer to [**MathWorld**] for further discussion.

B1. (52, 13, 54, ..., 4, 2, 30, 43) 60.1%
   Show that the curve $x^3 + 3xy + y^3 = 1$ **contains only one set of three distinct points, A, B, and C, which are vertices of an equilateral triangle, and find its area.**

Answer. The area of the triangle is $3\sqrt{3}/2$.

Solution. The "curve" $x^3 + 3xy + y^3 - 1 = 0$ is actually reducible, because the left side factors as

$$(x + y - 1)(x^2 - xy + y^2 + x + y + 1).$$

Moreover, the second factor is

$$\frac{1}{2}((x + 1)^2 + (y + 1)^2 + (x - y)^2),$$

so it only vanishes at $(-1, -1)$. Thus the curve in question consists of the single point $(-1, -1)$ together with the line $x + y = 1$. To form a triangle with three points on this curve, one of its vertices must be $(-1, -1)$. The other two vertices lie on the line $x + y = 1$, so the length of the altitude from $(-1, -1)$ is the distance from $(-1, -1)$ to $(1/2, 1/2)$, or $3\sqrt{2}/2$. The area of an equilateral triangle of height h is $h^2\sqrt{3}/3$, so the desired area is $3\sqrt{3}/2$.

Remark. The factorization used above is a special case of the fact that

$$x^3 + y^3 + z^3 - 3xyz = (x + y + z)(x + \omega y + \omega^2 z)(x + \omega^2 y + \omega z),$$

where ω denotes a primitive cube root of unity. That fact in turn follows from the evaluation of the determinant of the *circulant matrix*

$$\begin{pmatrix} x & y & z \\ z & x & y \\ y & z & x \end{pmatrix}$$

by reading off the eigenvalues of the eigenvectors $(1, \omega^i, \omega^{2i})$ for $i = 0, 1, 2$.

B2. (123, 28, 16, ..., 3, 0, 13, 15) 84.3%
   Prove that, for every set $X = \{x_1, x_2, \ldots, x_n\}$ of n real numbers, there exists a nonempty subset S of X and an integer m such that

$$\left| m + \sum_{s \in S} s \right| \le \frac{1}{n+1}.$$

Solution. Let $\{x\} = x - \lfloor x \rfloor$ denote the fractional part of x. For $i = 0, \ldots, n$, put $s_i = x_1 + \cdots + x_i$ (so that $s_0 = 0$). Sort the numbers $\{s_0\}, \ldots, \{s_n\}$ into ascending order, and call the result $t_0, \ldots, t_n$. Since $0 = t_0 \le \cdots \le t_n < 1$, the differences

$$t_1 - t_0, \ldots, t_n - t_{n-1}, 1 - t_n$$

are nonnegative and add up to 1. Hence by the pigeonhole principle, one of these differences is no more than $1/(n+1)$. If it is anything other than $1 - t_n$, it equals $\pm(\{s_i\} - \{s_j\})$ for some $0 \le i < j \le n$. Put $S = \{x_{i+1}, \ldots, x_j\}$ and $m = \lfloor s_i \rfloor - \lfloor s_j \rfloor$. Then

$$\left| m + \sum_{s \in S} s \right| = |m + s_j - s_i|$$

$$= |\{s_j\} - \{s_i\}|$$

$$\le \frac{1}{n+1},$$

as desired. In case $1 - t_n \le 1/(n+1)$, take $S = \{x_1, \ldots, x_n\}$ and $m = -\lceil s_n \rceil$, and again obtain the desired conclusion.

B3. (15, 12, 23, ..., 54, 25, 33, 36) 25.3%

Let S be a finite set of points in the plane. A *linear partition* of S is an unordered pair $\{A, B\}$ of subsets of S such that $A \cup B = S$, $A \cap B = \emptyset$, and A and B lie on opposite sides of some straight line disjoint from S (A or B may be empty). Let L_S be the number of linear partitions of S. For each positive integer n, find the maximum of L_S over all sets S of n points.

Answer. The maximum is $\binom{n}{2} + 1$.

Solution 1. The value $\binom{n}{2} + 1$ is achieved by a convex n-gon: besides the trivial partition (in which all of the points are in one part), each linear partition occurs by drawing a line crossing a unique pair of edges.

We prove the upper bound by induction on n. When $n = 1$, there is only $1 = \binom{1}{2} + 1$ linear partition. Assume that the upper bound holds for sets containing $n - 1 \geq 1$ points, and let S contain n points. Choose a point $P \in S$, and let $S' = S \setminus \{P\}$. By the induction hypothesis, there are at most $\binom{n-1}{2} + 1$ linear partitions of S'. Each linear partition of S restricts to a linear partition of S'. Moreover, if two linear partitions of S restrict to the same linear partition of S', then that partition of S' is achieved by a line through P.

Rotations of a line through P result in at most $n-1$ partitions of S' because the partition only changes when the rotating line passes through one of the points of S. Thus the number of linear partitions of S is at most $\binom{n-1}{2}+1+(n-1) = \binom{n}{2}+1$, which completes the induction.

Solution 2. To show that $L_S \leq \binom{n}{2} + 1$ in any configuration, it may be assumed that no two lines joining points of S are parallel. Otherwise, given a maximal configuration, the points can be moved slightly to get another maximal configuration in which this assumption is satisfied. Also, assume $n \geq 3$, as the cases $n = 1, 2$ are trivially valid.

Let P be the line at infinity in the real projective plane; that is, P is the set of possible directions of lines in the plane, viewed as a circle. Removing the directions corresponding to lines through two points of S leaves behind $\binom{n}{2}$ intervals.

Given a direction in one of the intervals, consider the set of linear partitions achieved by lines parallel to that direction. The resulting collection of partitions depends only on the interval. The collections associated to adjacent intervals differ in only one element.

The trivial partition that puts all of S on one side is in every such collection. We now verify that for any other linear partition $\{A, B\}$, the set of intervals to which $\{A, B\}$ belongs is:

(a) a consecutive block of intervals, but

(b) not all of them.

To check (a), note that if ℓ_1, ℓ_2 are nonparallel lines achieving the same partition, then we can rotate around their point of intersection to achieve all of the intermediate directions on one side or the other. To check (b), note that the case $n = 3$ is evident. To reduce the general case to this case, take points P, Q, R such that P lies on the opposite side of the partition from Q and R.

It follows now that each linear partition, except for the trivial one, occurs in exactly one place as the partition associated to some interval but not to its immediate counterclockwise neighbor. In other words, the number of linear partitions is one more than the number of intervals, or $\binom{n}{2} + 1$ as desired.

Solution 3. (Noam Elkies) We enlarge the plane to a projective plane by adding a line at infinity, then apply the polar duality map centered at one of the points $O \in S$. This turns the rest of S into a set S' of $n - 1$ lines in the dual projective plane. Let O' be the point in the dual plane corresponding to the original line at infinity; it does not lie on any of the lines in S'.

Let ℓ be a line in the original plane, corresponding to a point P in the dual plane. If we form the linear partition induced by ℓ, then the points of $S \setminus \{O\}$ lying in the same part as O correspond to the lines of S' which cross the segment $\overline{O'P}$. If we consider the dual affine plane as being divided into regions by the lines of S', then the lines of S' crossing the segment $\overline{O'P}$ are determined by which region P lies in.

Thus our original maximum is equal to the maximum number of regions into which $n - 1$ lines divide an affine plane. By induction on n, this number is seen to be $\binom{n}{2} + 1$.

Solution 4. (Florian Herzig) Say that an *S-line* is a line that intersects S in at least two points. We claim that the nontrivial linear partitions of S are in natural bijection with pairs $(\ell, \{X, Y\})$ consisting of an S-line ℓ and a nontrivial linear partition $\{X, Y\}$ of $\ell \cap S$. Since an S-line ℓ admits precisely $|\ell \cap S| - 1 \leq \binom{|\ell \cap S|}{2}$ nontrivial linear partitions, the claim implies that $L_S \leq \binom{n}{2} + 1$ with equality iff no three points of S are collinear.

Let P be the line at infinity in the real projective plane. Given any nontrivial linear partition $\{A, B\}$ of S, the set of directions of lines inducing this partition is a proper, open, connected subset I of P. (It is proper because it has to omit directions of S-lines that pass through both parts of the partition and open because we can vary the separating line. It is connected because if two such lines are not parallel, we can rotate through their point of intersection to get all intermediate directions.) Among all S-lines that intersect both A and B choose a line ℓ whose direction is minimal (in the clockwise direction) with respect to the interval I; also, pick an arbitrary line ℓ' that induces $\{A, B\}$. By rotating ℓ' clockwise to ℓ about their point of intersection, we see that the direction of ℓ is the least upper bound of I. (We cannot hit any point of S during the rotation because of the minimality property of ℓ.) The line ℓ is in fact unique because if the (parallel) lines $\overleftrightarrow{pq}$ and $\overleftrightarrow{rs}$ are two choices for ℓ, with $p, q \in A$ and $r, s \in B$, then one of the diagonals $\overline{ps}, \overline{qr}$ would contradict the minimality property of ℓ. To define the above bijection we send $\{A, B\}$ to $(\ell, \{A \cap \ell, B \cap \ell\})$.

Conversely, suppose that we are given an S-line ℓ and a nontrivial linear partition $\{X, Y\}$ of $\ell \cap S$. Pick any point $p \in \ell$ that induces the partition $\{X, Y\}$. If we rotate the line ℓ about p in the counterclockwise direction by a sufficiently small amount, we get a nontrivial linear partition of S that is independent of all choices. (It is obtained from the partition of $S - \ell$ induced by ℓ by adjoining X to one part and Y to the other.) This defines a map in the other direction.

By construction these two maps are inverse to each other, and this proves the claim.

Remark. Given a finite set S of points in $\mathbb{R}^n$, a *non-Radon partition* of S is a pair (A, B) of complementary subsets that can be separated by a hyperplane. *Radon's theorem* states that if $\#S \geq n + 2$, then not every (A, B) is a non-Radon partition. The result of this problem has been greatly extended, especially within the context of matroid theory and oriented matroid theory. Richard Stanley suggests the references [**Bryl, Zasl**].

B4. $(22, 7, 4, \ldots, 9, 17, 91, 48)$ 16.7%
Let Z denote the set of points in $\mathbb{R}^n$ whose coordinates are 0 or 1. (Thus Z has 2^n elements, which are the vertices of a unit hypercube in $\mathbb{R}^n$.) Given a vector subspace V of $\mathbb{R}^n$, let $Z(V)$ denote the number of members of Z that lie in V. Let k be given, $0 \leq k \leq n$. Find the maximum, over all vector subspaces $V \subseteq \mathbb{R}^n$ of dimension k, of the number of points in $V \cap Z$.

Remark. The proposers probably intended to write $Z(V)$ instead of "the number of points in $V \cap Z$", but this changes nothing.

Answer. The maximum is 2^k.

Solution 1. (Catalin Zara) The claimed maximum is achieved by the subspace

$$\{(x_1, \ldots, x_n) \in \mathbb{R}^n : x_1 = \cdots = x_{n-k} = 0\},$$

so it remains to prove that this is best possible. Let V be a k-dimensional subspace. Form the matrix whose rows are the elements of $V \cap Z$; by construction, it has row rank at most k. It thus also has column rank at most k; in particular, we can choose k coordinates such that each point of $V \cap Z$ is determined by those k of its coordinates. Since each coordinate of a point in Z can only take two values, $V \cap Z$ can have at most 2^k elements.

Solution 2. More generally, we show that any affine k-dimensional plane in $\mathbb{R}^n$ can contain at most 2^k points in Z. The proof is by induction on $k + n$. The case $k = n = 0$ is clearly true.

Suppose that V is an affine k-dimensional plane in $\mathbb{R}^n$. Denote the hyperplanes $\{x_n = 0\}$ and $\{x_n = 1\}$ by V_0 and V_1, respectively. If $V \cap V_0$ and $V \cap V_1$ are each at most $(k-1)$-dimensional, then $V \cap V_0 \cap Z$ and $V \cap V_1 \cap Z$ each have cardinality at most 2^{k-1} by the induction assumption, and hence $V \cap Z$ has at most 2^k elements. Otherwise, if $V \cap V_0$ or $V \cap V_1$ is k-dimensional, then $V \subset V_0$ or $V \subset V_1$; now apply the induction hypothesis on V, viewed as a subset of $\mathbb{R}^{n-1}$ by dropping the last coordinate.

Solution 3. Let S be a subset of Z contained in a k-dimensional subspace of V. This is equivalent to asking that any $t_1, \ldots, t_{k+1} \in S$ satisfy a nontrivial linear dependence $c_1 t_1 + \cdots + c_{k+1} t_{k+1} = 0$ with $c_1, \ldots, c_{k+1} \in \mathbb{R}$. Since $t_1, \ldots, t_{k+1} \in \mathbb{Q}^n$, given such a dependence we can always find another one with $c_1, \ldots, c_{k+1} \in \mathbb{Q}$. Then by clearing denominators, we can find one with $c_1, \ldots, c_{k+1} \in \mathbb{Z}$ and not all having a common factor.

Let $\mathbb{F}_2$ denote the field of two elements, and let $\overline{S} \subseteq \mathbb{F}_2^n$ be the reductions modulo 2 of the points of S. Then any $t_1, \ldots, t_{k+1} \in \overline{S}$ satisfy a nontrivial linear dependence, because we can take the dependence from the end of the previous paragraph and reduce modulo 2. Hence $\overline{S}$ is contained in a k-dimensional subspace of $\mathbb{F}_{2^n}$, and the latter has cardinality exactly 2^k. Thus $\overline{S}$ has at most 2^k elements, as does S.

Variant. (David Savitt) If $\overline{S}$ contained $k + 1$ linearly independent elements, the $(k+1) \times n$ matrix formed by these would have a nonvanishing maximal minor. The lift of that minor back to $\mathbb{R}$ would also not vanish, so S would contain $k + 1$ linearly independent elements.

Remark. By coincidence, this problem appeared on AoPS (topic 105991) about three months before the exam.

B5. $(93, 17, 6, \ldots, 6, 1, 15, 60)$ 58.6%

For each continuous function $f : [0,1] \to \mathbb{R}$, let $I(f) = \int_0^1 x^2 f(x)\,dx$ and $J(x) = \int_0^1 x\,(f(x))^2\,dx$. Find the maximum value of $I(f) - J(f)$ over all such functions f.

Answer. The maximum is $1/16$.

Solution 1. Consider the inner product on the space of continuous functions on $[0,1]$ defined by

$$\langle f, g \rangle = \int_0^1 x f(x) g(x)\,dx.$$

Letting $g(x) = x$, we have $I(f) = \langle f, g \rangle$ and $J(f) = \langle f, f \rangle$. By the Cauchy-Schwarz inequality

$$I(f) - J(f) = \langle f, g \rangle - \langle f, f \rangle \le \sqrt{\langle f, f \rangle \langle g, g \rangle} - \langle f, f \rangle.$$

Note that $\langle g, g \rangle = \int_0^1 x^3 dx = 1/4$. So if $y = \sqrt{\langle f, f \rangle}$, the quantity in question is at most $y/2 - y^2$. This attains its maximum value when $2y = 1/2$ or when $y = 1/4$. Thus

$$I(f) - J(f) \le 1/8 - 1/16 = 1/16.$$

Equality is obtained when $f = g/2$.

Solution 2. For any f,

$$\int_0^1 x^2 f(x) \, dx - \int_0^1 x(f(x))^2 \, dx$$

$$= \int_0^1 (x^3/4 - x(f(x) - x/2)^2) \, dx$$

$$\le \int_0^1 x^3/4 \, dx = 1/16,$$

with equality when $f(x) = x/2$.

B6. (6, 2, 0, …, 7, 5, 42, 136) 4.0%
    Let k be an integer greater than 1. Suppose $a_0 > 0$, and define

$$a_{n+1} = a_n + \frac{1}{\sqrt[k]{a_n}}$$

for $n > 0$. Evaluate

$$\lim_{n \to \infty} \frac{a_n^{k+1}}{n^k}.$$

Answer. The limit is

$$\left(\frac{k+1}{k} \right)^k.$$

Solution 1. We start with some loose upper and lower bounds on a_n. We write $O(f(n))$ and $\Omega(f(n))$ for functions $g(n)$ such that $f(n)/g(n)$ and $g(n)/f(n)$, respectively, are bounded above. Since a_n is a nondecreasing sequence, $a_{n+1} - a_n$ is bounded above, so $a_n = O(n)$. That means $a_n^{-1/k} = \Omega(n^{-1/k})$, so

$$a_n = \Omega \left(\sum_{i=1}^n i^{-1/k} \right) = \Omega(n^{(k-1)/k}).$$

In fact, all we will need is that $a_n \to \infty$ as $n \to \infty$.

By Taylor's theorem with remainder, for $1 < m < 2$ and $x > 0$,

$$|(1 + x)^m - 1 - mx| \le \frac{m(m - 1)}{2} x^2.$$

Taking $m = (k + 1)/k$ and $x = a_{n+1}/a_n = 1 + a_n^{-(k+1)/k}$, we obtain

$$\left| a_{n+1}^{(k+1)/k} - a_n^{(k+1)/k} - \frac{k + 1}{k} \right| \le \frac{k + 1}{2k^2} a_n^{-(k+1)/k}.$$

In particular,

$$\lim_{n \to \infty} a_{n+1}^{(k+1)/k} - a_n^{(k+1)/k} = \frac{k + 1}{k}.$$

In general, if x_n is a sequence with $\lim_{n \to \infty} x_n = c$, then also

$$\lim_{n \to \infty} \frac{1}{n} \sum_{i=1}^{n} x_i = c$$

by Cesaro's lemma. Explicitly, for any $\epsilon > 0$, we can find N such that $|x_n - c| \le \epsilon/2$ for $n \ge N$, and then

$$\left| c - \frac{1}{n} \sum_{i=1}^{n} x_i \right| \le \frac{n - N}{n} \frac{\epsilon}{2} + \frac{N}{n} \left| \sum_{i=1}^{N} (c - x_i) \right|;$$

for n large, the right side is smaller than ϵ.

In our case, we deduce that

$$\lim_{n \to \infty} \frac{a_n^{(k+1)/k}}{n} = \frac{k + 1}{k}$$

and so

$$\lim_{n \to \infty} \frac{a_n^{k+1}}{n^k} = \left(\frac{k + 1}{k} \right)^k,$$

as desired.

Remark. The use of Cesaro's lemma above is the special case $b_n = n$ of the *Cesaro-Stolz theorem*: if a_n, b_n are sequences such that b_n is positive, strictly increasing, and unbounded, and

$$\lim_{n \to \infty} \frac{a_{n+1} - a_n}{b_{n+1} - b_n} = L,$$

then

$$\lim_{n \to \infty} \frac{a_n}{b_n} = L.$$

Solution 2. In this solution, rather than applying Taylor's theorem with remainder to $(1 + x)^m$ for $1 < m < 2$ and $x > 0$, we only apply convexity to deduce that $(1 + x)^m \ge 1 + mx$. This gives

$$a_{n+1}^{(k+1)/k} - a_n^{(k+1)/k} \ge \frac{k + 1}{k},$$

and so

$$a_n^{(k+1)/k} \geq \frac{k+1}{k} n + c$$

for some $c \in \mathbb{R}$. In particular,

$$\liminf_{n \to \infty} \frac{a_n^{(k+1)/k}}{n} \geq \frac{k+1}{k}$$

and so

$$\liminf_{n \to \infty} \frac{a_n}{n^{k/(k+1)}} \geq \left(\frac{k+1}{k} \right)^{k/(k+1)}.$$

But turning this around, the fact that

$$a_{n+1} - a_n = a_n^{-1/k} \leq \left(\frac{k+1}{k} \right)^{-1/(k+1)} n^{-1/(k+1)}(1 + o(1)),$$

where $o(1)$ denotes a function tending to 0 as $n \to \infty$, yields

$$a_n \leq \left(\frac{k+1}{k} \right)^{-1/(k+1)} \sum_{i=1}^{n} i^{-1/(k+1)}(1 + o(1))$$

$$= \frac{k+1}{k} \left(\frac{k+1}{k} \right)^{-1/(k+1)} n^{k/(k+1)}(1 + o(1))$$

$$= \left(\frac{k+1}{k} \right)^{k/(k+1)} n^{k/(k+1)}(1 + o(1)),$$

so

$$\limsup_{n \to \infty} \frac{a_n}{n^{k/(k+1)}} \leq \left(\frac{k+1}{k} \right)^{k/(k+1)}$$

and this completes the proof.

Solution 3. We argue that $a_n \to \infty$ as in the first solution. Write $b_n = a_n - L n^{k/(k+1)}$, for a value of L to be determined later. Then

$$b_{n+1} = b_n + a_n^{-1/k} - L((n+1)^{k/(k+1)} - n^{k/(k+1)}) = e_1 + e_2,$$

where

$$e_1 = b_n + a_n^{-1/k} - L^{-1/k} n^{-1/(k+1)}$$

$$e_2 = L((n+1)^{k/(k+1)} - n^{k/(k+1)})$$

$$\quad - L^{-1/k} n^{-1/(k+1)}.$$

Next estimate e_1. For $-1 < m < 0$, by the convexity of $(1+x)^m$ and $(1+x)^{1-m}$,

$$1 + mx \leq (1+x)^m \leq 1 + mx(1+x)^{m-1}.$$

Hence

$$-\frac{1}{k} L^{-(k+1)/k} n^{-1} b_n \leq e_1 - b_n \leq -\frac{1}{k} b_n a_n^{-(k+1)/k}.$$

Both bounds have sign opposite to b_n; moreover, by the bound $a_n = \Omega(n^{(k-1)/k})$, both bounds have absolute value strictly less than that of b_n for n sufficiently large. Consequently, for n large,

$$|e_1| \leq |b_n|.$$

We now work on e_2. By Taylor's theorem with remainder applied to $(1 + x)^m$ for $x > 0$ and $0 < m < 1$,

$$1 + mx \geq (1 + x)^m$$

$$\geq 1 + mx + \frac{m(m-1)}{2}x^2.$$

The "main term" of $L((n + 1)^{k/(k+1)} - n^{k/(k+1)})$ is $L\frac{k}{k+1}n^{-1/(k+1)}$. To make this coincide with $L^{-1/k}n^{-1/(k+1)}$, we take

$$L = \left(\frac{k+1}{k}\right)^{k/(k+1)}.$$

We then find that

$$|e_2| = O(n^{-2}),$$

and because $b_{n+1} = e_1 + e_2$, $|b_{n+1}| \leq |b_n| + |e_2|$. Hence

$$|b_n| = O\left(\sum_{i=1}^{n} i^{-2}\right) = O(1),$$

and so

$$\lim_{n \to \infty} \frac{a_n^{k+1}}{n^k} = L^{k+1} = \left(\frac{k+1}{k}\right)^k.$$

Remark. The case $k = 2$ appeared on the 2004 Romanian Olympiad (district level).

Remark. One can make a similar argument for any sequence given by $a_{n+1} = a_n + f(a_n)$, when f is a *decreasing* function.

Remark. Richard Stanley suggests a heuristic for determining the asymptotic behavior of sequences of this type: replace the given recursion

$$a_{n+1} - a_n = a_n^{-1/k}$$

by the differential equation

$$y' = y^{-1/k}$$

and determine the asymptotics of the latter. See 2012B4 for another example of this.

**The Sixty-Eighth William Lowell Putnam
Mathematical Competition—December 1, 2007**

A1. (29, 6, 30, ..., 96, 12, 23, 10) 31.6%
 Find all values of α for which the curves $y = \alpha x^2 + \alpha x + \frac{1}{24}$ and $x = \alpha y^2 + \alpha y + \frac{1}{24}$ are tangent to each other.

Answer. The only such α are 2/3, 3/2, and $(13 \pm \sqrt{601})/12$.

Solution 1. Let C_1 and C_2 be the curves $y = \alpha x^2 + \alpha x + \frac{1}{24}$ and $x = \alpha y^2 + \alpha y + \frac{1}{24}$, respectively, and let L be the line $y = x$. There are three cases.
  If C_1 is tangent to L, then the point of tangency (x, x) satisfies

$$2\alpha x + \alpha = 1, \qquad x = \alpha x^2 + \alpha x + \frac{1}{24}.$$

By symmetry, C_2 is tangent to L there, so C_1 and C_2 are tangent. Writing $\alpha = 1/(2x + 1)$ in the first equation and substituting into the second yields

$$x = \frac{x^2 + x}{2x + 1} + \frac{1}{24},$$

which simplifies to $0 = 24x^2 - 2x - 1 = (6x + 1)(4x - 1)$, or $x \in \{1/4, -1/6\}$. This gives $\alpha = 1/(2x + 1) \in \{2/3, 3/2\}$.
  If C_1 does not intersect L, then C_1 and C_2 are separated by L and so cannot be tangent.
  If C_1 intersects L in two distinct points P_1, P_2, then it is not tangent to L at either point. Suppose at one of these points, say P_1, the tangent to C_1 is perpendicular to L. Then by symmetry, the same will be true of C_2, so C_1 and C_2 will be tangent at P_1. In this case, the point $P_1 = (x, x)$ satisfies

$$2\alpha x + \alpha = -1, \qquad x = \alpha x^2 + \alpha x + \frac{1}{24}.$$

Writing $\alpha = -1/(2x + 1)$ in the first equation and substituting into the second yields

$$x = -\frac{x^2 + x}{2x + 1} + \frac{1}{24},$$

or $x = (-23 \pm \sqrt{601})/72$. This gives $\alpha = -1/(2x + 1) = (13 \pm \sqrt{601})/12$.
  If instead the tangents to C_1 at P_1, P_2 are not perpendicular to L, then there cannot be any point where C_1 and C_2 are tangent. Indeed, if counting the intersections of C_1 and C_2 (by using C_1 to substitute for y in C_2, then solving for y), gives at most four solutions counting multiplicity. Two of these are P_1 and P_2, and any point of tangency counts for two more. However, off of L, any point of tangency would have a mirror image which is also a point of tangency, and there cannot be six solutions. This identifies all possible α.

Solution 2. For any nonzero value of α, the two conics will intersect in four points in the complex projective plane $\mathbb{P}^2(\mathbb{C})$. To determine the y-coordinates of these intersection points, subtract the two equations to obtain

$$(y - x) = \alpha(x - y)(x + y) + \alpha(x - y).$$

Therefore at a point of intersection either $x = y$, or $x = -1/\alpha - (y + 1)$. Substituting these two possible linear conditions into the second equation shows that the y-coordinate of a point of intersection is a root of either $Q_1(y) = \alpha y^2 + (\alpha - 1)y + 1/24$ or $Q_2(y) = \alpha y^2 + (\alpha + 1)y + 25/24 + 1/\alpha$.

If the two curves are tangent, then the y-coordinates of at least two of the intersection points will coincide. The converse is also true because one of the curves is the graph of a function in x. The coincidence occurs precisely when either the discriminant of at least one of Q_1 or Q_2 is zero, or there is a common root of Q_1 and Q_2. Computing the discriminants of Q_1 and Q_2 yields (up to constant factors) $f_1(\alpha) = 6\alpha^2 - 13\alpha + 6$ and $f_2(\alpha) = 6\alpha^2 - 13\alpha - 18$, respectively. If on the other hand Q_1 and Q_2 have a common root, it must be also a root of $Q_2(y) - Q_1(y) = 2y + 1 + 1/\alpha$, yielding $y = -(1 + \alpha)/(2\alpha)$ and $0 = Q_1(y) = -f_2(\alpha)/(24\alpha)$.

Thus the values of α for which the two curves are tangent must be contained in the set of zeros of f_1 and f_2, namely $2/3, 3/2, (13 \pm \sqrt{601})/12$.

Remark. The fact that the two conics in $\mathbb{P}^2(\mathbb{C})$ meet in four points, counted with multiplicities, is a special case of *Bézout's theorem*: two curves in $\mathbb{P}^2(\mathbb{C})$ of degrees m, n and not sharing any common component meet in exactly mn points when counted with multiplicity.

Many solvers were surprised that the proposers chose the parameter $1/24$ to give two rational roots and two nonrational roots. In fact, they had no choice in the matter: attempting to make all four roots rational by replacing $1/24$ by β amounts to asking for $\beta^2 + \beta$ and $\beta^2 + \beta + 1$ to be perfect squares. This cannot happen outside of trivial cases ($\beta = 0, -1$) ultimately because the elliptic curve 24A1 (in Cremona's notation) over $\mathbb{Q}$ has rank 0. (Thanks to Noam Elkies for providing this computation.)

However, there are choices that make the radical milder, for example, $\beta = 1/3$ gives $\beta^2 + \beta = 4/9$ and $\beta^2 + \beta + 1 = 13/9$, while $\beta = 3/5$ gives $\beta^2 + \beta = 24/25$ and $\beta^2 + \beta + 1 = 49/25$.

A2. (106, 33, 12, ..., 16, 7, 17, 15) 73.3%
    Find the least possible area of a convex set in the plane that intersects both branches of the hyperbola $xy = 1$ and both branches of the hyperbola $xy = -1$. (A set S in the plane is called *convex* if for any two points in S the line segment connecting them is contained in S.)

Answer. The minimum is 4.

Solution 1. The value 4 is achieved by the square with vertices $(\pm 1, \pm 1)$. To prove that 4 is a lower bound, let S be a convex set of the desired form. Choose $A, B, C, D \in S$ lying on the branches of the two hyperbolas, with A in the upper right quadrant, B in the upper left, C in the lower left, D in the lower right. Then the area of the quadrilateral $ABCD$ is a lower bound for the area of S.

Write $A = (a, 1/a)$, $B = (-b, 1/b)$, $C = (-c, -1/c)$, $D = (d, -1/d)$ with $a, b, c, d > 0$. Then the area of the quadrilateral $ABCD$ is

$$\frac{1}{2}\left(\frac{a}{b} + \frac{b}{c} + \frac{c}{d} + \frac{d}{a} + \frac{b}{a} + \frac{c}{b} + \frac{d}{c} + \frac{a}{d}\right),$$

which by the arithmetic mean/geometric mean inequality is at least 4.

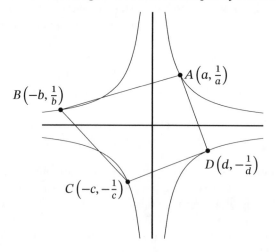

Solution 2. Choose A, B, C, D as in the first solution. Both the hyperbolas and the area of the convex hull of $ABCD$ are invariant under the transformation $(x, y) \mapsto (xm, y/m)$ for any $m > 0$. For m small, the counterclockwise angle from the line $\overleftrightarrow{AC}$ to the line $\overleftrightarrow{BD}$ approaches 0; for m large, this angle approaches π. By continuity, for some m this angle becomes $\pi/2$, that is, $\overleftrightarrow{AC}$ and $\overleftrightarrow{BD}$ become perpendicular. The area of $ABCD$ is then $AC \cdot BD$.

It thus suffices to note that $AC \geq 2\sqrt{2}$ (and similarly for BD). This holds because A and C lie outside the region between the tangent lines to the hyperbola $xy = 1$ at the points $(1, 1)$ and $(-1, -1)$. The orthogonal projection of the segment $\overline{AC}$ onto the line $x = y = 1$ has length at least $2\sqrt{2}$, so $\overline{AC}$ must as well.

Solution 3. (Richard Stanley) Choose A, B, C, D as in the first solution. Now fixing A and C, move B and D to the points at which the tangents to the curve are parallel to the line $\overleftrightarrow{AC}$. This does not increase the area of the quadrilateral $ABCD$ (even if this quadrilateral is not convex).

Note that B and D are now diametrically opposite. Write $B = (-x, 1/x)$ and $D = (x, -1/x)$. Repeating the procedure by fixing B and D and moving A and C to the points where the tangents are parallel to $\overleftrightarrow{BD}$, moves A and C to $(x, 1/x)$ and $(-x, -1/x)$, respectively, forming a rectangle of area 4.

Solution 4. (David Savitt and Chris Brewer) Choose A, B, C, D as in the first solution. Since $\overline{AD}$ and $\overline{BC}$ cross the positive and negative x-axes, respectively, the convex hull of $ABCD$ contains the origin O. Setting $A = (a, 1/a)$ and $B = (-1/b, b)$, the area of $\triangle ABO$ is

$$\frac{ab + \frac{1}{ab}}{2} \geq 1.$$

Similarly, the areas of $\triangle BCO$, $\triangle CDO$, $\triangle DAO$ are all at least 1, and the result follows.

A3. (126, 0, 0, $\ldots$, 49, 6, 9, 16) 61.2%
   Let k be a positive integer. Suppose that the integers $1, 2, 3, \ldots, 3k + 1$ are written down in random order. What is the probability that at no time during this process, the sum of the integers that have been written up to that time is a positive integer divisible by 3? Your answer should be in closed form, but may include factorials.

Answer. The probability is $\frac{k!(k+1)!}{(3k+1)(2k)!}$.

Solution. Assume that an ordering of $1, 2, \ldots, 3k + 1$ has no initial subsequence that sums to 0 modulo 3. Removing the multiples of 3 from this ordering leaves a sequence whose reduction modulo 3 must look like one of $1, 1, -1, 1, -1, \ldots$ or $-1, -1, 1, -1, 1, \ldots$. Since there is one more integer in the ordering congruent to 1 modulo 3 than to -1, the sequence modulo 3 must look like $1, 1, -1, 1, -1, \ldots$.
   It follows that the ordering satisfies the given condition if and only if the following two conditions hold: the first element in the ordering is not divisible by 3, and the sequence modulo 3 (ignoring zeros) is of the form $1, 1, -1, 1, -1, \ldots$. The two conditions are independent, and the probability of the first is $(2k+1)/(3k+1)$ while the probability of the second is $1/\binom{2k+1}{k}$, since there are $\binom{2k+1}{k}$ ways to order $(k + 1)$ 1's and k -1's. Hence the desired probability is the product of these two, or $\frac{k!(k+1)!}{(3k+1)(2k)!}$.

A4. (12, 19, 14, $\ldots$, 10, 2, 91, 58) 21.8%
   A *repunit* is a positive integer whose digits in base 10 are all ones. Find all polynomials f with real coefficients such that if n is a repunit, then so is $f(n)$.

Answer. The desired polynomials f are those of the form

$$f(n) = \frac{1}{9}(10^c(9n+1)^d - 1)$$

for $d \geq 0, c \geq 1 - d$.

Solution 1. Note that n is a repunit if and only if $9n + 1 = 10^m$ for some power of 10 greater than 1. Consequently, if we put

$$g(n) = 9f\left(\frac{n-1}{9}\right) + 1,$$

then f takes repunits to repunits if and only if g takes powers of 10 greater than 1 to powers of 10 greater than 1. We will show that the only such functions g are those of the form $g(n) = 10^c n^d$ for $d \geq 0, c \geq 1 - d$ (all of which clearly work), which will mean that the desired polynomials f are those of the specified form.

It is convenient to allow "powers of 10" to be of the form 10^k for any integer k. With this convention, it suffices to check that the polynomials g taking powers of 10 greater than 1 to powers of 10 are of the form $10^c n^d$ for any integers c, d with $d \geq 0$.

Suppose that the leading term of $g(x)$ is ax^d, where necessarily $a > 0$. Then $g(x)/x^d \to a$ as $x \to \infty$. However, for x a power of 10 greater than 1, $g(x)/x^d$ is a power of 10. The set of powers of 10 has no positive limit point, so $g(x)/x^d$ must be equal to a for $x = 10^k$ with k sufficiently large, and $a = 10^c$ for some c. The polynomial $g(x) - 10^c x^d$ has infinitely many roots, so must be identically zero.

Solution 2. Given the above definition of g, it suffices to prove that any $g(n)$ that takes powers of 10 to powers of 10 must be of the form $10^c n^d$ for some integers c, d with $d \geq 0$.

We proceed by induction on $d = \deg(g)$. If $d = 0$, then $g(n) = 10^c$ for some c. Otherwise g has rational coefficients by Lagrange's interpolation formula (this applies to any polynomial of degree d taking at least $d+1$ different rational numbers to rational numbers), so $g(0) = t$ is rational. Moreover, g takes each value only finitely many times, so the sequence $g(10^0), g(10^1), \ldots$ includes arbitrarily large powers of 10. Suppose that $t \neq 0$; then there exists a positive integer h such that the numerator of t is not divisible by 10^h. But for c large enough, $g(10^c) - t$ has numerator divisible by 10^b for some $b > h$, a contradiction.

Consequently $t = 0$, and we may apply the induction hypothesis to $g(n)/n$ to deduce the claim.

Remark. The second solution amounts to the fact that g, being a polynomial with rational coefficients, is continuous for the 2-adic and 5-adic topologies on $\mathbb{Q}$. By contrast, the first solution uses the "∞-adic" topology, which is to say the usual real topology.

A5. $(7, 5, 2, \ldots, 6, 7, 91, 88)$ 6.8%

Suppose that a finite group has exactly n elements of order p, where p is a prime. Prove that either $n = 0$ or p divides $n + 1$.

Solution 1. Let G denote the finite group in question, and let m be the order of G. By Lagrange's theorem, if m is not divisible by p, then $n = 0$. Otherwise let S be the set of p-tuples $(a_0, \ldots, a_{p-1}) \in G^p$ such that $a_0 \cdots a_{p-1} = e$. Then S has cardinality m^{p-1}, which is divisible by p. Note that this set is invariant under cyclic permutation, that is, if $(a_0, \ldots, a_{p-1}) \in S$, then $(a_1, \ldots, a_{p-1}, a_0) \in S$ also. The fixed points under this operation are the tuples $(a, \ldots, a)$ with $a^p = e$. All other tuples can be grouped into orbits under cyclic permutation, each of which has size p. Consequently, the number of $a \in G$ with $a^p = e$ is divisible by p. Since that number is $n + 1$ (only e has order 1), this proves the claim.

Solution 2. (Anand Deopurkar) Assume that $n > 0$, and let H be any subgroup of G of order p. Let S be the set of all elements of $G \setminus H$ of order dividing p, and let H act on G by conjugation. Each orbit has size p except for those which consist of individual elements g which commute with H. For each such g, g and H generate an elementary abelian subgroup of G of order p^2. However, we can group these g into sets of size $p^2 - p$ based on which subgroup they generate together with H. Hence the cardinality of S is divisible by p; adding the $p - 1$ nontrivial elements of H gives $n \equiv -1 \pmod{p}$ as desired.

Solution 3. Let S be the set of elements in G having order dividing p, and let H be an elementary abelian p-group of maximal order in G. If $|H| = 1$, then we are done. So assume $|H| = p^k$ for some $k \geq 1$, and let H act on S by conjugation. Let $T \subset S$ denote the set of fixed points of this action. Then the size of every H-orbit on S divides p^k, and so $|S| \equiv |T| \pmod{p}$. On the other hand, $H \subset T$, and if T contained an element not in H, then that would contradict the maximality of H. It follows that $H = T$, and so $|S| \equiv |T| = |H| = p^k \equiv 0 \pmod{p}$, that is, $|S| = n + 1$ is a multiple of p.

Remark. This result is a theorem of Cauchy; the first solution above is due to McKay. A more general (and more difficult) result was proved by Frobenius: for any positive integer m, if G is a finite group of order divisible by m, then the number of elements of G of order dividing m is a multiple of m.

A6. $(3, 0, 0, \ldots, 0, 4, 69, 130)$ 1.5%

A *triangulation* $\mathcal{T}$ of a polygon P is a finite collection of triangles whose union is P, and such that the intersection of any two triangles is either empty, or a shared vertex, or a shared side. Moreover, each side is a side of exactly one triangle in $\mathcal{T}$. Say that $\mathcal{T}$ is admissible if every internal vertex is shared by 6 or more triangles. For example

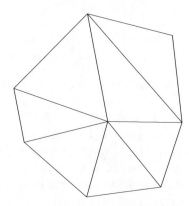

Prove that there is an integer M_n, depending only on n, such that any admissible triangulation of a polygon P with n sides has at most M_n triangles.

Solution. For an admissible triangulation $\mathcal{T}$, number the vertices of P consecutively $v_1, \ldots, v_n$, and let a_i be the number of edges in $\mathcal{T}$ emanating from v_i. Note that $a_i \geq 2$ for all i.

We first claim that $a_1 + \cdots + a_n \leq 4n - 6$. Let V, E, F denote the number of vertices, edges, and faces in $\mathcal{T}$. By Euler's formula, $(F+1) - E + V = 2$ (one must add 1 to the face count for the region exterior to P). Each face has three edges, and each edge but the n outside edges belongs to two faces; hence $3F = 2E - n$. On the other hand, each edge has two endpoints, and each of the $V - n$ internal vertices is an endpoint of at least 6 edges; hence $a_1 + \cdots + a_n + 6(V - n) \leq 2E$. Combining this inequality with the previous two equations gives

$$a_1 + \cdots + a_n \leq 2E + 6n - 6(1 - F + E)$$
$$= 4n - 6,$$

as claimed.

Now set $A_3 = 1$ and $A_n = A_{n-1} + 2n - 3$ for $n \geq 4$; we will prove by induction on n that $\mathcal{T}$ has at most A_n triangles. For $n = 3$, since $a_1 + a_2 + a_3 = 6, a_1 = a_2 = a_3 = 2$ and hence $\mathcal{T}$ consists of just one triangle.

Next assume that an admissible triangulation of an $(n-1)$-gon has at most A_{n-1} triangles, and let $\mathcal{T}$ be an admissible triangulation of an n-gon. If any $a_i = 2$, then removing the triangle of $\mathcal{T}$ containing vertex v_i yields an admissible triangulation of an $(n-1)$-gon; the number of triangles in $\mathcal{T}$ is at most $A_{n-1} + 1 < A_n$ by induction. Otherwise all $a_i \geq 3$. Now the average of $a_1, \ldots, a_n$ is less than 4, and thus there are more $a_i = 3$ than $a_i \geq 5$. It follows that there is a sequence of k consecutive vertices in P whose degrees are $3, 4, 4, \ldots, 4, 3$ in order, for some k with $2 \leq k \leq n - 1$ (possibly $k = 2$, in which case there are no degree 4 vertices separating the degree 3 vertices). Removing from $\mathcal{T}$ the $2k - 1$ triangles which contain at least one of these vertices yields an admissible triangulation of an $(n-1)$-gon. It follows that there are at most $A_{n-1}+2k-1 \le A_{n-1}+2n-3 = A_n$ triangles in $\mathcal{T}$. This completes the induction step and the proof.

Remark. We can refine the bound A_n somewhat. Supposing that $a_i \ge 3$ for all i, the fact that $a_1 + \cdots + a_n \le 4n - 6$ implies that there are at least six more indices i with $a_i = 3$ than with $a_i \ge 5$. Thus there exist six sequences with degrees $3, 4, \ldots, 4, 3$, of total length at most $n + 6$. We may thus choose a sequence of length $k \le \lfloor \frac{n}{6} \rfloor + 1$, thus improving the upper bound to $A_n = A_{n-1} + 2\lfloor \frac{n}{6} \rfloor + 1$, or asymptotically $\frac{1}{6}n^2$.

However (as noted by Noam Elkies), a hexagonal swatch of a triangular lattice, with the boundary as close to regular as possible, achieves asymptotically $\frac{1}{6}n^2$ triangles.

B1. $(189, 10, 3, \ldots, 3, 0, 0, 1)$ 98.1%
   Let f be a polynomial with positive integer coefficients. Prove that if n is a positive integer, then $f(n)$ divides $f(f(n) + 1)$ if and only if $n = 1$.

Remark. The problem fails if f is allowed to be constant. We thus assume that f is nonconstant.

Solution. Write $f(n) = \sum_{i=0}^{d} a_i n^i$ with $a_i > 0$. Then

$$f(f(n) + 1) = \sum_{i=0}^{d} a_i(f(n) + 1)^i$$

$$\equiv f(1) \pmod{f(n)}.$$

If $n = 1$, then this implies that $f(f(n) + 1)$ is divisible by $f(n)$. Otherwise, $0 < f(1) < f(n)$ since f is nonconstant and has positive coefficients, so $f(f(n) + 1)$ cannot be divisible by $f(n)$.

B2. $(80, 11, 9, \ldots, 27, 21, 34, 24)$ 48.5%
   Suppose that $f : [0, 1] \to \mathbb{R}$ has a continuous derivative and that $\int_0^1 f(x)\,dx = 0$. Prove that for every $\alpha \in (0, 1)$,

$$\left| \int_0^\alpha f(x)\,dx \right| \le \frac{1}{8} \max_{0 \le x \le 1} |f'(x)|.$$

Solution. Put $B = \max_{0 \le x \le 1} |f'(x)|$ and $g(x) = \int_0^x f(y)\,dy$. Since $g(0) = g(1) = 0$, the maximum value of $|g(x)|$ must occur at a critical point $y \in (0, 1)$ satisfying $g'(y) = f(y) = 0$. Thus take $\alpha = y$ hereafter.

Since $\int_0^\alpha f(x)\,dx = -\int_0^{1-\alpha} f(1 - x)\,dx$, we may assume that $\alpha \le 1/2$. By then substituting $-f(x)$ for $f(x)$ if needed, we may assume that $\int_0^\alpha f(x)\,dx \ge 0$.

From the inequality $f'(x) \geq -B$, we deduce $f(x) \leq B(\alpha - x)$ for $0 \leq x \leq \alpha$, so

$$
\begin{aligned}
\int_0^\alpha f(x)\,dx &\leq \int_0^\alpha B(\alpha - x)\,dx \\
&= -\frac{1}{2}B(\alpha - x)^2 \Big|_0^\alpha \\
&= \frac{\alpha^2}{2}B \leq \frac{1}{8}B
\end{aligned}
$$

as desired.

B3. $(65, 12, 10, \ldots, 10, 10, 29, 70)$ 42.2%
   Let $x_0 = 1$ and for $n \geq 0$, let $x_{n+1} = 3x_n + \lfloor x_n\sqrt{5}\rfloor$. **In particular, $x_1 = 5$, $x_2 = 26$, $x_3 = 136$, $x_4 = 712$. Find a closed-form expression for x_{2007}. ($\lfloor a\rfloor$ means the largest integer $\leq a$.)**

Answer. One valid expression is

$$
x_{2007} = \frac{2^{2006}}{\sqrt{5}}(\alpha^{3997} - \alpha^{-3997}).
$$

Solution 1. Observing that $x_2/2 = 13$, $x_3/4 = 34$, $x_4/8 = 89$, we guess that $x_n = 2^{n-1}F_{2n+3}$, where F_k is the kth Fibonacci number. We will show this in the form that $x_n = \frac{2^{n-1}}{\sqrt{5}}(\alpha^{2n+3} - \alpha^{-(2n+3)})$, where $\alpha = \frac{1+\sqrt{5}}{2}$; this will give the specified answer.
   We prove the claim by induction. The base case $x_0 = 1$ is true, and so it suffices to show that the recursion $x_{n+1} = 3x_n + \lfloor x_n\sqrt{5}\rfloor$ is satisfied for our formula for x_n. Indeed, since $\alpha^2 = \frac{3+\sqrt{5}}{2}$, it follows that

$$
\begin{aligned}
x_{n+1} - (3 + \sqrt{5})x_n &= \frac{2^{n-1}}{\sqrt{5}}(2(\alpha^{2n+5} - \alpha^{-(2n+5)}) \\
&\quad - (3 + \sqrt{5})(\alpha^{2n+3} - \alpha^{-(2n+3)})) \\
&= 2^n\alpha^{-(2n+3)}.
\end{aligned}
$$

Now $2^n\alpha^{-(2n+3)} = (\frac{1-\sqrt{5}}{2})^3(3 - \sqrt{5})^n$ is between -1 and 0. The recursion follows since x_n, x_{n+1} are integers.

Solution 2. (Catalin Zara) Since x_n is rational, $0 < x_n\sqrt{5} - \lfloor x_n\sqrt{5}\rfloor < 1$. This gives the inequalities

$$x_{n+1} - 3x_n < x_n\sqrt{5} < x_{n+1} - 3x_n + 1,$$
$$(3 + \sqrt{5})x_n - 1 < x_{n+1} < (3 + \sqrt{5})x_n,$$
$$4x_n - (3 - \sqrt{5}) < (3 - \sqrt{5})x_{n+1} < 4x_n,$$
$$3x_{n+1} - 4x_n < x_{n+1}\sqrt{5} < 3x_{n+1} - 4x_n + (3 - \sqrt{5}).$$

Since $0 < 3-\sqrt{5} < 1$, this yields $\lfloor x_{n+1}\sqrt{5}\rfloor = 3x_{n+1}-4x_n$, so rewrite the recursion as $x_{n+1} = 6x_n - 4x_{n-1}$ for $n \geq 2$. It is routine to solve this recursion to obtain the same solution as above.

Remark. With an initial 1 prepended, this becomes sequence A018903 in the OEIS. Therein, the sequence is described as the case $S(1,5)$ of the sequence $S(a_0, a_1)$ in which a_{n+2} is the least integer for which $a_{n+2}/a_{n+1} > a_{n+1}/a_n$; the reference given is [**Boyd**].

B4. (45, 10, 4, ..., 2, 5, 75, 65) 28.6%
  Let n be a positive integer. Find the number of pairs P, Q of polynomials with real coefficients such that

$$(P(X))^2 + (Q(X))^2 = X^{2n} + 1$$

and $\deg P > \deg Q$.

Answer. The number of pairs is 2^{n+1}.

Solution. The degree condition forces P to have degree n and leading coefficient ± 1. Count pairs in which P has leading coefficient 1 and multiply the answer by 2 afterward.
  Factor both sides:

$$(P(X) + Q(X)i)(P(X) - Q(X)i)$$
$$= \prod_{j=0}^{n-1}(X - \exp(2\pi i(2j + 1)/(4n)))$$
$$\cdot \prod_{j=0}^{n-1}(X + \exp(2\pi i(2j + 1)/(4n))).$$

Each choice of P, Q corresponds to equating $P(X) + Q(X)i$ with the product of some n factors on the right, choosing exactly one of the two factors for each $j = 0,\ldots, n - 1$. Exactly n factors must be chosen because, as a polynomial in X with complex coefficients, $P(X) + Q(X)i$ has degree exactly n. One factor must be chosen for each j to ensure that $P(X) + Q(X)i$ and $P(X) - Q(X)i$ are complex conjugates, so that P, Q have real coefficients. Thus there are 2^n such pairs. Multiplying by 2 to allow P to have leading coefficient -1 yields the desired result.

Remark. If P and Q are allowed to have complex coefficients but still are required to satisfy $\deg(P) > \deg(Q)$, then the number of pairs increases to $2\binom{2n}{n}$, as we may choose any n of the $2n$ factors of $X^{2n} + 1$ to use to form $P(X) + Q(X)i$.

B5. (39, 3, 6, ..., 4, 2, 28, 124) 23.3%
  Let k be a positive integer. Prove that there exist polynomials $P_0(n)$, $P_1(n), \ldots, P_{k-1}(n)$ (which may depend on k) such that for any integer n,

$$\left\lfloor \frac{n}{k} \right\rfloor^k = P_0(n) + P_1(n)\left\lfloor \frac{n}{k} \right\rfloor + \cdots + P_{k-1}(n)\left\lfloor \frac{n}{k} \right\rfloor^{k-1}.$$

Solution. For n an integer, $\left\lfloor \frac{n}{k} \right\rfloor = \frac{n-j}{k}$ for j the unique integer in $\{0, \ldots, k-1\}$ congruent to n modulo k; hence

$$\prod_{j=0}^{k-1}\left(\left\lfloor \frac{n}{k} \right\rfloor - \frac{n-j}{k}\right) = 0.$$

By expanding this out, we obtain the desired polynomials $P_0(n), \ldots, P_{k-1}(n)$.

Remark. Variants of this solution are possible that construct the P_i less explicitly, using Lagrange interpolation or Vandermonde determinants.

B6. (2, 2, 0, ..., 1, 2, 28, 171) 1.9%
  For each positive integer n, let $f(n)$ be the number of ways to make $n!$ cents using an unordered collection of coins, each worth $k!$ cents for some k, $1 \le k \le n$. Prove that for some constant C, independent of n,

$$n^{n^2/2 - Cn} e^{-n^2/4} \le f(n) \le n^{n^2/2 + Cn} e^{-n^2/4}.$$

Remark. It should be assumed that $n \ge 2$, as otherwise the problem is trivially false.

Solution. (Suggested by Oleg Golberg) Throughout this proof, any C_i will be a positive constant whose exact value is immaterial. As in the proof of Stirling's approximation, we estimate for any fixed $c \in \mathbb{R}$,

$$\sum_{i=1}^{n}(i + c)\log i = \frac{1}{2}n^2 \log n - \frac{1}{4}n^2 + O(n \log n)$$

by comparing the sum to an integral. This gives

$$n^{n^2/2 - C_1 n} e^{-n^2/4} \le 1^{1+c} 2^{2+c} \cdots n^{n+c}$$

$$\le n^{n^2/2 + C_2 n} e^{-n^2/4}.$$

Interpret $f(n)$ as counting the number of n-tuples $(a_1, \ldots, a_n)$ of nonnegative integers such that

$$a_1 1! + \cdots + a_n n! = n!.$$

For an upper bound on $f(n)$, use the inequalities $0 \le a_i \le n!/i!$ to deduce that there are at most $n!/i! + 1 \le 2(n!/i!)$ choices for a_i. Hence

$$f(n) \le 2^n \frac{n!}{1!} \cdots \frac{n!}{n!}$$

$$= 2^n 2^1 3^2 \cdots n^{n-1}$$

$$\le n^{n^2/2 + C_3 n} e^{-n^2/4}.$$

For a lower bound on $f(n)$, note that if $0 \le a_i < (n-1)!/i!$ for $i = 2, \ldots, n-1$ and $a_n = 0$, then $0 \le a_2 2! + \cdots + a_n n! \le n!$, so there is a unique choice of a_1 to complete this to a solution of $a_1 1! + \cdots + a_n n! = n!$. Hence

$$f(n) \ge \frac{(n-1)!}{2!} \cdots \frac{(n-1)!}{(n-1)!}$$

$$= 3^1 4^2 \cdots (n-1)^{n-3}$$

$$\ge n^{n^2/2 + C_4 n} e^{-n^2/4}.$$

**The Sixty-Ninth William Lowell Putnam
Mathematical Competition—December 6, 2008**

A1. $(177, 5, 4, \ldots, 0, 3, 0, 0)$ 98.4%

Let $f : \mathbb{R}^2 \to \mathbb{R}$ **be a function such that** $f(x, y) + f(y, z) + f(z, x) = 0$ **for all real numbers** x, y, **and** z. **Prove that there exists a function** $g : \mathbb{R} \to \mathbb{R}$ **such that** $f(x, y) = g(x) - g(y)$ **for all real numbers** x **and** y.

Solution. The function $g(x) = f(x, 0)$ works. Substituting $(x, y, z) = (0, 0, 0)$ into the given functional equation yields $f(0, 0) = 0$, whence substituting $(x, y, z) = (x, 0, 0)$ yields $f(x, 0) + f(0, x) = 0$. Finally, substituting $(x, y, z) = (x, y, 0)$ yields $f(x, y) = -f(y, 0) - f(0, x) = g(x) - g(y)$.

Remark. A similar argument shows that the possible functions g are precisely those of the form $f(x, 0) + c$ for some c.

A2. $(136, 14, 10, \ldots, 0, 0, 14, 15)$ 84.7%

Alan and Barbara play a game in which they take turns filling entries of an initially empty 2008×2008 array. Alan plays first. At each turn, a player chooses a real number and places it in a vacant entry. The game ends when all the entries are filled. Alan wins if the determinant of the resulting matrix is nonzero; Barbara wins if it is zero. Which player has a winning strategy?

Answer. Barbara has a winning strategy.

Solution 1. Pair each entry of the first row with the entry directly below it in the second row. If Alan ever writes a number in one of the first two rows, Barbara writes the same number in the other entry in the pair. If Alan writes a number anywhere other than the first two rows, Barbara does likewise. At the end, the resulting matrix will have two identical rows, so its determinant will be zero.

Solution 2. Whenever Alan writes a number x in an entry in some row, Barbara writes $-x$ in some other entry in the same row. At the end, the resulting matrix will have all rows summing to zero, so it cannot have full rank.

Remark. The strategies used in both solutions work for any $n \times n$ matrix with n even.

A3. $(67, 25, 47, \ldots, 32, 3, 10, 5)$ 73.5%

Start with a finite sequence $a_1, a_2, \ldots, a_n$ of positive integers. If possible, choose two indices $j < k$ such that a_j does not divide a_k, and replace

a_j and a_k by $\gcd(a_j, a_k)$ and $\mathrm{lcm}(a_j, a_k)$, **respectively. Prove that if this process is repeated, it must eventually stop and the final sequence does not depend on the choices made. (Note: gcd means greatest common divisor and lcm means least common multiple.)**

Solution. We first prove that the process stops. Note first that the product $a_1 \cdots a_n$ remains constant, because $a_j a_k = \gcd(a_j, a_k) \mathrm{lcm}(a_j, a_k)$. Moreover, the last number in the sequence can never decrease, because it is always replaced by its least common multiple with another number. Since it is bounded above (by the product of all of the numbers), the last number must eventually reach its maximum value, after which it remains constant throughout. After this happens, the next-to-last number will never decrease, so it eventually becomes constant, and so on. After finitely many steps, all of the numbers will achieve their final values, so no more steps will be possible. This only happens when a_j divides a_k for all pairs $j < k$.

We next check that there is only one possible final sequence. For p a prime and m a nonnegative integer, we claim that the number of integers in the list divisible by p^m never changes. To see this, suppose we replace a_j, a_k by $\gcd(a_j, a_k)$, $\mathrm{lcm}(a_j, a_k)$. If neither of a_j, a_k is divisible by p^m, then neither of $\gcd(a_j, a_k)$, $\mathrm{lcm}(a_j, a_k)$ is either. If exactly one a_j, a_k is divisible by p^m, then $\mathrm{lcm}(a_j, a_k)$ is divisible by p^m but $\gcd(a_j, a_k)$ is not.

If we started out with exactly h numbers not divisible by p^m, then in the final sequence $a'_1, \ldots, a'_n$, the numbers $a'_{h+1}, \ldots, a'_n$ are divisible by p^m while the numbers $a'_1, \ldots, a'_h$ are not. Repeating this argument for each pair (p, m) such that p^m divides the initial product $a_1, \ldots, a_n$, we can determine the exact prime factorization of each of $a'_1, \ldots, a'_n$. This proves that the final sequence is unique.

Remark. (David Savitt and Noam Elkies) Here are two other ways to prove the termination. One is to observe that $\prod_j a_j^j$ is *strictly* increasing at each step, and bounded above by $(a_1 \cdots a_n)^n$. The other is to notice that a_1 is nonincreasing but always positive, so eventually becomes constant. Then a_2 is nonincreasing but always positive, and so on.

Reinterpretation. For each p, consider the sequence consisting of the exponents of p in the prime factorizations of $a_1, \ldots, a_n$. At each step, we pick two positions i and j such that the exponents of some prime p are in the wrong order at positions i and j. We then sort these two positions into the correct order for every prime p simultaneously.

It is clear that this can only terminate with all sequences being sorted into the correct order. We must still check that the process terminates; however, since all but finitely many of the exponent sequences consist of all zeros, and each step makes a nontrivial switch in at least one of the other exponent sequences, it is enough to check the case of a single exponent sequence. This can be done as in the first solution.

Remark. (Abhinav Kumar) The following argument proves that the process always terminates in at most $\binom{n}{2}$ steps. (This is a variant of the worst-case analysis of the *bubble sort* algorithm.)

Consider the number of pairs (k, l) with $1 \leq k < l \leq n$ such that a_k does not divide a_l (call these *bad pairs*). At each step, we eliminate one bad pair (i, j), and we do not touch any pairs that do not involve either i or j. If $i < k < j$, then neither of the pairs (i, k) or (k, j) can become bad, because a_i is replaced by a divisor of itself, while a_j is replaced by a multiple of itself. If $k < i$, then (k, i) can only become a bad pair if a_k divided a_i but not a_j, in which case (k, j) stops being bad. Similarly, if $k > j$, then (i, k) and (j, k) either stay the same or switch status. Hence the number of bad pairs goes down by at least 1 each time. Since it is at most $\binom{n}{2}$ to begin with, this is an upper bound for the number of steps.

Remark. This problem is closely related to the classification theorem for finite abelian groups. Namely, if $a_1, \ldots, a_n$ and $a'_1, \ldots, a'_n$ are the sequences obtained at two different steps in the process, then the abelian groups $\mathbb{Z}/a_1\mathbb{Z} \times \cdots \times \mathbb{Z}/a_n\mathbb{Z}$ and $\mathbb{Z}/a'_1\mathbb{Z} \times \cdots \times \mathbb{Z}/a'_n\mathbb{Z}$ are isomorphic. The final sequence gives a canonical presentation of this group. The terms of this sequence are called the *elementary divisors* or *invariant factors* of the group.

Remark. (Tom Belulovich) A *lattice* is a partially ordered set L in which for any two $x, y \in L$, there is a unique minimal element z with $z \geq x$ and $z \geq y$, called the *join* and denoted $x \wedge y$, and there is a unique maximal element z with $z \leq x$ and $z \leq y$, called the *meet* and denoted $x \vee y$. In terms of a lattice L, one can pose the following generalization of the given problem. Start with $a_1, \ldots, a_n \in L$. If $i < j$ but $a_i \not\leq a_j$, it is permitted to replace a_i, a_j by $a_i \vee a_j, a_i \wedge a_j$, respectively. The same argument as above shows that this always terminates in at most $\binom{n}{2}$ steps. The question is, under what conditions on the lattice L is the final sequence uniquely determined by the initial sequence?

It turns out that this holds if and only if L is *distributive*, that is, for any $x, y, z \in L$,

$$x \wedge (y \vee z) = (x \wedge y) \vee (x \wedge z).$$

(This is equivalent to the same axiom with the operations interchanged.) For example, if L is a *Boolean algebra* (the set of subsets of a given set S under inclusion) then $\wedge$ is union, $\vee$ is intersection, and the distributive law holds. Conversely, any finite distributive lattice is contained in a Boolean algebra by a theorem of Birkhoff. The correspondence takes each $x \in L$ to the set of $y \in L$ such that $x \geq y$ and y cannot be written as a join of two elements of $L \setminus \{y\}$. (See for instance [**Birk**].)

On one hand, if L is distributive, it can be shown that the jth term of the final sequence is equal to the meet of $a_{i_1} \wedge \cdots \wedge a_{i_j}$ over all sequences $1 \leq i_1 < \cdots < i_j \leq n$. For instance, this can be checked by forming the smallest subset L' of L containing $a_1, \ldots, a_n$ and closed under meet and join, then embedding L' into a Boolean algebra using Birkhoff's theorem, then checking the claim for all Boolean algebras. It can also be checked directly (as suggested by Nghi Nguyen) by showing that for $j = 1, \ldots, n$, the meet of all joins of j-element subsets of $a_1, \ldots, a_n$ is invariant at each step.

On the other hand, a lattice fails to be distributive if and only if it contains five elements $a, b, c, 0, 1$ such that either the only relations among them are implied by

$$1 \geq a, b, c \geq 0$$

(this lattice is sometimes called the *diamond*), or the only relations among them are implied by

$$1 \geq a \geq b \geq 0, \qquad 1 \geq c \geq 0$$

(this lattice is sometimes called the *pentagon*). (For a proof, see the Birkhoff reference given above.) For each of these examples, the initial sequence a, b, c fails to determine the final sequence; for the diamond, we can end up with $0, *, 1$ for any of $* = a, b, c$, whereas for the pentagon we can end up with $0, *, 1$ for any of $* = a, b$.

Consequently, the final sequence is determined by the initial sequence if and only if L is distributive.

A4. (74, 29, 13, ..., 5, 2, 34, 32) 61.4%
   Define $f : \mathbb{R} \to \mathbb{R}$ **by**

$$f(x) = \begin{cases} x & \text{if } x \leq e, \\ xf(\ln x) & \text{if } x > e. \end{cases}$$

Does $\sum_{n=1}^{\infty} \frac{1}{f(n)}$ **converge?**

Answer. No, the sum diverges.

Solution. By definition, $f(x) = x$ on $[1, e]$, $x \log x$ on $(e, e^e]$, $x \log x \log \log x$ on $(e^e, e^{e^e}]$, and so forth. It follows that on $[1, \infty)$, f is positive, continuous, and increasing. Thus $\sum_{n=1}^{\infty} \frac{1}{f(n)}$, if it converges, is bounded below by $\int_1^{\infty} \frac{dx}{f(x)}$; it suffices to prove that the integral diverges.

Write $\log^1 x = \log x$ and $\log^k x = \log(\log^{k-1} x)$ for $k \geq 2$; similarly write $\exp^1 x = e^x$ and $\exp^k x = e^{\exp^{k-1} x}$. If we write $y = \log^k x$, then $x = \exp^k y$ and $dx = (\exp^k y)(\exp^{k-1} y) \cdots (\exp^1 y) dy = x(\log^1 x) \cdots (\log^{k-1} x) dy$. Now for $x \in$

$[\exp^{k-1} 1, \exp^{k} 1]$, $f(x) = x(\log^1 x) \cdots (\log^{k-1} x)$ and thus substituting $y = \log^k x$ yields

$$\int_{\exp^{k-1} 1}^{\exp^k 1} \frac{dx}{f(x)} = \int_0^1 dy = 1.$$

It follows that $\int_1^\infty \frac{dx}{f(x)} = \sum_{k=1}^\infty \int_{\exp^{k-1} 1}^{\exp^k 1} \frac{dx}{f(x)}$ diverges, as desired.

A5. (32, 9, 13, ..., 6, 5, 71, 53) 28.6%

Let $n \geq 3$ **be an integer. Let** $f(x)$ **and** $g(x)$ **be polynomials with real coefficients such that the points** $(f(1), g(1)), (f(2), g(2)), \ldots, (f(n), g(n))$ **in** $\mathbb{R}^2$ **are the vertices of a regular n-gon in counterclockwise order. Prove that at least one of** $f(x)$ **and** $g(x)$ **has degree greater than or equal to** $n - 1$.

Solution 1. Form the polynomial $P(z) = f(z) + ig(z)$ with complex coefficients. It suffices to prove that P has degree at least $n - 1$, as then one of f, g must have degree at least $n - 1$.

By replacing $P(z)$ with $aP(z) + b$ for suitable $a, b \in \mathbb{C}$, the regular n-gon can be made to have vertices $\zeta_n, \zeta_n^2, \ldots, \zeta_n^n$ for $\zeta_n = \exp(2\pi i/n)$. It thus suffices to check that there cannot exist a polynomial $P(z)$ of degree at most $n - 2$ such that $P(i) = \zeta_n^i$ for $i = 1, \ldots, n$.

More generally for any complex number $t \notin \{0, 1\}$, and any integer $m \geq 1$, any polynomial $Q(z)$ for which $Q(k) = t^k$ for $k = 1, \ldots, m$ has degree at least $m - 1$. There are several ways to do this. For example, if $Q(z)$ has degree d and leading coefficient c, then $R(z) = Q(z+1) - tQ(z)$ has degree d and leading coefficient $(1 - t)c$. However, by hypothesis, $R(z)$ has the distinct roots $1, 2, \ldots, m-1$, so $d \geq m - 1$.

Solution 2. Given the definition of $P(z)$ introduced in the first solution, proceed by induction on m. For the base case $m = 1$, $Q(1) = t^1 \neq 0$, so Q must be nonzero, and its degree is at least 0. Given the assertion for $m - 1$, if $Q(i) = t^i$ for $i = 1, \ldots, m$, then the polynomial $R(z) = (t - 1)^{-1}(Q(z + 1) - Q(z))$ has degree one less than that of Q, and satisfies $R(i) = t^i$ for $i = 1, \ldots, m - 1$. Since R must have degree at least $m - 2$ by the induction hypothesis, Q must have degree at least $m - 1$.

Solution 3. Again using the same construction of $P(z)$, use the method of *finite differences* (as in the second solution) but without induction. Namely, the $(m - 1)$st finite difference of P evaluated at 1 equals

$$\sum_{j=0}^{m-1} (-1)^j \binom{m-1}{j} Q(m - j) = t(1 - t)^{m-1} \neq 0,$$

which is impossible if Q has degree less than $m - 1$.

Remark. One can also establish the claim by computing a Vandermonde-type determinant, or by using the Lagrange interpolation formula to compute the leading coefficient of Q.

A6. $(11, 5, 2, \ldots, 7, 13, 26, 125)$ 9.5%
   Prove that there exists a constant $c > 0$ such that in every nontrivial finite group G there exists a sequence of length at most $c \log |G|$ with the property that each element of G equals the product of some subsequence. (The elements of G in the sequence are not required to be distinct. A *subsequence* of a sequence is obtained by selecting some of the terms, not necessarily consecutive, without reordering them; for example, $4, 4, 2$ is a subsequence of $2, 4, 6, 4, 2$, but $2, 2, 4$ is not.)

Remark. For notational convenience, we will interpret the problem as allowing the empty subsequence, whose product is the identity element of the group. To solve the problem in the interpretation where the empty subsequence is not allowed, simply append the identity element to the sequence given by one of the following solutions.

Solution 1. Put $n = |G|$. Say that a sequence S *produces* an element $g \in G$ if g occurs as the product of some subsequence of S. Let H be the set of elements produced by the sequence S.
   Start with S equal to the empty sequence. If at any point the set $H^{-1}H = \{h_1 h_2 : h_1^{-1}, h_2 \in H\}$ fails to be all of G, extend S by appending an element g of G not in $H^{-1}H$. Then $Hg \cap H$ must be empty, otherwise there would be an equation of the form $h_1 g = h_2$ with $h_1, h_2 \in G$, or $g = h_1^{-1}h_2$, a contradiction. Thus S can be extended by one element and double the size of H.
   After $k \leq \log_2 n$ steps, we must obtain a sequence $S = a_1, \ldots, a_k$ for which $H^{-1}H = G$. Then the sequence $a_k^{-1}, \ldots, a_1^{-1}, a_1, \ldots, a_k$ produces all of G and has length at most $(2/\log 2) \log n$.

Solution 2. Put $m = |H|$. One element g can be added to S so that the resulting sequence of $k + 1$ elements will produce at least $2m - m^2/n$ elements of G. To do this, compute

$$\sum_{g \in G} |H \cup Hg| = \sum_{g \in G} (|H| + |Hg| - |H \cap Hg|)$$

$$= 2mn - \sum_{g \in G} |H \cap Hg|$$

$$= 2mn - |\{(g,h) \in G^2 : h \in H \cap Hg\}|$$

$$= 2mn - \sum_{h \in H} |\{g \in G : h \in Hg\}|$$

$$= 2mn - \sum_{h \in H} |H^{-1}h|$$

$$= 2mn - m^2.$$

By the pigeonhole principle, $|H \cup Hg| \geq 2m - m^2/n$ for some choice of g, as claimed.

In other words, by extending the sequence by one element, the ratio $s = 1 - m/n$ (which is the fraction of elements of G not generated by S) can be replaced by a quantity no greater than

$$1 - (2m - m^2/n)/n = s^2.$$

We start out with $k = 0$ and $s = 1 - 1/n$. After k steps, $s \leq (1 - 1/n)^{2^k}$. It is enough to prove that for some $c > 0$, one can always find an integer $k \leq c \log n$ such that

$$\left(1 - \frac{1}{n}\right)^{2^k} < \frac{1}{n},$$

as then $n - m < 1$ and hence $H = G$.

To obtain this last inequality, put

$$k = \lfloor 2 \log_2 n \rfloor < (2/\log 2) \log n,$$

so that $2^{k+1} \geq n^2$. From the facts that $\log n \leq \log 2 + (n-2)/2 \leq n/2$ and $\log(1 - 1/n) < -1/n$ for all $n \geq 2$,

$$2^k \log\left(1 - \frac{1}{n}\right) < -\frac{n^2}{2n} = -\frac{n}{2} < -\log n,$$

yielding the desired inequality.

Remark. An alternate approach in the second solution is to distinguish between the cases of H small (meaning $m < n^{1/2}$, in which case m can be replaced by a value no less than $2m-1$) and H large. This strategy is used in a number of recent results concerning *small doubling* or *small tripling* of subsets of finite groups; a typical example of this is [**Helf**].

In the second solution, if we avoid the rather weak inequality $\log n \leq n/2$, we instead get sequences of length $\log_2(n \log n) = \log_2(n) + \log_2(\log n)$. This is close to optimal: one cannot use fewer than $\log_2 n$ terms because the number of subsequences must be at least n.

B1. (118, 2, 44, ..., 0, 0, 19, 6) 86.8%
   What is the maximum number of rational points that can lie on a circle in $\mathbb{R}^2$ whose center is not a rational point? (A *rational point* is a point both of whose coordinates are rational numbers.)

Answer. There are at most two such points.

Solution 1. The points $(0,0)$ and $(1,0)$ lie on a circle with center $(1/2, x)$ for any real number x, not necessarily rational. It thus remains to show that if three distinct rational points $P = (a, b), Q = (c, d), R = (e, f)$ lie on a circle, then the center of the circle is rational.
   Let (x, y) be the center of the circle. Then
$$(x - a)^2 + (y - b)^2 = (x - c)^2 + (y - d)^2 = (x - e)^2 + (y - f)^2,$$
which simplifies to
$$2(a - c)x + 2(b - d)y = a^2 + b^2 - c^2 - d^2,$$
$$2(a - e)x + 2(b - f)y = a^2 + b^2 - e^2 - f^2.$$
Because the points P, Q, R lie on a circle, they cannot be collinear and so $(a - c)(b - f) - (a - e)(b - d)$ is nonzero. Consequently, this system of two linear equations in two unknowns with rational coefficients has a unique rational point as its solution.

Variant. Given three rational points $(x_1, y_1), (x_2, y_2), (x_3, y_3)$, the circle through them is defined by the equation
$$0 = \det \begin{pmatrix} x_1^2 + y_1^2 & x_1 & y_1 & 1 \\ x_2^2 + y_2^2 & x_2 & y_2 & 1 \\ x_3^2 + y_3^2 & x_3 & y_3 & 1 \\ x^2 + y^2 & x & y & 1 \end{pmatrix}$$
which has the form $a(x^2 + y^2) + dx + ey + f = 0$ for a, d, e, f rational. (One has $a = 0$ if and only if the circle degenerates because the three points are collinear.) The center of this circle is $(-d/(2a), -e/(2a))$, which is again a rational point.

Solution 2. Define a *rational line* to be a line defined by an equation with rational coefficients. By elementary linear algebra, any two distinct rational points lie on a rational line, and any two nonparallel rational lines intersect in a rational point. Similarly, the midpoint between two given rational points is a rational point, and the line through a given rational point perpendicular to a rational line is a rational line.

Let P, Q, R be three noncollinear rational points. The perpendicular bisector L_1 of $\overline{PQ}$ is the line through the midpoint between the two rational points P and Q perpendicular to the rational line $\overleftrightarrow{PQ}$, and hence is a rational line. Similarly, the perpendicular bisector L_2 of $\overline{QR}$ is a rational line. The center of the circle through P, Q, R is the intersection of the rational lines L_1 and L_2, and so is a rational point.

Remark. Both solutions apply with the rational numbers replaced by any field of characteristic not equal to 2.

B2. (83, 17, 6, ..., 45, 4, 15, 19) 56.1%

Let $F_0(x) = \ln x$. For $n \geq 0$ and $x > 0$, let $F_{n+1}(x) = \int_0^x F_n(t)\,dt$. **Evaluate**

$$\lim_{n\to\infty} \frac{n!\,F_n(1)}{\ln n}.$$

Answer. The limit is -1.

Solution. We claim that $F_n(x) = (\log x - a_n)x^n/n!$, where $a_n = \sum_{k=1}^n 1/k$. Indeed, temporarily write $G_n(x) = (\log x - a_n)x^n/n!$ for $x > 0$ and $n \geq 1$. Then $\lim_{x\to 0} G_n(x) = 0$ and $G_n'(x) = (\log x - a_n + 1/n)x^{n-1}/(n-1)! = G_{n-1}(x)$, and the claim follows by the fundamental theorem of calculus and induction on n.

Given the claim, $F_n(1) = -a_n/n!$, and so it remains to evaluate

$$-\lim_{n\to\infty} \frac{a_n}{\log n}.$$

But since the function $1/x$ is strictly decreasing for x positive, $\sum_{k=2}^n 1/k = a_n - 1$ is bounded below by $\int_2^n dx/x = \log n - \log 2$ and above by $\int_1^n dx/x = \log n$. It follows that $\lim_{n\to\infty} \frac{a_n}{\log n} = 1$, and the desired limit is -1.

B3. (19, 7, 3, ..., 16, 5, 54, 85) 15.3%

What is the largest possible radius of a circle contained in a 4-dimensional hypercube of side length 1?

Answer. The largest possible radius is $\frac{\sqrt{2}}{2}$.

Solution. It will be convenient instead to solve the problem for a hypercube of side length 2 by showing that the largest radius is then $\sqrt{2}$. Choose coordinates so that the hypercube with its interior is the set $H = [-1, 1]^4$ in $\mathbb{R}^4$. Let C be a circle centered at the point P. Then C is contained both in H and its reflection across P. These intersect in a rectangular parallelepiped each of whose pairs of opposite faces are at most 2 units apart. Consequently, translating C so that its center moves to the point $O = (0, 0, 0, 0)$ at the center of H, then C remains entirely inside H.

This means that the answer equals the largest possible radius of a circle C contained in H *and centered at* O. Let $v_1 = (v_{11}, \ldots, v_{14})$ and $v_2 = (v_{21}, \ldots, v_{24})$ be two points on C lying on radii perpendicular to each other. Then the points of the circle can be expressed as $v_1 \cos \theta + v_2 \sin \theta$ for $0 \le \theta < 2\pi$. Thus C lies in H if and only if for each i,

$$|v_{1i} \cos \theta + v_{2i} \sin \theta| \le 1 \qquad (0 \le \theta < 2\pi).$$

In geometric terms, the vector (v_{1i}, v_{2i}) in $\mathbb{R}^2$ has dot product at most 1 with every unit vector. Since this holds for the unit vector in the same direction as (v_{1i}, v_{2i}), it must be that

$$v_{1i}^2 + v_{2i}^2 \le 1 \qquad (i = 1, \ldots, 4).$$

Conversely, if this holds, then the Cauchy-Schwarz inequality and the above analysis imply that C lies in H.

If r is the radius of C, then

$$2r^2 = \sum_{i=1}^{4} v_{1i}^2 + \sum_{i=1}^{4} v_{2i}^2$$

$$= \sum_{i=1}^{4} (v_{1i}^2 + v_{2i}^2)$$

$$\le 4,$$

so $r \le \sqrt{2}$. Since this is achieved by the circle through $(1, 1, 0, 0)$ and $(0, 0, 1, 1)$, it is the desired maximum.

Remark. One may similarly ask for the radius of the largest k-dimensional ball inside an n-dimensional unit hypercube. The given problem is the case $(n, k) = (4, 2)$. Here is an argument to show that the maximum radius in this case is $\frac{1}{2}\sqrt{\frac{n}{k}}$. Again, scale up by a factor of 2, and show that the maximum radius r of a k-dimensional ball contained in the hypercube $[-1, 1]^n$ is $\sqrt{\frac{n}{k}}$. As above, there is no loss of generality in centering the ball at the origin. Let $T : \mathbb{R}^k \to \mathbb{R}^n$ be a similitude carrying the unit ball to this embedded k-ball. Then there exists a vector $v_i \in \mathbb{R}^k$ such that for $e_1, \ldots, e_n$ the standard basis of $\mathbb{R}^n$, $x \cdot v_i = T(x) \cdot e_i$ for all $x \in \mathbb{R}^k$. The condition of the problem is equivalent to requiring $|v_i| \le 1$ for all i, while the radius r of the embedded ball is determined by the fact that for all $x \in \mathbb{R}^k$,

$$r^2(x \cdot x) = T(x) \cdot T(x) = \sum_{i=1}^{n} (x \cdot v_i)^2.$$

Let M be the matrix with columns $v_1, \ldots, v_k$; then $MM^T = r^2 I_k$, for I_k the $k \times k$ identity matrix. Then

$$kr^2 = \text{Trace}(r^2 I_k) = \text{Trace}(MM^T)$$

$$= \text{Trace}(M^T M) = \sum_{i=1}^{n} |v_i|^2$$

$$\leq n,$$

yielding the upper bound $r \leq \sqrt{\frac{n}{k}}$.

To show that this bound is optimal, it is enough to show that one can find an orthogonal projection of $\mathbb{R}^n$ onto $\mathbb{R}^k$ so that the projections of the e_i all have the same norm. One can then rescale to get the desired configuration of $v_1, \ldots, v_n$. Construct such a configuration by a "smoothing" argument. Start with any projection. Let $w_1, \ldots, w_n$ be the projections of $e_1, \ldots, e_n$. If the desired condition is not achieved, choose i, j such that

$$|w_i|^2 < \frac{1}{n}(|w_1|^2 + \cdots + |w_n|^2) < |w_j|^2.$$

By precomposing with a suitable rotation that fixes e_h for $h \neq i, j$, we can vary $|w_i|, |w_j|$ without varying $|w_i|^2 + |w_j|^2$ or $|w_h|$ for $h \neq i, j$. We can thus choose such a rotation to force one of $|w_i|^2, |w_j|^2$ to become equal to $\frac{1}{n}(|w_1|^2 + \cdots + |w_n|^2)$. Repeating at most $n - 1$ times gives the desired configuration.

B4. (81, 17, 7, ..., 16, 5, 23, 40) 55.6%
    Let p be a prime number. Let $h(x)$ be a polynomial with integer coefficients such that $h(0), h(1), \ldots, h(p^2 - 1)$ are distinct modulo p^2. Show that $h(0), h(1), \ldots, h(p^3 - 1)$ are distinct modulo p^3.

Solution. We use the identity given by Taylor's theorem:

$$h(x + y) = \sum_{i=0}^{\deg(h)} \frac{h^{(i)}(x)}{i!} y^i.$$

In this expression, $h^{(i)}(x)/i!$ is a polynomial in x with integer coefficients, so its value at an integer x is an integer.

For $x = 0, \ldots, p - 1$, we deduce that

$$h(x + p) \equiv h(x) + ph'(x) \pmod{p^2}.$$

(This can also be deduced more directly using the binomial theorem.) Since we assumed $h(x)$ and $h(x + p)$ are distinct modulo p^2, we conclude that $h'(x) \not\equiv 0 \pmod{p}$. Since h' is a polynomial with integer coefficients, $h'(x) \equiv h'(x + mp) \pmod{p}$ for any integer m, and so $h'(x) \not\equiv 0 \pmod{p}$ for *all* integers x.

Now for $x = 0, \ldots, p^2 - 1$ and $y = 0, \ldots, p - 1$, we write

$$h(x + yp^2) \equiv h(x) + p^2 yh'(x) \pmod{p^3}.$$

Thus $h(x), h(x+p^2), \ldots, h(x+(p-1)p^2)$ run over all of the residue classes modulo p^3 congruent to $h(x)$ modulo p^2. Since the $h(x)$ themselves cover all the residue classes modulo p^2, this proves that $h(0), \ldots, h(p^3 - 1)$ are distinct modulo p^3.

Remark. More generally, the same proof shows that for any integers $d, e > 1$, h permutes the residue classes modulo p^d if and only if it permutes the residue classes modulo p^e. The argument used in the proof is related to a general result in number theory known as *Hensel's lemma.*

B5. (17, 25, 8, ..., 6, 6, 65, 62) 26.5%
    Find all continuously differentiable functions $f : \mathbb{R} \to \mathbb{R}$ such that for every rational number q, the number $f(q)$ is rational and has the same denominator as q. (The denominator of a rational number q is the unique positive integer b such that $q = a/b$ for some integer a with $\gcd(a, b) = 1$.) (Note: gcd means greatest common divisor.)

Answer. The only such functions are $f(x) = x + n$ and $f(x) = -x + n$ for some integer n.

Solution. The functions $f(x) = x + n$ and $f(x) = -x + n$ for any integer n clearly satisfy the condition of the problem. It thus remains to check that these are the only ones. We claim that these are the only possible f. Let $q = a/b$ be any rational number with $\gcd(a, b) = 1$ and $b > 0$. For n any positive integer,

$$\frac{f(\frac{an+1}{bn}) - f(\frac{a}{b})}{\frac{1}{bn}} = bnf\left(\frac{an+1}{bn}\right) - nbf\left(\frac{a}{b}\right)$$

is an integer by the property of f. Since f is differentiable at a/b, the left-hand side has a limit. It follows that for sufficiently large n, both sides must be equal to some integer $c = f'(\frac{a}{b})$: $f(\frac{an+1}{bn}) = f(\frac{a}{b}) + \frac{c}{bn}$. Now c cannot be 0, since otherwise $f(\frac{an+1}{bn}) = f(\frac{a}{b})$ for sufficiently large n has denominator b rather than bn. Similarly, $|c|$ cannot be greater than 1: otherwise if we take $n = k|c|$ for k a sufficiently large positive integer, then $f(\frac{a}{b}) + \frac{c}{bn}$ has denominator bk, contradicting the fact that $f(\frac{an+1}{bn})$ has denominator bn. It follows that $c = f'(\frac{a}{b}) = \pm 1$.
    Thus the derivative of f at any rational number is ± 1. Since f is continuously differentiable, we conclude that $f'(x) = 1$ for all real x or $f'(x) = -1$ for all real x. Since $f(0)$ must be an integer (a rational number with denominator 1), $f(x) = x + n$ or $f(x) = -x + n$ for some integer n.

Remark. After showing that $f'(q)$ is an integer for each q, one can instead argue that f' is a continuous function taking the rationals to the integers, so must be constant. One can then write $f(x) = ax + b$ and check that $b \in \mathbb{Z}$ by evaluation at $a = 0$, and that $a = \pm 1$ by evaluation at $x = 1/a$.

B6. (12, 3, 0, ..., 4, 4, 32, 134) 7.9%

   Let n and k be positive integers. Say that a permutation σ of $\{1, 2, \ldots, n\}$ is k-*limited* if $|\sigma(i) - i| \le k$ for all i. Prove that the number of k-limited permutations of $\{1, 2, \ldots, n\}$ is odd if and only if $n \equiv 0$ or $1 \pmod{2k + 1}$.

Solution 1. (Yufei Zhao) Let $F_{n,k}$ be the number of k-limited permutations of $\{1, \ldots, n\}$. Let $M_{n,k}$ be the $n \times n$ matrix with

$$(M_{n,k})_{ij} = \begin{cases} 1 & |i - j| \le k, \\ 0 & \text{otherwise.} \end{cases}$$

Write $\det(M_{n,k})$ as the sum over permutations σ of $\{1, \ldots, n\}$ of $(M_{n,k})_{1\sigma(1)} \cdots (M_{n,k})_{n\sigma(n)}$ times the signature of σ. Then σ contributes ± 1 to $\det(M_{n,k})$ if σ is k-limited and 0 otherwise. We conclude that

$$\det(M_{n,k}) \equiv F_{n,k} \pmod 2.$$

For the rest of the solution, we interpret $M_{n,k}$ as a matrix over the field of two elements. We compute its determinant using linear algebra modulo 2.

   We first show that for $n \ge 2k + 1$,

$$F_{n,k} \equiv F_{n-2k-1,k} \pmod 2,$$

provided that we interpret $F_{0,k} = 1$. We do this by computing $\det(M_{n,k})$ using row and column operations. We will verbally describe these operations for general k, while illustrating with the example $k = 3$.

   To begin with, $M_{n,k}$ has the following form.

$$\left(\begin{array}{ccccccc|c} 1 & 1 & 1 & 1 & 0 & 0 & 0 & \emptyset \\ 1 & 1 & 1 & 1 & 1 & 0 & 0 & \emptyset \\ 1 & 1 & 1 & 1 & 1 & 1 & 0 & \emptyset \\ 1 & 1 & 1 & 1 & 1 & 1 & 1 & \emptyset \\ 0 & 1 & 1 & 1 & 1 & 1 & 1 & ? \\ 0 & 0 & 1 & 1 & 1 & 1 & 1 & ? \\ 0 & 0 & 0 & 1 & 1 & 1 & 1 & ? \\ \hline \emptyset & \emptyset & \emptyset & \emptyset & ? & ? & ? & * \end{array} \right)$$

In this presentation, the first $2k + 1$ rows and columns are shown explicitly; the remaining rows and columns are shown in a compressed format. The symbol $\emptyset$ indicates that the unseen entries are all zeros, while the symbol ? indicates that they are not. The symbol $*$ in the lower right corner represents the matrix $F_{n-2k-1,k}$. We will preserve the unseen structure of the matrix by only adding the first $k + 1$ rows or columns to any of the others.

We first add row 1 to each of rows $2, \dots, k+1$.

$$
\begin{pmatrix}
1 & 1 & 1 & 1 & 0 & 0 & 0 & \emptyset \\
0 & 0 & 0 & 0 & 1 & 0 & 0 & \emptyset \\
0 & 0 & 0 & 0 & 1 & 1 & 0 & \emptyset \\
0 & 0 & 0 & 0 & 1 & 1 & 1 & \emptyset \\
0 & 1 & 1 & 1 & 1 & 1 & 1 & ? \\
0 & 0 & 1 & 1 & 1 & 1 & 1 & ? \\
0 & 0 & 0 & 1 & 1 & 1 & 1 & ? \\
\emptyset & \emptyset & \emptyset & \emptyset & ? & ? & ? & *
\end{pmatrix}
$$

We next add column 1 to each of columns $2, \dots, k+1$.

$$
\begin{pmatrix}
1 & 0 & 0 & 0 & 0 & 0 & 0 & \emptyset \\
0 & 0 & 0 & 0 & 1 & 0 & 0 & \emptyset \\
0 & 0 & 0 & 0 & 1 & 1 & 0 & \emptyset \\
0 & 0 & 0 & 0 & 1 & 1 & 1 & \emptyset \\
0 & 1 & 1 & 1 & 1 & 1 & 1 & ? \\
0 & 0 & 1 & 1 & 1 & 1 & 1 & ? \\
0 & 0 & 0 & 1 & 1 & 1 & 1 & ? \\
\emptyset & \emptyset & \emptyset & \emptyset & ? & ? & ? & *
\end{pmatrix}
$$

For $i = 2$, for each of $j = i+1, \dots, 2k+1$ for which the $(j, k+i)$-entry is nonzero, add row i to row j.

$$
\begin{pmatrix}
1 & 0 & 0 & 0 & 0 & 0 & 0 & \emptyset \\
0 & 0 & 0 & 0 & 1 & 0 & 0 & \emptyset \\
0 & 0 & 0 & 0 & 0 & 1 & 0 & \emptyset \\
0 & 0 & 0 & 0 & 0 & 1 & 1 & \emptyset \\
0 & 1 & 1 & 1 & 0 & 1 & 1 & ? \\
0 & 0 & 1 & 1 & 0 & 1 & 1 & ? \\
0 & 0 & 0 & 1 & 0 & 1 & 1 & ? \\
\emptyset & \emptyset & \emptyset & \emptyset & \emptyset & ? & ? & *
\end{pmatrix}
$$

Repeat the previous step for $i = 3, \dots, k+1$ in succession.

$$
\begin{pmatrix}
1 & 0 & 0 & 0 & 0 & 0 & 0 & \emptyset \\
0 & 0 & 0 & 0 & 1 & 0 & 0 & \emptyset \\
0 & 0 & 0 & 0 & 0 & 1 & 0 & \emptyset \\
0 & 0 & 0 & 0 & 0 & 0 & 1 & \emptyset \\
0 & 1 & 1 & 1 & 0 & 0 & 0 & ? \\
0 & 0 & 1 & 1 & 0 & 0 & 0 & ? \\
0 & 0 & 0 & 1 & 0 & 0 & 0 & ? \\
\emptyset & \emptyset & \emptyset & \emptyset & \emptyset & \emptyset & \emptyset & *
\end{pmatrix}
$$

Repeat the two previous steps with the roles of the rows and columns reversed. That is, for $i = 2, \ldots, k+1$, for each of $j = i+1, \ldots, 2k+1$ for which the $(j, k+i)$-entry is nonzero, add row i to row j.

$$\begin{pmatrix} 1 & 0 & 0 & 0 & 0 & 0 & 0 & \varnothing \\ 0 & 0 & 0 & 0 & 1 & 0 & 0 & \varnothing \\ 0 & 0 & 0 & 0 & 0 & 1 & 0 & \varnothing \\ 0 & 0 & 0 & 0 & 0 & 0 & 1 & \varnothing \\ 0 & 1 & 0 & 0 & 0 & 0 & 0 & \varnothing \\ 0 & 0 & 1 & 0 & 0 & 0 & 0 & \varnothing \\ 0 & 0 & 0 & 1 & 0 & 0 & 0 & \varnothing \\ \hline \varnothing & \varnothing & \varnothing & \varnothing & \varnothing & \varnothing & \varnothing & * \end{pmatrix}$$

We now have a block diagonal matrix in which the top left block is a $(2k + 1) \times (2k + 1)$ matrix with nonzero determinant (it results from reordering the rows of the identity matrix), the bottom right block is $M_{n-2k-1,k}$, and the other two blocks are zero. We conclude that

$$\det(M_{n,k}) \equiv \det(M_{n-2k-1,k}) \pmod{2},$$

proving the desired congruence.

To prove the desired result, we must now check that $F_{0,k}, F_{1,k}$ are odd and $F_{2,k}, \ldots, F_{2k,k}$ are even. For $n = 0, \ldots, k+1$, the matrix $M_{n,k}$ consists of all ones, so its determinant is 1 if $n = 0, 1$ and 0 otherwise. (Alternatively, $F_{n,k} = n!$ for $n = 0, \ldots, k+1$ since every permutation of $\{1, \ldots, n\}$ is k-limited.) For $n = k+2, \ldots, 2k$, observe that rows k and $k + 1$ of $M_{n,k}$ both consist of all ones, so $\det(M_{n,k}) = 0$ as desired.

Solution 2. (Tom Belulovich) Define $F_{n,k}$ and $M_{n,k}$ as in the first solution. We prove $\det(M_{n,k})$ is odd for $n \equiv 0, 1 \pmod{2k + 1}$ and even otherwise, by directly determining whether or not $M_{n,k}$ is invertible as a matrix over the field of two elements.

Let r_i denote row i of $M_{n,k}$. We first check that if $n \equiv 2, \ldots, 2k \pmod{2k+1}$, then $M_{n,k}$ is not invertible. In this case, we can find integers $0 \le a < b \le k$ such that $n + a + b \equiv 0 \pmod{2k + 1}$. Put $j = (n + a + b)/(2k + 1)$. We can then write the all-ones vector both as

$$\sum_{i=0}^{j-1} r_{k+1-a+(2k+1)i}$$

and as

$$\sum_{i=0}^{j-1} r_{k+1-b+(2k+1)i}.$$

Hence $M_{n,k}$ is not invertible.

We next check that if $n \equiv 0, 1 \pmod{2k+1}$, then $M_{n,k}$ is invertible. Suppose that $a_1, \ldots, a_n$ are scalars such that $a_1 r_1 + \cdots + a_n r_n$ is the zero vector. The mth coordinate of this vector equals $a_{m-k} + \cdots + a_{m+k}$, where we regard a_i as zero if $i \notin \{1, \ldots, n\}$. By comparing consecutive coordinates, we obtain

$$a_{m-k} = a_{m+k+1} \qquad (1 \le m < n).$$

In particular, the a_i repeat with period $2k+1$. Taking $m = 1, \ldots, k$ further yields that

$$a_{k+2} = \cdots = a_{2k+1} = 0$$

while taking $m = n-k, \ldots, n-1$ yields

$$a_{n-2k} = \cdots = a_{n-1-k} = 0.$$

For $n \equiv 0 \pmod{2k+1}$, the latter can be rewritten as

$$a_1 = \cdots = a_k = 0$$

whereas for $n \equiv 1 \pmod{2k+1}$, it can be rewritten as

$$a_2 = \cdots = a_{k+1} = 0.$$

In either case, since we also have

$$a_1 + \cdots + a_{2k+1} = 0$$

from the $(k+1)$st coordinate, we deduce that all of the a_i must be zero, and so $M_{n,k}$ must be invertible.

Remark. The matrices $M_{n,k}$ are examples of *banded matrices*, which occur frequently in numerical applications of linear algebra. They are also examples of *Toeplitz matrices*.

Solution 3. (Jacob Tsimerman) A permutation is k-limited if and only if its inverse is k-limited. Consequently, the number of k-limited permutations of $\{1, \ldots, n\}$ is the same as the number of k-limited involutions (permutations equal to their inverses) of $\{1, \ldots, n\}$ modulo 2.

We use the following fact several times: the number of involutions of $\{1, \ldots, n\}$ is odd if $n = 0, 1$ and even otherwise. This follows from the fact that noninvolutions come in pairs, so the number of involutions has the same parity as the number of permutations, namely $n!$.

For $n \le k+1$, all involutions are k-limited. By the previous paragraph, $F_{n,k}$ is odd for $n = 0, 1$ and even for $n = 2, \ldots, k+1$.

For $n > k+1$, group the k-limited involutions into classes based on their actions on $k+2, \ldots, n$. For C a class and $\sigma \in C$, the set of elements of $A = \{1, \ldots, k+1\}$ which map into A under σ depends only on C, not on σ. Call this set $S(C)$; then the size of C is exactly the number of involutions of $S(C)$. Consequently, $|C|$ is even unless $S(C)$ has at most one element. However, the element

1 cannot map out of A because we are looking at k-limited involutions. Hence if $S(C)$ has one element and $\sigma \in C$, then $\sigma(1) = 1$. Since σ is k-limited and $\sigma(2)$ cannot belong to A, it must be that $\sigma(2) = k+2$. By induction, for $i = 3, \dots, k+1$, it follows that $\sigma(i) = k+i$.

If $n < 2k+1$, this shows that no class C of odd cardinality can exist, so $F_{n,k}$ must be even. If $n \geq 2k+1$, the classes of odd cardinality are in bijection with k-limited involutions of $\{2k+2, \dots, n\}$, so $F_{n,k}$ has the same parity as $F_{n-2k-1,k}$. By induction on n, we deduce the desired result.

The Seventieth William Lowell Putnam
Mathematical Competition—December 5, 2009

A1. $(193, 4, 2, \ldots, 0, 0, 1, 0)$ 99.5%

Let f be a real-valued function on the plane such that for every square $ABCD$ in the plane, $f(A)+f(B)+f(C)+f(D) = 0$. Does it follow that $f(P) = 0$ for all points P in the plane?

Answer. Yes, it does follow.

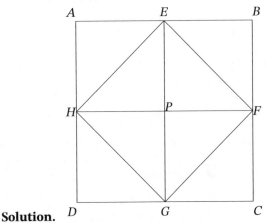

Solution.

Let P be any point in the plane. Let $ABCD$ be any square with center P. Let E, F, G, H be the midpoints of the segments $\overline{AB}, \overline{BC}, \overline{CD}, \overline{DA}$, respectively. The function f must satisfy the equations

$$0 = f(A) + f(B) + f(C) + f(D),$$
$$0 = f(E) + f(F) + f(G) + f(H),$$
$$0 = f(A) + f(E) + f(P) + f(H),$$
$$0 = f(B) + f(F) + f(P) + f(E),$$
$$0 = f(C) + f(G) + f(P) + f(F),$$
$$0 = f(D) + f(H) + f(P) + f(G).$$

Adding the last four equations, then subtracting the first equation and twice the second equation, yields $0 = 4f(P)$.

Remark. Problem 1 of the 1996 Romanian IMO team selection exam asks the same question with squares replaced by regular polygons of any (fixed) number of vertices.

A2. (84, 22, 24, ..., 6, 8, 40, 16) 65.0%

   Functions f, g, h are differentiable on some open interval around 0 and satisfy the equations and initial conditions

$$f' = 2f^2gh + \frac{1}{gh}, \quad f(0) = 1,$$

$$g' = fg^2h + \frac{4}{fh}, \quad g(0) = 1,$$

$$h' = 3fgh^2 + \frac{1}{fg}, \quad h(0) = 1.$$

Find an explicit formula for $f(x)$, valid in some open interval around 0.

Answer. One valid formula is $f(x) = 2^{-1/12} \left(\frac{\sin(6x+\pi/4)}{\cos^2(6x+\pi/4)} \right)^{1/6}$.

Solution. Multiplying the first differential equation by gh, the second by fh, and the third by fg, and summing gives

$$(fgh)' = 6(fgh)^2 + 6.$$

Write $k(x) = f(x)g(x)h(x)$, so that $k' = 6k^2 + 6$ and $k(0) = 1$. One solution for this differential equation with this initial condition is $k(x) = \tan(6x + \pi/4)$; by standard uniqueness, this must necessarily hold for x in some open interval around 0. Now the first given equation becomes

$$f'/f = 2k(x) + 1/k(x)$$

$$= 2\tan(6x + \pi/4) + \cot(6x + \pi/4).$$

Integrating both sides gives

$$\log(f(x)) = \frac{-2\log\cos(6x + \pi/4) + \log\sin(6x + \pi/4)}{6} + c,$$

whence $f(x) = e^c \left(\frac{\sin(6x+\pi/4)}{\cos^2(6x+\pi/4)} \right)^{1/6}$. Substituting $f(0) = 1$ gives $e^c = 2^{-1/12}$, yielding the claimed formula.

Remark. The answer can be put in alternate forms using trigonometric identities. One particularly simple one is

$$f(x) = (\sec 12x)^{1/12}(\sec 12x + \tan 12x)^{1/4}.$$

A3. (81, 6, 6, ..., 6, 2, 39, 60) 46.5%

   Let d_n be the determinant of the $n \times n$ matrix whose entries, from left to right and then from top to bottom, are $\cos 1, \cos 2, \ldots, \cos n^2$. (For example,

$$d_3 = \begin{vmatrix} \cos 1 & \cos 2 & \cos 3 \\ \cos 4 & \cos 5 & \cos 6 \\ \cos 7 & \cos 8 & \cos 9 \end{vmatrix}.$$

The argument of cos is always in radians, not degrees.) Evaluate $\lim_{n\to\infty} d_n$.

Answer. The limit is 0.

Solution 1. We show that $d_n = 0$ for all $n \geq 3$. Starting from the given matrix, adding the third column to the first column does not change the determinant. However, thanks to the identity $\cos x + \cos y = 2\cos\frac{x+y}{2}\cos\frac{x-y}{2}$, the resulting matrix has the form

$$\begin{pmatrix} 2\cos 2\cos 1 & \cos 2 & \cdots \\ 2\cos(n+2)\cos 1 & \cos(n+2) & \cdots \\ 2\cos(2n+2)\cos 1 & \cos(2n+2) & \cdots \\ \vdots & \vdots & \ddots \end{pmatrix}$$

with the first column being a multiple of the second. Hence $d_n = 0$.

Solution 2. Recall that for any two matrices A and B, the rank of $A + B$ is at most the sum of the ranks of A and B. (That is because the row span of $A + B$ is contained in the sum of the row spans of A and B, or similarly for column spans.) It will thus suffice to write the given matrix as a sum $A + B$ of two matrices of rank 1, for each $n \geq 3$. One way to do this is to take

$$A_{jk} = \cos(j-1)n\cos k, \quad B_{jk} = -\sin(j-1)n\sin k,$$

exploiting the identity

$$\cos((j-1)n+k) = \cos(j-1)n\cos k - \sin(j-1)n\sin k.$$

Another is to take

$$A_{jk} = \frac{1}{2}e^{i((j-1)n+k)}, \quad B_{jk} = \frac{1}{2}e^{-i(j-1)n+k},$$

exploiting the identity $\cos x = \frac{1}{2}e^{ix} + \frac{1}{2}e^{-ix}$.

Remark. Although the problem statement specifies that the argument of cos is always in radians, not degrees, this does not have any effect on either solution.

A4. (49, 27, 23, ..., 6, 11, 54, 30) 49.5%
   Let S be a set of rational numbers such that

(a) $0 \in S$;

(b) If $x \in S$, then $x + 1 \in S$ and $x - 1 \in S$; and

(c) If $x \in S$ and $x \notin \{0, 1\}$, then $\frac{1}{x(x-1)} \in S$.

Must S contain all rational numbers?

Answer. No, S need not contain all rational numbers.

Solution. We show that the set $S = \mathbb{Q} \setminus \{n + 2/5 \mid n \in \mathbb{Z}\}$ satisfies the given conditions. By its definition, S satisfies (a) and (b). To verify (c), it suffices to show that if $x = \frac{p}{q}$ is a fraction with $(p, q) = 1$ and $p > 0$, then it is impossible to have $\frac{1}{x(x-1)} = n + 2/5$ for an integer n. Suppose otherwise; then

$$\frac{q^2}{p(p-q)} = \frac{5n+2}{5}.$$

Since p and q are relatively prime, p and $p - q$ are each relatively prime to q^2, and so the fraction on the left is already in lowest terms except possibly up to sign. In particular, $p(p-q) = \pm 5$; since $p > 0$, this implies $(p, p - q) \in \{(1, 5), (1, -5), (5, 1), (5, -1)\}$. In these four cases, $5n + 2 \in \{\pm 16, \pm 36\}$ and so n cannot be an integer.

Remark. Instead of comparing denominators, one can also complete the proof by comparing numerators: we cannot have $q^2 = \pm(5n+2)$ because neither of ± 2 is a quadratic residue modulo 5.

A5. (26, 5, 1, ..., 6, 6, 70, 86) 16.0%
   Is there a finite abelian group G such that the product of the orders of all its elements is 2^{2009}?

Answer. No, there is no such group.

Solution. Suppose by way of contradiction that G is such a group. By the fundamental theorem of finite abelian groups, G is isomorphic to a product of cyclic groups. If any of these factors has odd order, then G has an element of odd order, so the product of the orders of all of its elements cannot be a power of 2. Consequently, there exists an isomorphism

$$G \cong \mathbb{Z}/2^{e_1}\mathbb{Z} \times \cdots \times \mathbb{Z}/2^{e_k}\mathbb{Z}$$

for some positive integers $e_1, \ldots, e_k$.
   For $i = 1, \ldots, k$, let m_i be the number of cyclic subgroups of G of order 2^i. Each such subgroup contains $\phi(2^i) = 2^{i-1}$ distinct generators, so the number of elements of order 2^i is $2^{i-1}m_i$. Multiplying the orders together and taking the base-2 logarithm yields

$$2009 = m_1 + 2 \cdot 2m_2 + 4 \cdot 3m_3 + \cdots.$$

Reducing modulo 4 yields $m_1 \equiv 1 \pmod 4$. However, the number of elements of order 2 is exactly $2^k - 1$, which is congruent to 3 modulo 4 unless $k = 1$. That is, G must be a cyclic group.

Suppose then that $G \cong \mathbb{Z}/2^e\mathbb{Z}$ for some positive integer e. Then $m_1 = \cdots = m_e = 1$ and $m_i = 0$ for $i > e$, so

$$2009 = \sum_{i=1}^{e} i2^{i-1} = (e-1)2^e + 1.$$

However, $(e-1)2^e + 1$ is a strictly increasing function of e which equals 1793 for $e = 8$ and 4097 for $e = 9$, so it can never equal 2009. This proves the claim. This yields the desired contradiction.

Remark. A less calculation-intensive way to rule out the possibility that $G \cong \mathbb{Z}/2^e\mathbb{Z}$ is to note that $(e-1)2^e + 1 < 2009$ for $e = 1, 2$, whereas for $e \geq 3$ the claimed equality would imply

$$2009 \equiv 1 + 2 \cdot 2 + 4 \cdot 3 \pmod{16},$$

which is again a contradiction.

A6. $(5, 2, 1, \ldots, 0, 0, 53, 139)$ 4.0%
   Let $f : [0,1]^2 \to \mathbb{R}$ be a continuous function on the closed unit square such that $\frac{\partial f}{\partial x}$ and $\frac{\partial f}{\partial y}$ exist and are continuous on the interior $(0,1)^2$. Let $a = \int_0^1 f(0, y)\, dy$, $b = \int_0^1 f(1, y)\, dy$, $c = \int_0^1 f(x, 0)\, dx$, $d = \int_0^1 f(x, 1)\, dx$. **Prove or disprove: There must be a point (x_0, y_0) in $(0,1)^2$ such that**

$$\frac{\partial f}{\partial x}(x_0, y_0) = b - a \quad \text{and} \quad \frac{\partial f}{\partial y}(x_0, y_0) = d - c.$$

Answer. We disprove the assertion.

Solution 1. (Kent Merryfield) Consider functions of the form $f(x, y) = g(x)h(y)$. For such f,

$$a = g(0) \int_0^1 h(y)\, dy, \quad b = g(1) \int_0^1 h(y)\, dy,$$

$$c = h(0) \int_0^1 g(x)\, dx, \quad d = h(1) \int_0^1 g(x)\, dx$$

and

$$\frac{\partial f}{\partial x}(x_0, y_0) = g'(x_0)h(y_0), \quad \frac{\partial f}{\partial y}(x_0, y_0) = g(x_0)h'(y_0).$$

By taking $g(x) = \sin(2\pi x)$, which satisfies $g(0) = g(1) = \int_0^1 g(x) = 0$, we ensure that $a = b = c = d = 0$ no matter what h is. For $x_0 \in (0,1)$, $g(x_0)$ vanishes only for $x_0 = 1/2$ and $g'(x_0) = -2\pi \cos(2\pi x_0)$ vanishes only for $x_0 = 1/4, 3/4$. We thus get an example of the desired form by taking any function h for which $h(y), h'(y)$ are both nonvanishing for $y \in (0, 1)$; for instance, $h(y) = y$ works.

Remark. Some other functions of the form $f(x, y) = g(x)h(y)$ that are compara-bly easy to verify are $x^{1/3}y^{2/3}$ (suggested by Catalin Zara) and $xy(1-y)$ (suggested by Qingchun Ren).

Solution 2. Take
$$f(x, y) = 3(1 + y)(2x - 1)^2 - y;$$
for this function, $a = b$ because $f(x, y) = f(1 - x, y)$. By direct computation,

$$c = \int_0^1 3(2x - 1)^2\, dx = 1,$$

$$d = \int_0^1 (6(2x - 1)^2 - 1)\, dx = 1.$$

The partial derivatives

$$\frac{\partial f}{\partial x}(x_0, y_0) = 3(1 + y_0)(8x_0 - 4),$$

$$\frac{\partial f}{\partial y}(x_0, y_0) = 3(2x_0 - 1)^2 - 1,$$

have no common zero in $(0, 1)^2$: the first partial can only vanish when $x_0 = 1/2$ since $1 + y_0$ is nowhere zero, but for $x_0 = 1/2$ the second partial cannot vanish.

Remark. One can also consider examples with symmetry along $y = x$. For in-stance, take
$$f(x, y) = \begin{cases} (y - 2x)^2 & \text{if } y \geq 2x, \\ (x - 2y)^2 & \text{if } x \geq 2y, \\ 0 & \text{otherwise.} \end{cases}$$
In this case $(b - a, d - c) = (-1/6, -1/6)$, but at every point, the gradient is either zero or orthogonal to one of the lines $y = 2x$ or $x = 2y$.

B1. (142, 33, 15, ..., 3, 2, 5, 0) 95.0%
   Show that every positive rational number can be written as a quotient of products of factorials of (not necessarily distinct) primes. For example,

$$\frac{10}{9} = \frac{2! \cdot 5!}{3! \cdot 3! \cdot 3!}.$$

Solution. Every positive rational number can be uniquely written in lowest terms as a/b for a, b positive integers. We prove the statement in the problem by induc-tion on the largest prime dividing either a or b (where this is considered to be 1 if $a = b = 1$). For the base case, write $1/1 = 2!/2!$. For a general a/b, let p be the largest prime dividing either a or b; then $a/b = p^k a'/b'$ for some $k \neq 0$

and positive integers a', b' whose largest prime factors are strictly less than p. Then $a/b = (p!\,)^k \frac{a'}{(p-1)!^k b'}$, and all prime factors of a' and $(p-1)!^k\, b'$ are strictly less than p. By the induction assumption, $\frac{a'}{(p-1)!^k b'}$ can be written as a quotient of products of prime factorials, and so $a/b = (p!\,)^k \frac{a'}{(p-1)!^k b'}$ can as well. This completes the induction.

Remark. (Noam Elkies) The representations are unique up to rearranging and canceling common factors.

B2. $(62, 3, 0, \ldots, 63, 13, 49, 10)$ 32.5%
   A game involves jumping to the right on the real number line. If a and b are real numbers and $b > a$, the cost of jumping from a to b is $b^3 - ab^2$. For what real numbers c can one travel from 0 to 1 in a finite number of jumps with total cost exactly c?

Answer. The desired real numbers c are those for which $1/3 < c \le 1$.

Solution. For any positive integer m and any sequence $0 = x_0 < x_1 < \cdots < x_m = 1$, the cost of jumping along this sequence is $\sum_{i=1}^m (x_i - x_{i-1})x_i^2$. Since

$$1 = \sum_{i=1}^m (x_i - x_{i-1}) \ge \sum_{i=1}^m (x_i - x_{i-1})x_i^2$$
$$> \sum_{i=1}^m \int_{x_{i-1}}^{x_i} t^2\,dt$$
$$= \int_0^1 t^2\,dt = \frac{1}{3},$$

one can only achieve costs c for which $1/3 < c \le 1$.

   It remains to check that any such c can be achieved. Suppose $0 = x_0 < \cdots < x_m = 1$ is a sequence with $m \ge 1$. For $i = 1, \ldots, m$, let c_i be the cost of the sequence $0, x_i, x_{i+1}, \ldots, x_m$. For $i > 1$ and $0 < y \le x_{i-1}$, the cost of the sequence $0, y, x_i, \ldots, x_m$ is

$$c_i + y^3 + (x_i - y)x_i^2 - x_i^3 = c_i - y(x_i^2 - y^2),$$

which is less than c_i but approaches c_i as $y \to 0$. By continuity, for $i = 2, \ldots, m$, every value in the interval $[c_{i-1}, c_i)$ can be achieved, as can $c_m = 1$ by the sequence $0, 1$.

   To show that all costs c with $1/3 < c \le 1$ can be achieved, it now suffices to check that for every $\epsilon > 0$, there exists a sequence with cost at most $1/3 + \epsilon$. For instance, for the sequence $0, 1/m, \ldots, (m-1)/m, 1$, the cost is

$$\frac{1}{m^3}(1^2 + \cdots + m^2) = \frac{(m+1)(2m+1)}{6m^2},$$

which converges to 1/3 as $m \to \infty$.

Reinterpretation. The cost of jumping along a particular sequence is an upper Riemann sum of the function t^2. The fact that this function admits a Riemann integral implies that for any $\epsilon > 0$, there exists δ_0 such that the cost of the sequence $x_0, \ldots, x_m$ is at most $1/3 + \epsilon$ as long as $\max_i\{x_i - x_{i-1}\} < \epsilon$. (The computation of the integral using the sequence $x_i = i/m$ was already known to Archimedes.)

B3. (105, 22, 9, ..., 6, 4, 26, 28) 68.0%
   Call a subset S of $\{1, 2, \ldots, n\}$ *mediocre* if it has the following property: **Whenever a and b are elements of S whose average is an integer, that average is also an element of S. Let $A(n)$ be the number of mediocre subsets of $\{1, 2, \ldots, n\}$. [For instance, every subset of $\{1, 2, 3\}$ except $\{1, 3\}$ is mediocre, so $A(3) = 7$.] Find all positive integers n such that $A(n + 2) - 2A(n + 1) + A(n) = 1$.**

Answer. The integers n in question are those of the form $2^k - 1$ for some integer $k \geq 1$.

Solution. There is a bijection between mediocre subsets of $\{1, \ldots, n\}$ and mediocre subsets of $\{2, \ldots, n + 1\}$ given by adding 1 to each element of the subset; thus $A(n+1) - A(n)$ is the number of mediocre subsets of $\{1, \ldots, n+1\}$ that contain 1. It follows that $A(n+2) - 2A(n+1) + A_n = (A(n+2) - A(n+1)) - (A(n+1) - A(n))$ is the difference between the number of mediocre subsets of $\{1, \ldots, n + 2\}$ containing 1 and the number of mediocre subsets of $\{1, \ldots, n + 1\}$ containing 1. This difference is precisely the number of mediocre subsets of $\{1, \ldots, n+2\}$ containing both 1 and $n + 2$, which we term "mediocre subsets containing the endpoints." Since $\{1, \ldots, n+2\}$ itself is a mediocre subset of itself containing the endpoints, it suffices to prove that this is the only mediocre subset of $\{1, \ldots, n + 2\}$ containing the endpoints if and only if $n = 2^k - 1$ for some k.
   If n is not of the form $2^k - 1$, then $n + 1 = 2^a b$ for some odd $b > 1$. In this case, the set $\{1 + mb \mid 0 \leq m \leq 2^a\}$ is a mediocre subset of $\{1, \ldots, n+2\}$ containing the endpoints: the average of $1 + m_1 b$ and $1 + m_2 b$, namely $1 + \frac{m_1 + m_2}{2} b$, is an integer if and only if $m_1 + m_2$ is even, in which case this average lies in the set.
   It remains to show that if $n = 2^k - 1$, then the only mediocre subset of $\{1, \ldots, n+2\}$ containing the endpoints is itself. We establish this by induction on k. For $k = 1$, the statement is true because the presence of both 1 and 3 immediately forces the presence of 2. For general k, any mediocre subset S of $\{1, \ldots, n + 2 = 2^k + 1\}$ containing 1 and $2^k + 1$ must also contain their average, $2^{k-1} + 1$. By the induction assumption, the only mediocre subset of $\{1, \ldots, 2^{k-1} + 1\}$ containing the endpoints is itself, and so S must contain all integers between 1 and $2^{k-1} + 1$. Similarly, a mediocre subset of $\{2^{k-1} + 1, \ldots, 2^k + 1\}$ containing the endpoints

gives a mediocre subset of $\{1, \ldots, 2^{k-1}+1\}$ containing the endpoints by subtracting 2^{k-1} from each element. By the induction assumption again, it follows that S must contain all integers between $2^{k-1}+1$ and 2^k+1. Thus $S = \{1, \ldots, 2^k+1\}$ and the induction is complete.

Remark. One can also argue that a nonempty subset of $\{1, \ldots, n\}$ is mediocre if and only if it is an arithmetic progression with odd common difference. Given this fact, the number of mediocre subsets of $\{1, \ldots, n+2\}$ containing the endpoints is seen to be the number of odd factors of $n+1$, from which the desired result is evident.

Remark. The sequence $A(n)$ appears as sequence A124197 in the OEIS.

B4. (56, 13, 3, ..., 1, 7, 59, 61) 36.0%
   Say that a polynomial with real coefficients in two variables, x, y, is *balanced* if the average value of the polynomial on each circle centered at the origin is 0. The balanced polynomials of degree at most 2009 form a vector space V over $\mathbb{R}$. Find the dimension of V.

Answer. The dimension of V is

$$(1 + \cdots + 2010) - 1005 = (2011 - 1) \times 1005 = 2020050.$$

Solution. Any polynomial $P(x, y)$ of degree at most 2009 can be written uniquely as a sum $\sum_{i=0}^{2009} P_i(x, y)$ in which $P_i(x, y)$ is a homogeneous polynomial of degree i. For $r > 0$, let C_r be the path $(r \cos \theta, r \sin \theta)$ for $0 \le \theta \le 2\pi$. Put $\lambda(P_i) = \oint_{C_1} P_i$; then for $r > 0$,

$$\oint_{C_r} P = \sum_{i=0}^{2009} r^i \lambda(P_i).$$

For fixed P, the right side is a polynomial in r, which vanishes for all $r > 0$ if and only if its coefficients vanish. In other words, P is balanced if and only if $\lambda(P_i) = 0$ for $i = 0, \ldots, 2009$.

   For i odd, $P_i(-x, -y) = -P_i(x, y)$. Hence $\lambda(P_i) = 0$ because the contributions to the integral from θ and $\theta + \pi$ cancel.

   For i even, $\lambda(P_i)$ is a linear function of the coefficients of P_i. This function is not identically zero: for $P_i = (x^2 + y^2)^{i/2}$, the integrand is always positive and so $\lambda(P_i) > 0$. The kernel of λ on the space of homogeneous polynomials of degree i is thus a subspace of codimension 1.

   To conclude, V is a subspace of codimension 1005 of a vector space of dimension $1 + \cdots + 2010$. This yields the claimed answer.

Remark. One can also make the calculation by replacing the variables x, y with $z = x + iy, \bar{z} = x - iy$.

B5. (7, 4, 3, …, 1, 6, 84, 95) 7.0%

    Let $f : (1, \infty) \to \mathbb{R}$ be a differentiable function such that

$$f'(x) = \frac{x^2 - f(x)^2}{x^2(f(x)^2 + 1)} \qquad \text{for all } x > 1.$$

Prove that $\lim_{x \to \infty} f(x) = \infty$.

Solution 1. If $f(x) \geq x$ for all $x > 1$, then $\lim_{x \to \infty} f(x) \geq \lim_{x \to \infty} x = \infty$. We thus assume hereafter that there exists $x_0 > 1$ for which $f(x_0) < x_0$.

    Rewrite the original differential equation as

$$f'(x) = 1 - \frac{x^2 + 1}{x^2} \frac{f(x)^2}{1 + f(x)^2}.$$

Put $c_0 = \min\{0, f(x_0) - 1/x_0\}$. For all $x \geq x_0$, $f'(x) > -1/x^2$ and so

$$f(x) \geq f(x_0) - \int_{x_0}^{x} dt/t^2 > c_0.$$

In the other direction, we show that $f(x) < x$ for all $x \geq x_0$. Suppose by way of contradiction that this fails; then by continuity, there is a least $x \geq x_0$ for which $f(x) \geq x$, and this least value satisfies $f(x) = x$. However, this forces $f'(x) = 0 < 1$ and so $f(x - \epsilon) > x - \epsilon$ for $\epsilon > 0$ small, which contradicts the choice of x.

    Put $x_1 = \max\{x_0, -c_0\}$. For $x \geq x_1$, $|f(x)| < x$ and so $f'(x) > 0$. In particular, the limit $L = \lim_{x \to \infty} f(x)$ exists.

    Suppose that $L < \infty$; then $\lim_{x \to \infty} f'(x) = 1/(1 + L^2) > 0$. Hence there exist $\epsilon > 0$ and $x_2 \geq x_1$ such that $f'(x) \geq \epsilon$ for $x \geq x_2$. But then $f(x) \geq f(x_2) + \epsilon(x - x_2)$, which contradicts $L < \infty$. Hence $L = \infty$, as desired.

Variant. (Leonid Shteyman) One obtains a similar argument by writing

$$f'(x) = \frac{1}{1 + f(x)^2} - \frac{f(x)^2}{x^2(1 + f(x)^2)},$$

so that

$$-\frac{1}{x^2} \leq f'(x) - \frac{1}{1 + f(x)^2} \leq 0.$$

Hence $f'(x) - 1/(1 + f(x)^2)$ tends to 0 as $x \to \infty$, so $f(x)$ is bounded below, and tends to ∞ if and only if the improper integral $\int dx/(1 + f(x)^2)$ diverges. However, convergence of the intergral would imply $1/(1 + f(x)^2) \to 0$ as $x \to \infty$; since f is bounded below, this would again force $f(x) \to \infty$ (which in this case yields a contradiction).

Solution 2. (Catalin Zara) The function $g(x) = f(x) + x$ satisfies the differential equation

$$g'(x) = 1 + \frac{1 - (g(x)/x - 1)^2}{1 + x^2(g(x)/x - 1)^2}.$$

This implies that $g'(x) > 0$ for all $x > 1$, so the limit $L_1 = \lim_{x \to \infty} g(x)$ exists. In addition, $L_1 < \infty$ would imply that $\lim_{x \to \infty} g'(x) = 0$, whereas the differential equation forces this limit to be 1. Hence $g(x) \to \infty$ as $x \to \infty$.

Similarly, the function $h(x) = -f(x) + x$ satisfies the differential equation

$$h'(x) = 1 - \frac{1 - (h(x)/x - 1)^2}{1 + x^2(h(x)/x - 1)^2}.$$

This implies that $h'(x) \geq 0$ for all $x > 1$, so the limit $L_2 = \lim_{x \to \infty} h(x)$ exists. In addition, $L_2 < \infty$ would imply that $\lim_{x \to \infty} h'(x) = 0$, whereas the differential equation forces this limit to be 1. Hence $h(x) \to \infty$ as $x \to \infty$.

Since g and h both tend to ∞ as $x \to \infty$, there exists $x_1 > 1$ such that $g(x), h(x) > 0$ for all $x \geq x_1$. For $x \geq x_1$, $|f(x)| < x$ and hence $f'(x) > 0$, so the limit $L = \lim_{x \to \infty} f(x)$ exists. Once again, $L < \infty$ would imply that $\lim_{x \to \infty} f'(x) = 0$, whereas the original differential equation (in the form given in the first solution) forces this limit to be $1/(1 + L^2) > 0$. Hence $f(x) \to \infty$ as $x \to \infty$, as desired.

Solution 3. (Noam Elkies) The function $g(x) = f(x) + \frac{1}{3}f(x)^3$ satisfies

$$g'(x) = f'(x)(1 + f(x)^2) = 1 - \frac{f(x)^2}{x^2} < 1$$

for $x > 1$. Since $g'(x) < 1$, $g(x) - x$ is bounded above for x large. As in the first solution, $f(x)$ is bounded below for x large, so $\frac{1}{3}f(x)^3 - x$ is bounded above by some $c > 0$. For $x \geq c$, we obtain $f(x) \leq (6x)^{1/3}$.

Since $f(x)/x \to 0$ as $x \to \infty$, $g'(x) \to 1$ and so $g(x)/x \to 1$. Since $g(x)$ tends to ∞, so does $f(x)$.

Remark. With extra work, one can show that $f(x)/(3x)^{1/3} \to 1$ as $x \to \infty$.

B6. $(2, 0, 3, \ldots, 1, 0, 47, 147)$ 2.5%

Prove that for every positive integer n, there is a sequence of integers $a_0, a_1, \ldots, a_{2009}$ with $a_0 = 0$ and $a_{2009} = n$ such that each term after a_0 is either an earlier term plus 2^k for some nonnegative integer k, or of the form $b \bmod c$ for some earlier positive terms b and c. [Here $b \bmod c$ denotes the remainder when b is divided by c, so $0 \leq (b \bmod c) < c$.]

Solution 1. (based on work of Yufei Zhao) Since any sequence of the desired form remains of the desired form upon multiplying each term by 2, we may reduce to the case where n is odd. In this case, take $x = 2^h$ for some positive integer

h for which $x \geq n$, then set

$$a_1 = 1,$$
$$a_2 = 2x + 1 = a_1 + 2x,$$
$$a_3 = (x + 1)^2 = a_2 + x^2,$$
$$a_4 = x^n + 1 = a_1 + x^n,$$
$$a_5 = n(x + 1) = a_4 \bmod a_3,$$
$$a_6 = x,$$
$$a_i = n = a_5 \bmod a_6 \qquad (i \geq 7).$$

Solution 2. (James Merryfield) Suppose first that n is not divisible by 3. Recall that since 2 is a primitive root modulo 3^2, it is also a primitive root modulo 3^h for any positive integer h. Choose h so that $3^{2h} > n$; then there exists a positive integer c for which $2^c \bmod 3^{2h} = n$. Now take b to be a positive integer for which $2^b > 3^{2h}$ and put

$$a_1 = 1,$$
$$a_2 = 3 = a_1 + 2,$$
$$a_3 = 3 + 2^b,$$
$$a_4 = 2^{2hb},$$
$$a_5 = 3^{2h} = a_4 \bmod a_3,$$
$$a_6 = 2^c,$$
$$a_i = n = a_6 \bmod a_5 \qquad (i \geq 7).$$

If n is divisible by 3, use a similar construction to ensure that $a_7 = n - 1$, then put $a_i = n = a_7 + 1$ for $i \geq 8$.

Remark. (Hendrik Lenstra, Ronald van Luijk, and Gabriele Della Torre) The following variant of the first solution requires only 6 steps. For n odd and x as in the first solution, set

$$a_1 = 1,$$
$$a_2 = x + 1 = a_1 + x,$$
$$a_3 = x^n + x + 1 = a_2 + x^n,$$
$$a_4 = x^{(n-1)(\phi(a_3)-1)},$$
$$a_5 = \frac{x^n + 1}{x + 1} = a_4 \bmod a_3,$$
$$a_i = n = a_5 \bmod a_2 \qquad (i \geq 6).$$

Remark. Improving upon the previous remark seems to depend on some deep number-theoretic conjectures. For example, if there exist infinitely many positive integers m for which $p = 2^m + 3$ is prime and 2 is a primitive root modulo p, then we can find some such m for which $p > m$, and for suitable e we may then take

$$a_1 = 1,$$
$$a_2 = 3 = a_1 + 2,$$
$$a_3 = p = a_2 + 2^m,$$
$$a_4 = 2^e,$$
$$a_i = n = a_4 \bmod a_3 \qquad (i \geq 5).$$

However, it is not even known whether there are infinitely many primes satisfying one of the two conditions; for the second condition, this question is Artin's conjecture on primitive roots.

The Seventy-First William Lowell Putnam
Mathematical Competition—December 4, 2010

A1. $(181, 0, 0, \ldots, 0, 0, 7, 0)$ 96.3%

Given a positive integer n, what is the largest k such that the numbers $1, 2, \ldots, n$ can be put into k boxes so that the sum of the numbers in each box is the same? [When $n = 8$, the example $\{1, 2, 3, 6\}, \{4, 8\}, \{5, 7\}$ shows that the largest k is *at least* 3.]

Answer. The largest such k is $\left\lfloor \frac{n+1}{2} \right\rfloor = \left\lceil \frac{n}{2} \right\rceil$.

Solution. For n even, this value is achieved by the partition

$$\{1, n\}, \{2, n-1\}, \ldots;$$

for n odd, it is achieved by the partition

$$\{n\}, \{1, n-1\}, \{2, n-2\}, \ldots.$$

One way to see that this is optimal is to note that the common sum can never be less than n, since n itself belongs to one of the boxes. This implies that $k \leq (1 + \cdots + n)/n = (n+1)/2$. Another argument is that if $k > (n+1)/2$, then there would have to be two boxes with one number each (by the pigeonhole principle), but such boxes could not have the same sum.

Remark. A much subtler question would be to find the smallest k (as a function of n) for which no such arrangement exists.

A2. $(103, 42, 26, \ldots, 6, 2, 7, 2)$ 91.0%

Find all differentiable functions $f : \mathbb{R} \to \mathbb{R}$ such that

$$f'(x) = \frac{f(x+n) - f(x)}{n}$$

for all real numbers x and all positive integers n.

Answer. These are the functions of the form $f(x) = cx+d$ for some real numbers c and d.

Solution. To see that these are the only functions, suppose that f has the desired property. Then for any $x \in \mathbb{R}$,

$$2f'(x) = f(x+2) - f(x)$$
$$= (f(x+2) - f(x+1)) + (f(x+1) - f(x))$$
$$= f'(x+1) + f'(x).$$

Consequently, $f'(x+1) = f'(x)$.

Define the function $g : \mathbb{R} \to \mathbb{R}$ by $g(x) = f(x+1) - f(x)$, and put $c = g(0)$, $d = f(0)$. For all $x \in \mathbb{R}$, $g'(x) = f'(x+1) - f'(x) = 0$, so $g(x) = c$ identically. Applying the condition of the problem with $n = 1$ yields $f'(x) = f(x+1) - f(x) = g(x) = c$, so $f(x) = cx + d$ identically as desired.

A3. (30, 43, 6, ..., 5, 0, 56, 48) 42.0%
   Suppose that the function $h : \mathbb{R}^2 \to \mathbb{R}$ has continuous partial derivatives and satisfies the equation

$$h(x, y) = a\frac{\partial h}{\partial x}(x, y) + b\frac{\partial h}{\partial y}(x, y)$$

for some constants a, b. Prove that if there is a constant M such that $|h(x, y)| \le M$ for all $(x, y) \in \mathbb{R}^2$, then h is identically zero.

Solution. If $a = b = 0$, then the desired result holds trivially, so we assume that at least one of a, b is nonzero. Pick any point $(a_0, b_0) \in \mathbb{R}^2$, and let L be the line given by the parametric equation $L(t) = (a_0, b_0) + (a, b)t$ for $t \in \mathbb{R}$. Let $f = h \circ L$; by the chain rule and the given equation, $f'(t) = f(t)$ for all t. It follows that $f(t) = Ce^t$ for some constant C; since $|f(t)| \le M$ for all t, we must have $C = 0$. It follows that $h(a_0, b_0) = 0$; since (a_0, b_0) was an arbitrary point, h is identically 0 over all of $\mathbb{R}^2$.

A4. (90, 29, 1, ..., 2, 2, 25, 39) 63.8%
   Prove that for each positive integer n, the number $10^{10^{10^n}} + 10^{10^n} + 10^n - 1$ is not prime.

Solution. Put
$$N = 10^{10^{10^n}} + 10^{10^n} + 10^n - 1.$$
Write $n = 2^m k$ with m a nonnegative integer and k a positive odd integer. For any nonnegative integer j,
$$10^{2^m j} \equiv (-1)^j \pmod{10^{2^m} + 1}.$$
Since $10^n \ge n \ge 2^m \ge m + 1$, 10^n is divisible by 2^n and hence by 2^{m+1}, and similarly 10^{10^n} is divisible by 2^{10^n} and hence by 2^{m+1}. It follows that
$$N \equiv 1 + 1 + (-1) + (-1) \equiv 0 \pmod{10^{2^m} + 1}.$$
Since $N \ge 10^{10^n} > 10^n + 1 \ge 10^{2^m} + 1$, it follows that N is composite.

A5. (26, 9, 4, ..., 63, 4, 38, 44) 20.7%
   Let G be a group, with operation $*$. Suppose that

(i) **G is a subset of $\mathbb{R}^3$ (but $*$ need not be related to addition of vectors);**

(ii) **For each $a, b \in G$, either $a \times b = a * b$ or $a \times b = 0$ (or both), where $\times$ is the usual cross product in $\mathbb{R}^3$.**

Prove that $a \times b = 0$ for all $a, b \in G$.

Solution. We start with three lemmas.

Lemma 1. If $x, y \in G$ are nonzero orthogonal vectors, then $x * x$ is parallel to y.

Proof. Put $z = x \times y \neq 0$, so that x, y, and $z = x * y$ are nonzero and mutually orthogonal. Then $w = x \times z \neq 0$, so $w = x * z$ is nonzero and orthogonal to x and z. However, if $(x * x) \times y \neq 0$, then $w = x * (x * y) = (x * x) * y = (x * x) \times y$ is also orthogonal to y, a contradiction. $\square$

Lemma 2. If $x \in G$ is a nonzero vector, and there exists $y \in G$ which is nonzero and orthogonal to x, then $x * x = 0$.

Proof. Lemma 1 implies that $x * x$ is parallel to both y and $x \times y = x * y$, so it must be zero. $\square$

Lemma 3. If $x, y \in G$ commute, then $x \times y = 0$.

Proof. If $x \times y \neq 0$, then $y \times x$ is nonzero and distinct from $x \times y$. Consequently, $x * y = x \times y$ and $y * x = y \times x \neq x * y$. $\square$

We proceed now to the problem at hand. Assume by way of contradiction that there exist $a, b \in G$ with $a \times b \neq 0$. Put $c = a \times b = a * b$, so that a, b, c are nonzero and linearly independent. Let e be the identity element of G. Since e commutes with a, b, c, by Lemma 3 $e \times a = e \times b = e \times c = 0$. Since a, b, c span $\mathbb{R}^3$, $e \times x = 0$ for all $x \in \mathbb{R}^3$, so $e = 0$.

Since b, c, and $b \times c = b * c$ are nonzero and mutually orthogonal, Lemma 2 implies
$$b * b = c * c = (b * c) * (b * c) = 0 = e.$$
Hence $b * c = c * b$, contradicting Lemma 3 because $b \times c \neq 0$. The desired result follows.

A6. (12, 1, 4, ..., 2, 5, 44, 120) 9.0%

Let $f : [0, \infty) \to \mathbb{R}$ **be a strictly decreasing continuous function such that** $\lim_{x \to \infty} f(x) = 0$. **Prove that** $\int_0^\infty \frac{f(x) - f(x+1)}{f(x)} dx$ **diverges.**

Solution 1. (based on a suggestion of Greg Martin) The hypotheses on f imply that $f(x) > 0$ for all $x \in [0, \infty)$, so the integrand is a continuous function of f and the integral makes sense. Moreover, to show that it diverges, it suffices to produce an infinite sequence of disjoint intervals $I_1, I_2, \ldots$ such that the quantities
$$\int_{I_n} \frac{f(x) - f(x + 1)}{f(x)} dx \qquad (n = 1, 2, \ldots)$$

form a divergent series.

If $f(y) > 2f(y + 1)$, then either $f(y) > \sqrt{2}f(y + 1/2)$ or $f(y + 1/2) > \sqrt{2}f(y + 1)$; in either case,

$$\int_{y-1/2}^{y+1/2} \frac{f(x) - f(x+1)}{f(x)}\, dx > \frac{1}{2}\left(1 - \frac{1}{\sqrt{2}}\right) > \frac{1}{7}$$

because the integrand exceeds $1 - 1/\sqrt{2}$ on some interval of length $1/2$. If there exist arbitrarily large values of y for which $f(y) > 2f(y + 1)$, then the original integral is greater than any multiple of $1/7$, and so diverges.

We may thus assume without loss of generality that for some N, $f(x) \leq 2f(x + 1)$ for all $x \geq N$. By Taylor's theorem with remainder, for $t \in [0, 1/2]$,

$$-\log(1 - t) \leq t + \frac{t^2}{2} \sup_{t \in [0,1/2]} \left\{ \frac{1}{(1-t)^2} \right\}$$

$$= t + 2t^2 \leq 2t.$$

For each nonnegative integer $n \geq N$, we then have

$$\int_0^\infty \left(1 - \frac{f(x+1)}{f(x)}\right) dx \geq \int_N^n \left(1 - \frac{f(x+1)}{f(x)}\right) dx$$

$$= \sum_{i=N}^{n-1} \int_0^1 \left(1 - \frac{f(x+i+1)}{f(x+i)}\right) dx$$

$$\geq \frac{1}{2} \sum_{i=N}^{n-1} \int_0^1 \log \frac{f(x+i)}{f(x+i+1)}\, dx$$

$$= \frac{1}{2} \int_0^1 \left(\sum_{i=N}^{n-1} \log \frac{f(x+i)}{f(x+i+1)} \right) dx$$

$$= \frac{1}{2} \int_0^1 \log \frac{f(x+N)}{f(x+n)}\, dx.$$

For each $x \in [0, 1]$, $\log(f(x+N)/f(x+n))$ is a strictly increasing unbounded function of n. By the monotone convergence theorem, the definite integral $\int_0^1 \log(f(x+N)/f(x+n))\, dx$ grows without bound as $n \to \infty$. Thus the original integral diverges, as desired.

Remark. This solution is motivated by the commonly used fact that an infinite product $(1 + x_1)(1 + x_2) \cdots$ converges absolutely if and only if the sum $x_1 + x_2 + \cdots$ converges absolutely. The additional argument at the beginning is needed because one cannot bound $-\log(1 - t)$ by a fixed multiple of t uniformly for all $t \in [0, 1)$; an alternate argument for this step uses Lebesgue measure as follows.

For $n \geq 0$, define the Lebesgue measurable set

$$I_n = \{x \in [0,1] : 1 - \frac{f(x+n+1)}{f(x+n)} \leq 1/2\}.$$

If the original integral converges, then so does the sum $\sum_{n=0}^{\infty} \frac{1}{2}(1 - \mu(I_n))$; in particular, there exists a nonnegative integer N for which $\sum_{n=N}^{\infty}(1 - \mu(I_n)) < 1$. The intersection

$$I = \bigcup_{n=N}^{\infty} I_n = [0,1] - \bigcap_{n=N}^{\infty}([0,1] - I_n)$$

then has positive Lebesgue measure, so we may calculate that

$$\int_0^{\infty} \left(1 - \frac{f(x+1)}{f(x)}\right) dx \geq \int_N^n \left(1 - \frac{f(x+1)}{f(x)}\right) dx$$

$$\geq \sum_{i=N}^{n-1} \int_I \left(1 - \frac{f(x+i+1)}{f(x+i)}\right) dx,$$

then repeat the previous calculation with the integrals over $[0,1]$ replaced by integrals over I, to reach a contradiction under the assumption that the original integral converges.

Solution 2. (Paul Allen) Let $b > a$ be nonnegative integers. Then

$$\int_a^b \frac{f(x) - f(x+1)}{f(x)} dx = \sum_{k=a}^{b-1} \int_0^1 \frac{f(x+k) - f(x+k+1)}{f(x+k)} dx$$

$$= \int_0^1 \sum_{k=a}^{b-1} \frac{f(x+k) - f(x+k+1)}{f(x+k)} dx$$

$$\geq \int_0^1 \sum_{k=a}^{b-1} \frac{f(x+k) - f(x+k+1)}{f(x+a)} dx$$

$$= \int_0^1 \frac{f(x+a) - f(x+b)}{f(x+a)} dx.$$

Since $f(x) \to 0$, for each nonnegative integer a there exists some integer $l(a) > a$ for which $f(l(a)) < f(a+1)/2$. For all $x \in [0,1]$,

$$\frac{f(x+a) - f(x+l(a))}{f(x+a)} \geq 1 - \frac{f(l(a))}{f(a+1)} > \frac{1}{2}.$$

Define the sequence of integers a_n by $a_0 = 0$, $a_{n+1} = l(a_n)$; then

$$\int_0^\infty \frac{f(x) - f(x+1)}{f(x)} dx = \sum_{n=0}^\infty \int_{a_n}^{a_{n+1}} \frac{f(x) - f(x+1)}{f(x)} dx$$

$$> \sum_{n=0}^\infty \int_0^1 \frac{1}{2} dx,$$

and the final sum diverges.

Solution 3. (Joshua Rosenberg, via Catalin Zara) If the original integral converges, then on one hand the integrand $(f(x) - f(x+1))/f(x) = 1 - f(x+1)/f(x)$ cannot tend to 1 as $x \to \infty$. On the other hand, for any $a \geq 0$,

$$0 < \frac{f(a+1)}{f(a)}$$

$$< \frac{1}{f(a)} \int_a^{a+1} f(x) dx$$

$$= \frac{1}{f(a)} \int_a^\infty (f(x) - f(x+1)) dx$$

$$\leq \int_a^\infty \frac{f(x) - f(x+1)}{f(x)} dx,$$

and the last expression tends to 0 as $a \to \infty$. Hence by the sandwich theorem, $f(a+1)/f(a) \to 0$ as $a \to \infty$, a contradiction.

B1. (144, 24, 5, ..., 2, 4, 8, 1) 92.0%
Is there an infinite sequence of real numbers $a_1, a_2, a_3, \ldots$ such that

$$a_1^m + a_2^m + a_3^m + \cdots = m$$

for every positive integer m?

Answer. No, there is no such sequence.

Solution 1. (Catalin Zara) Suppose by way of contradiction that such a sequence exists. If $a_k^2 \in [0, 1]$ for all k, then $a_k^4 \leq a_k^2$ for all k, and so

$$4 = a_1^4 + a_2^4 + \cdots \leq a_1^2 + a_2^2 + \cdots = 2,$$

a contradiction. There thus exists a positive integer k for which $a_k^2 > 1$. However, in this case, for m large, $a_k^{2m} > 2m$ and so $a_1^{2m} + a_2^{2m} + \cdots \neq 2m$.

Solution 2. If such a sequence were to exist, then the Cauchy-Schwarz inequality would imply

$$8 = (a_1^2 + a_2^2 + \cdots)(a_1^4 + a_2^4 + \cdots)$$
$$\geq (a_1^3 + a_2^3 + \cdots)^2 = 9,$$

a contradiction.

Solution 3. We generalize the first solution to show that it is impossible for a sequence $a_1, a_2, \ldots$ of complex numbers to satisfy the given conditions for any positive integer k for which the series $a_1^k + a_2^k + \cdots$ converges absolutely. This includes the original problem by taking $k = 2$, in which case the series $a_1^2 + a_2^2 + \cdots$ consists of nonnegative real numbers and so converges absolutely if it converges at all.

Since the sum $\sum_{i=1}^{\infty} |a_i|^k$ converges by hypothesis, there exists a positive integer n such that $\sum_{i=n+1}^{\infty} |a_i|^k < 1$. For each positive integer d,

$$\left| kd - \sum_{i=1}^{n} a_i^{kd} \right| = \left| \sum_{i=n+1}^{\infty} a_i^{kd} \right| \leq \sum_{i=n+1}^{\infty} |a_i|^{kd} < 1.$$

Set $r = \max\{|a_1|, \ldots, |a_n|\}$; then $r > 1$, as otherwise the sum $\sum_{i=1}^{n} a_i^{kd}$ would be bounded in absolute value by n independently of d. For $\epsilon > 0$,

$$\limsup_{d \to \infty} (r - \epsilon)^{-kd} \left| \sum_{i=1}^{n} a_i^{kd} \right| > 0$$

and so the root test implies that the power series

$$\sum_{i=1}^{n} \frac{1}{1 - a_i^k z} = \sum_{d=0}^{\infty} \left(\sum_{i=1}^{n} a_i^{kd} \right) z^d$$

converges for $|z| < r$. This yields a contadiction because the power series represents a rational function with a pole within the circle $|z| \leq r^{-1/k}$.

Solution 4. (Noam Elkies) Since $\sum_k a_k^2 = 2$, for each positive integer k we have $a_k^2 \leq 2$ and so $a_k^4 \leq 2a_k^2$, with equality only for $a_k^2 \in \{0, 2\}$. Thus to have $\sum_k a_k^4 = 4$, there must be a single index k for which $a_k^2 = 2$, and the other a_k must all equal 0. But then $\sum_k a_k^{2m} = 2^m \neq 2m$ for any positive integer $m > 2$.

Remark. It is possible to construct sequences of complex numbers with the desired property if we drop the condition of absolute convergence. We give one such construction, of which several variants are possible.

For $n = 1, 2, \ldots$ and $z \in \mathbb{C}$, define the finite sequence

$$s_{n,z} = \left(\frac{1}{z} e^{2\pi i j/n} : j = 0, \ldots, n - 1 \right).$$

This sequence has the property that for any positive integer k, the sum of the kth powers of the terms of $s_{n,z}$ equals $1/z^k$ if k is divisible by n and 0 otherwise. Moreover, any partial sum of kth powers is bounded in absolute value by $n/|z|^k$.

The desired sequence will be constructed as follows. Suppose that we have a finite sequence which has the correct sum of kth powers for $k = 1, \ldots, m$. (For instance, for $m = 1$, we may start with the singleton sequence 1.) We may then extend it to a new sequence which has the correct sum of kth powers for $k = 1, \ldots, m + 1$, by appending r copies of $s_{m+1,z}$ for suitable choices of a positive integer r and a complex number z with $|z| < m^{-2}$. This last restriction ensures that the resulting infinite sequence $a_1, a_2, \ldots$ is such that for each positive integer m, the series $a_1^m + a_2^m + \cdots$ is convergent (though not absolutely convergent). Its partial sums include a subsequence equal to the constant value m, so the sum of the series must equal m as desired.

B2. (133, 5, 31, …, 10, 2, 4, 3) 89.9%
   Given that A, B, and C are noncollinear points in the plane with integer coordinates such that the distances AB, AC, and BC are integers, what is the smallest possible value of AB?

Answer. The smallest possible value is 3.

Solution. The value 3 is achieved by $A = (0,0)$, $B = (3,0)$, $C = (0,4)$. To check that this is best possible, it suffices to check that AB cannot equal 1 or 2. (It cannot equal 0 because if two of the points were to coincide, the three points would be collinear.)

The triangle inequality implies that $|AC - BC| \leq AB$, with equality if and only if A, B, C are collinear. If $AB = 1$, we may assume without loss of generality that $A = (0,0)$, $B = (1,0)$. To avoid collinearity, we must have $AC = BC$, but this forces $C = (1/2, y)$ for some $y \in \mathbb{R}$, a contradiction. (One can also treat this case by scaling by a factor of 2 to reduce to the case $AB = 2$, treated in the next paragraph.)

If $AB = 2$, then we may assume without loss of generality that $A = (0,0)$, $B = (2,0)$. The triangle inequality implies $|AC - BC| \in \{0,1\}$. Also, for $C = (x,y)$, $AC^2 = x^2 + y^2$ and $BC^2 = (2-x)^2 + y^2$ have the same parity; it follows that $AC = BC$. Hence $c = (1,y)$ for some $y \in \mathbb{R}$, so y^2 and $y^2 + 1 = BC^2$ are consecutive perfect squares. This can only happen for $y = 0$, but then A, B, C are collinear, a contradiction again.

Remark. More generally, a *Heronian triangle* (a triangle with integer sides and rational area) cannot have a side of length 1 or 2 (and again it is enough to treat the case of length 2). The original problem follows from this because a triangle whose vertices have integer coordinates has area equal to half an integer (by Pick's theorem or the shoelace formula).

B3. (152, 0, 0, ..., 0, 0, 32, 4) 80.9%

There are 2010 boxes labeled $B_1, B_2, \ldots, B_{2010}$, and 2010$n$ balls have been distributed among them, for some positive integer n. You may redistribute the balls by a sequence of moves, each of which consists of choosing an i and moving *exactly* i balls from box B_i into any one other box. For which values of n is it possible to reach the distribution with exactly n balls in each box, regardless of the initial distribution of balls?

Answer. It is possible if and only if $n \geq 1005$.

Solution. From the equality

$$1 + \cdots + 2009 = \frac{2009 \times 2010}{2} = 2010 \times 1004.5,$$

it follows that for $n \leq 1004$, there exists an initial distribution in which each box B_i starts with at most $i - 1$ balls (so in particular B_1 is empty). From such a distribution, no moves at all are possible, so it is impossible to reach the desired final distribution.

Suppose now that $n \geq 1005$. By the pigeonhole principle, at any time, there exists at least one index i for which the box B_i contains at least i balls; we describe any such index as being *eligible*. The following sequence of operations then has the desired effect.

(a) Find the largest eligible index i. If $i = 1$, proceed to (b). Otherwise, move i balls from B_i to B_1, then repeat (a).

(b) At this point, only the index $i = 1$ can be eligible (so it must be). Find the largest index j for which B_j is nonempty. If $j = 1$, proceed to (c). Otherwise, move 1 ball from B_1 to B_j; in case this makes j eligible, move j balls from B_j to B_1. Then repeat (b).

(c) At this point, all of the balls are in B_1. For $i = 2, \ldots, 2010$, move one ball from B_1 to B_i n times.

After these operations, we have the desired distribution.

B4. (37, 8, 3, ..., 3, 3, 78, 56) 25.5%

Find all pairs of polynomials $p(x)$ and $q(x)$ with real coefficients for which

$$p(x)q(x + 1) - p(x + 1)q(x) = 1.$$

Answer. The pairs (p, q) satisfying the given equation are those of the form $p(x) = ax + b, q(x) = cx + d$ for $a, b, c, d \in \mathbb{R}$ such that $bc - ad = 1$.

Solution 1. Suppose p and q satisfy the given equation; neither p nor q can be identically zero. Subtracting the equations

$$p(x)q(x+1) - p(x+1)q(x) = 1,$$
$$p(x-1)q(x) - p(x)q(x-1) = 1$$

yields

$$p(x)(q(x+1) + q(x-1)) = q(x)(p(x+1) + p(x-1)).$$

The original equation implies that $p(x)$ and $q(x)$ have no common nonconstant factor, so by unique factorization of polynomials, $p(x)$ divides $p(x+1) + p(x-1)$. Since each of $p(x+1)$ and $p(x-1)$ has the same degree and leading coefficient as p,

$$p(x+1) + p(x-1) = 2p(x).$$

Define the polynomials $r(x) = p(x+1) - p(x)$, $s(x) = q(x+1) - q(x)$; then $r(x+1) = r(x)$ and similarly $s(x+1) = s(x)$. Put

$$a = r(0), b = p(0), c = s(0), d = q(0).$$

Then $r(x) = a, s(x) = c$ for all $x \in \mathbb{Z}$, and hence identically; consequently, $p(x) = ax + b, q(x) = cx + d$ for all $x \in \mathbb{Z}$, and hence identically. For p and q of this form,

$$p(x)q(x+1) - p(x+1)q(x) = bc - ad,$$

so we get a solution if and only if $bc - ad = 1$, as claimed.

Solution 2. (Catalin Zara) Again, p and q must be nonzero. Write

$$p(x) = p_0 + p_1 x + \cdots + p_m x^m,$$
$$q(x) = q_0 + q_1 x + \cdots + q_n x^n$$

with $p_m, q_n \neq 0$, so that $m = \deg(p), n = \deg(q)$. It is enough to derive a contradiction assuming that $\max\{m, n\} > 1$, the remaining cases being treated as in the first solution.

Put $R(x) = p(x)q(x+1) - p(x+1)q(x)$. Since $m + n \geq 2$ by assumption, the coefficient of x^{m+n-1} in $R(x)$ must vanish. This coefficient equals $(m - n)p_m q_n$, so $m = n > 1$.

For $k = 1, \ldots, 2m - 2$, the coefficient of x^k in $R(x)$ is

$$\sum_{i+j>k, j>i} \left(\binom{j}{k-i} - \binom{i}{k-j} \right) (p_i q_j - p_j q_i)$$

and must vanish. For $k = 2m - 2$, the only summand is for $(i, j) = (m-1, m)$, so $p_{m-1}q_m = p_m q_{m-1}$.

Suppose now that $h \geq 1$ and that $p_i q_j = p_j q_i$ is known to vanish whenever $j > i \geq h$. (By the previous paragraph, we initially have this for $h = m-1$.) Take $k = m + h - 2$ and note that the conditions $i + j > h, j \leq m$ force $i \geq h - 1$. By the hypothesis, the only possible nonzero contribution to the coefficient of x^k in $R(x)$ is from $(i, j) = (h - 1, m)$. Hence $p_{h-1}q_m = p_m q_{h-1}$; since $p_m, q_m \neq 0$, this implies $p_{h-1}q_j = p_j q_{h-1}$ whenever $j > h - 1$.

By descending induction, $p_i q_j = p_j q_i$ whenever $j > i \geq 0$. Consequently, $p(x)$ and $q(x)$ are scalar multiples of each other, forcing $R(x) = 0$, a contradiction.

Solution 3. (David Feldman) As in the second solution, there are no solutions for which $m = \deg(p), n = \deg(q)$ are distinct and $m + n \geq 2$. Suppose p, q form a solution with $m = n \geq 2$. The desired identity asserts that the matrix

$$\begin{pmatrix} p(x) & p(x + 1) \\ q(x) & q(x + 1) \end{pmatrix}$$

has determinant 1. This condition is preserved by replacing $q(x)$ with $q(x) - tp(x)$ for any real number t. In particular, choosing t to force $\deg(q(x) - tp(x)) < m$ yields a contradiction.

B5. $(11, 9, 17, \ldots, 2, 3, 63, 83)$ 19.7%
   Is there a strictly increasing function $f : \mathbb{R} \to \mathbb{R}$ such that $f'(x) = f(f(x))$ for all x?

Answer. No, there is no such function.

Solution 1. Suppose otherwise. For the condition to make sense, f must be differentiable. Since f is strictly increasing, $f'(x) \geq 0$ for all x. Also, the function $f'(x)$ is strictly increasing: if $y > x$ then $f'(y) = f(f(y)) > f(f(x)) = f'(x)$. In particular, $f'(y) > 0$ for all $y \in \mathbb{R}$.

For any $x_0 \geq -1$, if $f(x_0) = b$ and $f'(x_0) = a > 0$, then $f'(x) > a$ for $x > x_0$ and thus $f(x) \geq a(x - x_0) + b$ for $x \geq x_0$. Then either $b < x_0$ or $a = f'(x_0) = f(f(x_0)) = f(b) \geq a(b - x_0) + b$. In the latter case, $b \leq a(x_0 + 1)/(a+1) \leq x_0 + 1$. In either case, $f(x_0) \leq x_0 + 1$ for all $x_0 \geq -1$.

We must then have $f(f(x)) = f'(x) \leq 1$ for all x, since otherwise $f(x) > x + 1$ for large x. Now by the above reasoning, if $f(0) = b_0$ and $f'(0) = a_0 > 0$, then $f(x) > a_0 x + b_0$ for $x > 0$. Thus for $x > \max\{0, -b_0/a_0\}$, $f(x) > 0$ and $f(f(x)) > a_0 x + b_0$. But then $f(f(x)) > 1$ for sufficiently large x, a contradiction.

Solution 2. (Catalin Zara) Suppose such a function exists. Since f is strictly increasing and differentiable, so is $f \circ f = f'$; in particular, f is twice differentiable. Also, $f''(x) = f'(f(x))f'(x)$ is the product of two strictly increasing nonnegative functions, so it is also strictly increasing and nonnegative. In particular, there exist $\alpha > 0$ and $M \in \mathbb{R}$ such that $f''(x) > 4\alpha$ for all $x \geq M$. Then for all $x \geq M$, by Taylor's theorem with remainder,

$$f(x) \geq f(M) + f'(M)(x - M) + 2\alpha(x - M)^2.$$

In particular, for some $M' > M$, $f(x) \geq \alpha x^2$ for all $x \geq M'$.

Pick $T > 0$ so that $\alpha T^2 > M'$. Then for $x \geq T$, $f(x) > M'$ and so $f'(x) = f(f(x)) \geq \alpha f(x)^2$. Now

$$\frac{1}{f(T)} - \frac{1}{f(2T)} = \int_T^{2T} \frac{f'(t)}{f(t)^2} \, dt \geq \int_T^{2T} \alpha \, dt;$$

however, as $T \to \infty$, the left side of this inequality tends to 0 while the right side tends to ∞, a contradiction.

Solution 3. (Noam Elkies) Since f is strictly increasing, for some y_0, f admits an inverse function $g(y)$ for $y \geq y_0$. Then $x = g(f(x))$ and differentiating yields $1 = g'(f(x))f'(x) = g'(f(x))f(f(x))$. It follows that $g'(y) = 1/f(y)$ for $y \geq y_0$; since g takes arbitrarily large values, the integral $\int_{y_0}^{\infty} dy/f(y)$ must diverge. One then gets a contradiction from any reasonable lower bound on $f(x)$ for x large, such as the bound $f(x) \geq \alpha x^2$ from the second solution. (One can also start with a linear lower bound $f(x) \geq \beta x$, then use the integral expression for g to deduce that $g(x) \leq \gamma \log x$, which in turn forces $f(x)$ to grow exponentially.)

B6. $(24, 4, 7, \ldots, 1, 7, 28, 117)$ 18.6%

Let A be an $n \times n$ matrix of real numbers for some $n \geq 1$. For each positive integer k, let $A^{[k]}$ be the matrix obtained by raising each entry to the kth power. Show that if $A^k = A^{[k]}$ for $k = 1, 2, \ldots, n+1$, then $A^k = A^{[k]}$ for all $k \geq 1$.

Solution. For any polynomial $p(x)$, let $[p(x)]A$ denote the $n \times n$ matrix obtained by replacing each entry A_{ij} of A by $p(A_{ij})$; thus $A^{[k]} = [x^k]A$. Let $P(x) = x^n + a_{n-1}x^{n-1} + \cdots + a_0$ denote the characteristic polynomial of A. By the Cayley-Hamilton theorem,

$$0 = A \cdot P(A)$$
$$= A^{n+1} + a_{n-1}A^n + \cdots + a_0 A$$
$$= A^{[n+1]} + a_{n-1}A^{[n]} + \cdots + a_0 A^{[1]}$$
$$= [xP(x)]A.$$

Thus each entry of A is a root of the polynomial $xP(x)$.

Now suppose $m \geq n + 1$. Then

$$0 = [x^{m+1-n}P(x)]A$$
$$= A^{[m+1]} + a_{n-1}A^{[m]} + \cdots + a_0 A^{[m+1-n]}$$

since each entry of A is a root of $x^{m+1-n}P(x)$. On the other hand,

$$0 = A^{m+1-n} \cdot P(A)$$
$$= A^{m+1} + a_{n-1}A^m + \cdots + a_0 A^{m+1-n}.$$

Therefore if $A^k = A^{[k]}$ for $m + 1 - n \le k \le m$, then $A^{m+1} = A^{[m+1]}$. The desired result follows by induction on m.

Remark. This problem was posed on AoPS in September 2010 (topic c7h364284).

Remark. If A is a diagonal matrix, then $A^k = A^{[k]}$ for all $k \ge 1$. The converse does not hold for $n \ge 2$: the matrix

$$A = \begin{pmatrix} 1 & \cdots & 1 \\ 0 & \cdots & 0 \\ \vdots & & \vdots \\ 0 & \cdots & 0 \end{pmatrix}$$

is not diagonal, but $A^k = A^{[k]} = A$ for all $k \ge 1$.

Remark. (David Feldman) The result is best possible in the case $n = 2$: there are 2×2 matrices A for which $A^2 = A^{[2]}$ but $A^3 \ne A^{[3]}$. One can even classify these matrices completely: they are the matrices of one of the forms

$$A = \begin{pmatrix} x & x+y \\ 0 & y \end{pmatrix}, \begin{pmatrix} x & 0 \\ x+y & y \end{pmatrix} \qquad (x, y, x+y \ne 0).$$

However, for $n = 3, 4$, any $n \times n$ matrix A for which $A^k = A^{[k]}$ for $k = 1, \ldots, n$ also satisfies $A^{n+1} = A^{[n+1]}$. To check this, we may assume (by symmetry and the previous remark) that the off-diagonal entry A_{12} is nonzero; the result is then confirmed by a few minutes of computation using the *Sage* computer algebra system (version 8.9). The cases $n \ge 5$ remain unsettled.

```
sage: for n in [3..4]:
....:     P = PolynomialRing(QQ, n^2+1, names=['x_%s'%i for i in [0..n^2]])
....:     A = Matrix(n, n, P.gens()[1:])
....:     d = {i: A^i - A.apply_map(lambda x: x^i) for i in [2..n+1]}
....:     I = ideal(_ for i in [2..n] for _ in d[i].list())
....:     I = (I + ideal([P('x_0')*P('x_2') - 1])).radical()
....:     print(I == I + ideal(d[n+1].list()))
....: # end for
True
True
```

The Seventy-Second William Lowell Putnam
Mathematical Competition—December 3, 2011

A1. (90, 11, 11, ..., 25, 5, 54, 1) 56.9%
Define a *growing spiral* in the plane to be a sequence of points with integer coordinates $P_0 = (0,0), P_1, \ldots, P_n$ such that $n \geq 2$ and:

a.   the directed line segments $P_0P_1, P_1P_2, \ldots, P_{n-1}P_n$ are in the successive coordinate directions east (for P_0P_1), north, west, south, east, etc.;

b.   the lengths of these line segments are positive and strictly increasing.

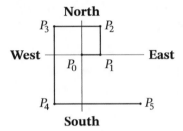

How many of the points (x, y) with integer coordinates $0 \leq x \leq 2011$, $0 \leq y \leq 2011$ *cannot* be the last point, P_n of any growing spiral?

Answer. The number of excluded points is

$$2012 + 2011 + 2011 + 2010 + 2009 = 10053.$$

Solution. We show that the set of points with $0 \leq x \leq 2011$ and $0 \leq y \leq 2011$ that cannot be the last point of a growing spiral are as follows: $(0, y)$ for $0 \leq y \leq 2011$; $(x, 0)$ and $(x, 1)$ for $1 \leq x \leq 2011$; $(x, 2)$ for $2 \leq x \leq 2011$; and $(x, 3)$ for $3 \leq x \leq 2011$. This will give the specified total.

The complement of this set is the set of (x, y) with $0 < x < y$, along with (x, y) with $x \geq y \geq 4$. Each point in the former set is achievable as P_2 in a growing spiral, while a point (x, y) in the latter set is P_6 in a growing spiral with successive lengths $1, 2, 3, x + 1, x + 2, x + y - 1$.

Write $x_1 < y_1 < x_2 < y_2 < \cdots$ for the lengths of the line segments in the spiral in order, so that $P_1 = (x_1, 0)$, $P_2 = (x_1, y_1)$, $P_3 = (x_1 - x_2, y_1)$, and so forth. Any point beyond P_0 has x-coordinate of the form $x_1 - x_2 + \cdots + (-1)^{n-1}x_n$ for $n \geq 1$; if n is odd, this sum can be regrouped as $x_1 + (-x_2 + x_3) + \cdots + (-x_{n-1} + x_n) > 0$, while if n is even, the sum can be regrouped as $(x_1 - x_2) + \cdots + (x_{n-1} - x_n) < 0$. Thus no point beyond P_0 can have x-coordinate 0; this rules out $(0, y)$ for $0 \leq y \leq 2011$.

Similarly, any point beyond P_3 has y-coordinate of the form $y_1 - y_2 + \cdots + (-1)^{n-1}y_n$ for $n \geq 2$; if n is even, this sum can be regrouped as $(y_1 - y_2) + \cdots + (y_{n-1} - y_n) < 0$, while if $n \geq 3$ is odd, the sum can be regrouped as

$$y_1 + (-y_2 + y_3) + \cdots + (-y_{n-1} + y_n) \geq y_1 + 2 \geq 4.$$

Hence of the points that must still be excluded, none can occur in a growing spiral except possibly as P_2 or P_3. However, no such point can occur as $P_3 = (x_1 - x_2, y_1)$ since $x_1 - x_2 < 0$, nor as $P_2 = (x_1, y_1)$ since it has y-coordinate at most equal to its x-coordinate.

A2. $(87, 21, 9, \ldots, 40, 10, 15, 15)$ 59.4%

Let $a_1, a_2, \ldots$ and $b_1, b_2, \ldots$ be sequences of positive real numbers such that $a_1 = b_1 = 1$ and $b_n = b_{n-1}a_n - 2$ for $n = 2, 3, \ldots$. Assume that the sequence (b_j) is bounded. Prove that

$$S = \sum_{n=1}^{\infty} \frac{1}{a_1 \cdots a_n}$$

converges, and evaluate S.

Answer. $S = 3/2$.

Solution. For $m \geq 1$, write

$$S_m = \frac{3}{2}\left(1 - \frac{b_1 \cdots b_m}{(b_1 + 2) \cdots (b_m + 2)}\right).$$

Then $S_1 = 1 = 1/a_1$ and a quick calculation yields

$$S_m - S_{m-1} = \frac{b_1 \cdots b_{m-1}}{(b_2 + 2) \cdots (b_m + 2)} = \frac{1}{a_1 \cdots a_m}$$

for $m \geq 2$, since $a_j = (b_j + 2)/b_{j-1}$ for $j \geq 2$. It follows that $S_m = \sum_{n=1}^{m} 1/(a_1 \cdots a_n)$.

Now if (b_j) is bounded above by B, then $\frac{b_j}{b_j + 2} \leq \frac{B}{B+2}$ for all j, and so $3/2 > S_m \geq 3/2(1 - (\frac{B}{B+2})^m)$. Since $\frac{B}{B+2} < 1$, it follows that the sequence (S_m) converges to $S = 3/2$.

Remark. One way to discover this solution is to work backwards in the following fashion. First, guess that there is a simple expression for $T_m = \sum_{n=1}^{m} 1/(a_1 \cdots a_n)$ in terms of the sequence (b_j). Second, notice that the recurrence relation can be written in the form

$$a_n = \frac{b_n + 2}{b_{n-1}}$$

and substitute to obtain the equality

$$T_m - T_{m-1} = \frac{1}{a_2 \cdots a_m} = \frac{b_1 \cdots b_{m-1}}{(b_2 + 2) \cdots (b_m + 2)}.$$

Third, write T_m in the form

$$\frac{U_m}{(b_2 + 2) \cdots (b_m + 2)}$$

and guess the general form of U_m from its first few values, then prove the guess by induction.

A3. (12, 0, 3, ..., 24, 12, 48, 98) 7.6%
   Find a real number c and a positive number L for which

$$\lim_{r \to \infty} \frac{r^c \displaystyle\int_0^{\pi/2} x^r \sin x \, dx}{\displaystyle\int_0^{\pi/2} x^r \cos x \, dx} = L.$$

Answer. We prove the claim with $(c, L) = (-1, 2/\pi)$.

Solution. Write $f(r) = \int_0^{\pi/2} x^r \sin x \, dx$. On one hand,

$$f(r) < \int_0^{\pi/2} x^r \, dx = \frac{(\pi/2)^{r+1}}{r + 1}.$$

On the other hand, since $\sin x \geq 2x/\pi$ for $x \leq \pi/2$,

$$f(r) > \int_0^{\pi/2} \frac{2x^{r+1}}{\pi} \, dx = \frac{(\pi/2)^{r+1}}{r + 2}.$$

It follows that

$$\lim_{r \to \infty} r \left(\frac{2}{\pi}\right)^{r+1} f(r) = 1,$$

whence

$$\lim_{r \to \infty} \frac{f(r)}{f(r + 1)} = \lim_{r \to \infty} \frac{r(2/\pi)^{r+1} f(r)}{(r + 1)(2/\pi)^{r+2} f(r + 1)} \cdot \frac{2(r + 1)}{\pi r} = \frac{2}{\pi}.$$

By integration by parts,

$$\int_0^{\pi/2} x^r \cos x \, dx = \frac{1}{r + 1} \int_0^{\pi/2} x^{r+1} \sin x \, dx = \frac{f(r + 1)}{r + 1}.$$

Thus setting $c = -1$ in the given limit yields

$$\lim_{r \to \infty} \frac{(r + 1)f(r)}{r f(r + 1)} = \frac{2}{\pi},$$

as desired.

Remark. The pair (c, L) is uniquely determined by the statement of the problem. To see this, let (c', L') be a second such pair. By taking the ratio of the two limits, we deduce that

$$\lim_{r \to \infty} r^{c'-c} = \frac{L'}{L}.$$

This is impossible if $c' > c$, in which case the limit is ∞, or if $c' < c$, in which case the limit is 0. Hence $c' = c$, which in turn forces $L' = L$.

A4. $(37, 8, 5, \dots, 6, 103, 12, 26)$ 25.4%
  For which positive integers n is there an $n \times n$ matrix with integer entries such that every dot product of a row with itself is even, while every dot product of two different rows is odd?

Answer. Such a matrix exists if and only if n is odd.

Solution. Let I denote the $n \times n$ identity matrix, and let A denote the $n \times n$ matrix all of whose entries are 1. If n is odd, then the matrix $A - I$ satisfies the conditions of the problem: the dot product of any row with itself is $n - 1$, and the dot product of any two distinct rows is $n - 2$.
  Conversely, suppose n is even, and suppose that the matrix M satisfied the conditions of the problem. Consider all matrices and vectors modulo 2. Since the dot product of a row with itself is equal modulo 2 to the sum of the entries of the row, $Mv = 0$ where v is the vector $(1, 1, \dots, 1)$, and so M is singular. On the other hand, $MM^T = A - I$; since

$$(A - I)^2 = A^2 - 2A + I = (n - 2)A + I = I,$$

$(\det M)^2 = \det(A - I) = 1$ and $\det M = 1$, contradicting the fact that M is singular.

A5. $(1, 0, 0, \dots, 0, 0, 15, 181)$ 0.5%
  Let $F : \mathbb{R}^2 \to \mathbb{R}$ and $g : \mathbb{R} \to \mathbb{R}$ be twice continuously differentiable functions with the following properties:

- $F(u, u) = 0$ **for every** $u \in \mathbb{R}$;

- **for every** $x \in \mathbb{R}$, $g(x) > 0$ **and** $x^2 g(x) \le 1$;

- **for every** $(u, v) \in \mathbb{R}^2$, **the vector** $\nabla F(u, v)$ **is either 0 or parallel to the vector** $\langle g(u), -g(v) \rangle$.

Prove that there exists a constant C such that for every $n \ge 2$ and any $x_1, \dots, x_{n+1} \in \mathbb{R}$, we have

$$\min_{i \ne j} |F(x_i, x_j)| \le \frac{C}{n}.$$

Solution. (Abhinav Kumar) Define $G : \mathbb{R} \to \mathbb{R}$ by $G(x) = \int_0^x g(t)\,dt$. By assumption, G is a strictly increasing, thrice continuously differentiable function. It is also bounded: for $x > 1$,

$$0 < G(x) - G(1) = \int_1^x g(t)\,dt \le \int_1^x dt/t^2 = 1,$$

and similarly for $x < -1$, $0 > G(x)-G(-1) \ge -1$. It follows that the image of G is some open interval (A,B) and that $G^{-1} : (A,B) \to \mathbb{R}$ is also thrice continuously differentiable.

Define $H : (A,B) \times (A,B) \to \mathbb{R}$ by $H(x,y) = F(G^{-1}(x), G^{-1}(y))$; it is twice continuously differentiable since F and G^{-1} are. By our assumptions about F,

$$\frac{\partial H}{\partial x} + \frac{\partial H}{\partial y} = \frac{\partial F}{\partial x}(G^{-1}(x), G^{-1}(y)) \cdot \frac{1}{g(G^{-1}(x))}$$
$$+ \frac{\partial F}{\partial y}(G^{-1}(x), G^{-1}(y)) \cdot \frac{1}{g(G^{-1}(y))} = 0.$$

Therefore H is constant along any line parallel to the vector $(1,1)$, or equivalently, $H(x,y)$ depends only on $x - y$. We may thus write $H(x,y) = h(x-y)$ for some function h on $(-(B-A), B-A)$, and then $F(x,y) = h(G(x) - G(y))$. Since $F(u,u) = 0$, $h(0) = 0$. Also, h is twice continuously differentiable (since it can be written as $h(x) = H((A+B+x)/2, (A+B-x)/2)$, so $|h'|$ is bounded on the closed interval $[-(B-A)/2, (B-A)/2]$, say by M.

Given $x_1, \ldots, x_{n+1} \in \mathbb{R}$ for some $n \ge 2$, the numbers $G(x_1), \ldots, G(x_{n+1})$ all belong to (A,B), so there exist indices i and j so that $|G(x_i)-G(x_j)| \le (B-A)/n \le (B-A)/2$. By the mean value theorem,

$$|F(x_i, x_j)| = |h(G(x_i) - G(x_j))| \le M\frac{B-A}{n},$$

so the claim holds with $C = M(B-A)$.

A6. $(1, 1, 1, \ldots, 6, 2, 8, 178)$ 1.5%
Let G be an abelian group with n elements, and let

$$\{g_1 = e, g_2, \ldots, g_k\} \subsetneq G$$

be a (not necessarily minimal) set of distinct generators of G. A special die, which randomly selects one of the elements $g_1, g_2, \ldots, g_k$ with equal probability, is rolled m times, and the selected elements are multiplied to produce an element $g \in G$. Prove that there exists a real number $b \in (0,1)$ such that

$$\lim_{m\to\infty} \frac{1}{b^{2m}} \sum_{x\in G} \left(\text{Prob}(g = x) - \frac{1}{n}\right)^2$$

is positive and finite.

Solution. Choose some ordering $h_1, \ldots, h_n$ of the elements of G with $h_1 = e$. Define an $n \times n$ matrix M by setting $M_{ij} = 1/k$ if $h_j = h_i g$ for some $g \in \{g_1, \ldots, g_k\}$ and $M_{ij} = 0$ otherwise. Let v denote the column vector $(1, 0, \ldots, 0)$. The probability that the product of m random elements of $\{g_1, \ldots, g_k\}$ equals h_i can then be interpreted as the ith component of the vector $M^m v$.

Let $\hat{G}$ denote the dual group of G, that is, the group $\operatorname{Hom}(G, \mathbb{C}^\times)$ of complex-valued characters of G. Let $\hat{e} \in \hat{G}$ denote the trivial character. For each $\chi \in \hat{G}$, the vector $v_\chi = (\chi(h_i))_{i=1}^n$ is an eigenvector of M with eigenvalue

$$\lambda_\chi = \frac{\chi(g_1) + \cdots + \chi(g_k)}{k}.$$

Since $\#\hat{G} = \#G = n$, these form a complete system of eigenvectors of M. In particular, $v_{\hat{e}}$, the all-ones vector, has eigenvalue $\lambda_{\hat{e}} = 1$. Put

$$b = \max\{|\lambda_\chi| : \chi \in \hat{G} - \{\hat{e}\}\};$$

we show that $b \in (0, 1)$ as follows.

First, suppose $b = 0$; then

$$1 = \sum_{\chi \in \hat{G}} \lambda_\chi = \frac{1}{k} \sum_{i=1}^k \sum_{\chi \in \hat{G}} \chi(g_i) = \frac{n}{k},$$

because

$$\sum_{\chi \in \hat{G}} \chi(g) = \begin{cases} n & g = e, \\ 0 & \text{otherwise.} \end{cases} \tag{1}$$

This yields $n = k$, which contradicts the hypothesis that $\{g_1, \ldots, g_k\}$ is not all of G. Hence $b > 0$.

Next, suppose $b = 1$, and choose $\chi \in \hat{G} - \{\hat{e}\}$ with $|\lambda_\chi| = 1$. Now $\chi(g_1), \ldots, \chi(g_k)$ are complex numbers of norm 1 whose sum has norm k, so the triangle inequality forces them all to be equal. Since $\chi(g_1) = \chi(e) = 1$, χ must map each of $g_1, \ldots, g_k$ to 1, and since $\{g_1, \ldots, g_k\}$ is a set of generators for G, it follows that $\chi = 1$ which is a contradiction. Hence $b < 1$.

By (1), $v = \frac{1}{n} \sum_{\chi \in \hat{G}} v_\chi$. Using $M v_\chi = \lambda_\chi v_\chi$,

$$M^m v - \frac{1}{n} v_{\hat{e}} = \frac{1}{n} \sum_{\chi \in \hat{G} - \{\hat{e}\}} \lambda_\chi^m v_\chi.$$

Since the vectors v_χ are pairwise orthogonal with respect to the standard Hermitian inner product on $\mathbb{C}^n$, the limit in question can be written as

$$\lim_{m \to \infty} \frac{1}{b^{2m}} \left(M^m v - \frac{1}{n} v_{\hat{e}}\right) \cdot \left(M^m v - \frac{1}{n} v_{\hat{e}}\right).$$

and then rewritten as

$$\lim_{m \to \infty} \frac{1}{b^{2m}} \sum_{\chi \in \hat{G} - \{\hat{e}\}} |\lambda_\chi|^{2m} = \#\{\chi \in \hat{G} : |\lambda_\chi| = b\}.$$

By construction, this last quantity is nonzero and finite.

Remark. The result fails if we do not assume $g_1 = e$: take $G = \mathbb{Z}/2\mathbb{Z}$, $n = 1$, and $g_1 = 1$.

Remark. (Harm Derksen) A similar argument applies even if G is not assumed to be abelian, provided that the operator $g_1 + \cdots + g_k$ in the group algebra $\mathbb{Z}[G]$ is *normal*, meaning that it commutes with the operator $g_1^{-1} + \cdots + g_k^{-1}$. This includes the cases where the set $\{g_1, \ldots, g_k\}$ is closed under taking inverses and where it is a union of conjugacy classes (which in turn includes the case of G abelian).

Remark. The matrix M used above has nonnegative entries with row sums equal to 1 (that is, it corresponds to a Markov chain), and there exists a positive integer m such that M^m has positive entries. For any such matrix, the Perron-Frobenius theorem implies that the sequence of vectors $M^m v$ converges to a limit w, and there exists $b \in [0, 1)$ such that

$$\limsup_{m \to \infty} \frac{1}{b^{2m}} \sum_{i=1}^{n} ((M^m v - w)_i)^2$$

is nonzero and finite. (The intended interpretation in case $b = 0$ is that $M^m v = w$ for all large m.) However, the lim sup need not equal the lim inf in general.

B1. (105, 8, 12, ..., 9, 9, 48, 6) 63.5%
     Let h and k be positive integers. Prove that for every $\epsilon > 0$, there are positive integers m and n such that

$$\epsilon < |h\sqrt{m} - k\sqrt{n}| < 2\epsilon.$$

Solution 1. We show that for n sufficiently large, the smallest positive integer m for which $h\sqrt{m} > k\sqrt{n} + \epsilon$ has the desired property. Since $h\sqrt{m} - k\sqrt{n} > \epsilon$ by construction, it will suffice to check that $h\sqrt{m} - k\sqrt{n} < 2\epsilon$.
     By the minimality of m,

$$h\sqrt{m-1} \leq k\sqrt{n} + \epsilon.$$

Since

$$\sqrt{m} - \sqrt{m-1} = \frac{m - (m-1)}{\sqrt{m} + \sqrt{m-1}} \leq \frac{1}{2\sqrt{m-1}}$$

and $m > k^2 n / h^2$, for n sufficiently large

$$h(\sqrt{m} - \sqrt{m-1}) < \epsilon$$

and hence

$$h\sqrt{m} - k\sqrt{n} < h\sqrt{m-1} - k\sqrt{n} + \epsilon < 2\epsilon.$$

Solution 2. Since the rational numbers are dense in the reals, there exist positive integers a, b such that

$$\frac{3\epsilon}{hk} < \frac{b}{a} < \frac{4\epsilon}{hk}.$$

By multiplying a and b by a suitably large positive integer, we can also ensure that $3a^2 > b$. Then

$$\frac{\epsilon}{hk} < \frac{b}{3a} < \frac{b}{\sqrt{a^2+b}+a} = \sqrt{a^2+b} - a$$

and

$$\sqrt{a^2+b} - a = \frac{b}{\sqrt{a^2+b}+a} \leq \frac{b}{2a} < 2\frac{\epsilon}{hk}.$$

We may then take $m = k^2(a^2+b), n = h^2a^2$.

Remark. One may discover this solution as follows. First, guess that one can achieve

$$\epsilon < h\sqrt{m} - k\sqrt{n} < 2\epsilon$$

by taking n of the form h^2a^2 for some positive integer a. Since we want $m > k^2a$, let $m = k^2(a^2+b)$ and solve for b.

B2. (141, 7, 14, ..., 6, 15, 12, 2) 82.2%
   Let S be the set of all ordered triples (p,q,r) of prime numbers for which at least one rational number x satisfies $px^2 + qx + r = 0$. Which primes appear in seven or more elements of S?

Answer. Only the primes 2 and 5 appear seven or more times.

Solution. The fact that the primes 2 and 5 appear seven or more times is demonstrated by the examples

$$(2,5,2), (2,5,3), (2,7,5), (2,11,5)$$

and their reversals. It remains to show that if either $\ell = 3$ or ℓ is a prime greater than 5, then ℓ occurs at most six times as an element of a triple in S. Note that $(p,q,r) \in S$ if and only if $q^2 - 4pr = a^2$ for some integer a; in particular, since $4pr \geq 16$, this forces $q \geq 5$. In particular, q is odd, as then is a, and so $q^2 \equiv a^2 \equiv 1$ (mod 8); consequently, one of p, r must equal 2. If $r = 2$, then $8p = q^2 - a^2 = (q+a)(q-a)$; since both factors are of the same sign and their sum is the positive number $2q$, both factors are positive. Since they are also both even, $q+a, q-a \in \{2, 4, 2p, 4p\}$ and so $q \in \{2p+1, p+2\}$. Similarly, if $p = 2$, then $q \in \{2r+1, r+2\}$.

Consequently, ℓ occurs at most twice as many times as there are prime numbers in the list

$$2\ell + 1, \ell + 2, \frac{\ell - 1}{2}, \ell - 2.$$

For $\ell = 3$, $\ell - 2 = 1$ is not prime. For $\ell \geq 7$, the numbers $\ell - 2, \ell, \ell + 2$ cannot all be prime, since one of them is always a nontrivial multiple of 3.

Remark. The above argument shows that the cases listed for 5 are the only ones that can occur. By contrast, there are infinitely many cases where 2 occurs if and only if either the twin prime conjecture holds or there are infinitely many Sophie Germain primes (both of which are expected to be true).

B3. (65, 13, 3, ..., 22, 19, 45, 30) 41.1%

Let f and g be (real-valued) functions defined on an open interval containing 0, with g nonzero and continuous at 0. If fg and f/g are differentiable at 0, must f be differentiable at 0?

Answer. Yes, f must be differentiable at 0.

Solution 1. Note first that because f/g and g are both continuous at 0, so is their product f. If $f(0) \neq 0$, then in some neighborhood of 0, f is either always positive or always negative. We can thus choose $\epsilon \in \{\pm 1\}$ so that ϵf is the composition of the differentiable function $(fg) \cdot (f/g)$ with the square root function. By the chain rule, f is differentiable at 0.

If $f(0) = 0$, then $(f/g)(0) = 0$, so

$$(f/g)'(0) = \lim_{x \to 0} \frac{f(x)}{xg(x)}.$$

Since g is continuous at 0, we may multiply limits to deduce that $\lim_{x \to 0} f(x)/x$ exists.

Solution 2. Choose a neighborhood N of 0 on which $g(x) \neq 0$. Define the following functions on $N \setminus \{0\}$:

$$h_1(x) = \frac{f(x)g(x) - f(0)g(0)}{x},$$

$$h_2(x) = \frac{f(x)g(0) - f(0)g(x)}{xg(0)g(x)},$$

$$h_3(x) = g(0)g(x),$$

$$h_4(x) = \frac{1}{g(x) + g(0)}.$$

By assumption, h_1, h_2, h_3, h_4 all have limits as $x \to 0$. On the other hand,

$$\frac{f(x) - f(0)}{x} = (h_1(x) + h_2(x)h_3(x))h_4(x),$$

and it follows that $\lim_{x \to 0} \frac{f(x) - f(0)}{x}$ exists, as desired.

B4. $(3, 1, 2, \ldots, 15, 20, 54, 102)$ 3.0%

In a tournament, 2011 players meet 2011 times to play a multiplayer game. Every game is played by all 2011 players together and ends with each of the players either winning or losing. The standings are kept in two 2011×2011 matrices, $T = (T_{hk})$ and $W = (W_{hk})$. Initially, $T = W = 0$. After every game, for every (h, k) (including for $h = k$), if players h and k tied (that is, both won or both lost), the entry T_{hk} is increased by 1, while if player h won and player k lost, the entry W_{hk} is increased by 1 and W_{kh} is decreased by 1.

Prove that at the end of the tournament, $\det(T + iW)$ is a nonnegative integer divisible by 2^{2010}.

Solution. Number the games $1, \ldots, 2011$, and let $A = (a_{jk})$ be the 2011×2011 matrix whose (j, k) entry is 1 if player k wins game j and $i = \sqrt{-1}$ if player k loses game j. Then $\overline{a_{hj}} a_{jk}$ is 1 if players h and k tie in game j; i if player h wins and player k loses in game j; and $-i$ if h loses and k wins. It follows that $T + iW = \overline{A}^T A$.

The determinant of A is unaffected by subtracting the first row of A from each of the other rows; this operation produces a matrix whose rows, besides the first one, each consist of integer multiples of $1 - i$. This means that $\det A = (1 - i)^{2010}(a + bi)$ for some integers a, b and that $\det(T + iW) = \det(\overline{A}^T A) = 2^{2010}(a^2 + b^2)$ is a nonnegative integer multiple of 2^{2010}, as desired.

B5. $(12, 3, 2, \ldots, 2, 1, 32, 145)$ 8.6%

Let $a_1, a_2, \ldots$ be real numbers. Suppose that there is a constant A such that for all n,

$$\int_{-\infty}^{\infty} \left(\sum_{i=1}^{n} \frac{1}{1 + (x - a_i)^2} \right)^2 dx \leq An.$$

Prove there is a constant $B > 0$ such that for all n,

$$\sum_{i,j=1}^{n} (1 + (a_i - a_j)^2) \geq Bn^3.$$

Solution. Define the function

$$f(y) = \int_{-\infty}^{\infty} \frac{dx}{(1 + x^2)(1 + (x + y)^2)}.$$

For $y \geq 0$, $-1 \leq x \leq 0$,

$$(1 + x^2)(1 + (x + y)^2) \leq (1 + 1)(1 + (1 + y)^2) = 2y^2 + 4y + 4$$
$$\leq 2y^2 + 4 + 2(y^2 + 1) \leq 6 + 6y^2.$$

This yields the lower bound

$$f(y) \geq \int_{-1}^{0} \frac{dx}{(1 + x^2)(1 + (x + y)^2)} \geq \frac{1}{6(1 + y^2)};$$

the same bound is valid for $y \leq 0$ because $f(y) = f(-y)$.

The original hypothesis can be written as

$$\sum_{i,j=1}^{n} f(a_i - a_j) \leq An$$

and thus implies that

$$\sum_{i,j=1}^{n} \frac{1}{1 + (a_i - a_j)^2} \leq 6An.$$

By the Cauchy-Schwarz inequality or the arithmetic mean/harmonic mean inequality, this implies

$$\sum_{i,j=1}^{n} (1 + (a_i - a_j)^2) \geq Bn^3$$

for $B = 1/(6A)$.

Remark. One can also compute explicitly (using partial fractions, Fourier transforms, or contour integration) that $f(y) = \frac{2\pi}{4+y^2}$.

Remark. (Praveen Venkataramana) The lower bound can be improved to Bn^4 as follows. For each $z \in \mathbb{Z}$, put $Q_{z,n} = \{i \in \{1,\ldots,n\} : a_i \in [z, z + 1)\}$ and $q_{z,n} = \#Q_{z,n}$. Then $\sum_z q_{z,n} = n$ and

$$6An \geq \sum_{i,j=1}^{n} \frac{1}{1 + (a_i - a_j)^2} \geq \sum_{z \in \mathbb{Z}} \frac{1}{2} q_{z,n}^2.$$

If exactly k of the $q_{z,n}$ are nonzero, then $\sum_{z \in \mathbb{Z}} q_{z,n}^2 \geq n^2/k$ by Jensen's inequality (or various other methods), so $k \geq n/(6A)$. Then

$$\sum_{i,j=1}^{n} (1 + (a_i - a_j)^2) \geq n^2 + \sum_{i,j=1}^{k} \max\{0, (|i - j| - 1)^2\}$$

$$\geq n^2 + \frac{k^4}{6} - \frac{2k^3}{3} + \frac{5k^2}{6} - \frac{k}{3}.$$

This is bounded below by Bn^4 for some $B > 0$.

In the opposite direction, one can weaken the initial upper bound to $An^{4/3}$ and still derive a lower bound of Bn^3. The argument is similar.

B6. $(0, 0, 0, \ldots, 0, 0, 38, 159)$ 0.0%

Let p be an odd prime. **Show that for at least $(p + 1)/2$ values of n in** $\{0, 1, 2, \ldots, p - 1\}$,

$$\sum_{k=0}^{p-1} k!\, n^k \qquad \text{is not divisible by } p.$$

Remark. In order to interpret the problem statement, one must choose a convention for the value of 0^0; we will take it to equal 1. (If one takes 0^0 to be 0, then the problem fails for $p = 3$.)

Solution 1. Define the polynomial f over $\mathbb{F}_p$ by

$$f(x) = \sum_{k=0}^{p-1} k!\, x^k.$$

Note that 0 is not a root of f. By Wilson's theorem,

$$k!\,(p - 1 - k)! \equiv (-1)^k (p - 1)! \equiv (-1)^{k+1} \pmod{p},$$

so for $x \not\equiv 0 \pmod{p}$,

$$f(x) \equiv -\sum_{k=0}^{p-1} \frac{(-x)^k}{(p - 1 - k)!} \equiv -x^{p-1} \sum_{k=0}^{p-1} \frac{(-x)^{-k}}{k!} \pmod{p}.$$

Replacing x by $-1/x$, it is thus equivalent to show that the polynomial

$$g(x) = \sum_{k=0}^{p-1} \frac{x^k}{k!}$$

has at most $(p - 1)/2$ nonzero roots in $\mathbb{F}_p$. To see this, write

$$h(x) = x^p - x + g(x)$$

and note that by Wilson's theorem again,

$$h'(x) = -1 + \sum_{k=1}^{p-1} \frac{x^{k-1}}{(k - 1)!} = x^{p-1} - 1 + g(x).$$

If $z \in \mathbb{F}_p$ is a nonzero root of g, then $z^{p-1} = 1$, so $h(z) = h'(z) = 0$ and so z is at least a double root of h. Since h is a polynomial of degree p, there can be at most $(p - 1)/2$ nonzero roots of g in $\mathbb{F}_p$, as desired.

Solution 2. (Noam Elkies) Put $t = (p - 1)/2$; for f as in the first solution, the problem statement is that f has at most t roots modulo p. Suppose the contrary; since $f(0) = 1$, this means that $f(x)$ is nonzero for at most $t - 1$ values of $x \in \mathbb{F}_p^*$. Denote these values by $x_1, \ldots, x_m$, where by assumption $m < t$, and define the polynomial Q over $\mathbb{F}_p$ by

$$Q(x) = \prod_{k=1}^{m}(x - x_m) = \sum_{k=0}^{t-1} Q_k x^k.$$

Then we can write

$$f(x) = \frac{P(x)}{Q(x)}(1 - x^{p-1})$$

where $P(x)$ is some polynomial of degree at most m. Thus the coefficients of $x^t, \ldots, x^{2t-1}$ in $f(x)Q(x) = P(x)(1 - x^{p-1})$ vanish. In other words, the product of the square matrix

$$A = [(i + j + 1)!]_{i,j=0}^{t-1}$$

with the nonzero column vector $(Q_{t-1}, \ldots, Q_0)$ is zero. However, by the following lemma, $\det(A)$ is nonzero modulo p, a contradiction.

Lemma. For any nonnegative integer m and any integer n,

$$\det((i + j + n)!)_{i,j=0}^{m} = \prod_{k=0}^{m} k!\,(k + n)!\,.$$

Proof. Define the $(m+1) \times (m+1)$ matrix $A_{m,n}$ by $(A_{m,n})_{i,j} = \binom{i+j+n}{i}$; the desired result is then that $\det(A_{m,n}) = 1$. Note that

$$(A_{m,n-1})_{i,j} = \begin{cases} (A_{m,n})_{i,j} & i = 0, \\ (A_{m,n})_{i,j} - (A_{m,n})_{i-1,j} & i > 0; \end{cases}$$

that is, $A_{m,n-1}$ can be obtained from $A_{m,n}$ by elementary row operations. Therefore $\det(A_{m,n}) = \det(A_{m,n-1})$, so $\det(A_{m,n})$ depends only on m. The claim now follows by observing that $A_{0,0}$ is the 1×1 matrix with entry 1 and that $A_{m,-1}$ has the block representation $\begin{pmatrix} 1 & * \\ 0 & A_{m-1,0} \end{pmatrix}$. $\qquad\square$

Remark. See http://mathoverflow.net/questions/82648 for a more detailed description by Elkies of the origins of this solution in the theory of orthogonal polynomials.

**The Seventy-Third William Lowell Putnam
Mathematical Competition—December 1, 2012**

A1. $(142, 28, 14, \ldots, 2, 0, 1, 2)$ 97.4%

Let $d_1, d_2, \ldots, d_{12}$ **be real numbers in the open interval** $(1, 12)$. **Show
that there exist distinct indices** i, j, k **such that** d_i, d_j, d_k **are the side lengths
of an acute triangle.**

Solution. Without loss of generality, assume $d_1 \leq d_2 \leq \cdots \leq d_{12}$. If $d_{i+2}^2 <$
$d_i^2 + d_{i+1}^2$ for some $i \leq 10$, then d_i, d_{i+1}, d_{i+2} are the side lengths of an acute
triangle, since in this case $d_i^2 < d_{i+1}^2 + d_{i+2}^2$ and $d_{i+1}^2 < d_i^2 + d_{i+2}^2$ as well. We
may thus assume that $d_{i+2}^2 \geq d_i^2 + d_{i+1}^2$ for all i. But then by induction, $d_i^2 \geq F_i d_1^2$
for all i, where F_i is the ith Fibonacci number (with $F_1 = F_2 = 1$): $i = 1$ is the
tautology $d_1^2 \geq d_1^2$, $i = 2$ follows from $d_2 \geq d_1$, and the induction step follows
from the assumed inequality. Setting $i = 12$ now gives $d_{12}^2 \geq 144 d_1^2$, contradicting
$d_1 > 1$ and $d_{12} < 12$.

Remark. A closely related problem appeared on the 2012 USA Mathematical
Olympiad and USA Junior Mathematical Olympiad.

A2. $(151, 21, 8, \ldots, 0, 0, 7, 2)$ 95.2%

Let $*$ **be a commutative and associative binary operation on a set** S.
Assume that for every x **and** y **in** S, **there exists** z **in** S **such that** $x * z = y$.
(**This** z **may depend on** x **and** y.) **Show that if** a, b, c **are in** S **and** $a * c = b * c$,
then $a = b$.

Solution. Write d for $a * c = b * c \in S$. For some $e \in S$, $d * e = a$, and thus for
$f = c * e$, $a * f = a * c * e = d * e = a$ and $b * f = b * c * e = d * e = a$. Let $g \in S$
satisfy $g * a = b$; then $b = g * a = g * (a * f) = (g * a) * f = b * f = a$, as desired.

Remark. With slightly more work, one can show that S, if nonempty, forms an
abelian group with the operation $*$. One can also drop the commutativity condition: if $\star$ is an associative binary operation on a nonempty set S such that for
every $a, b \in S$, there exist $c, d \in S$ such that $a \star c = d \star a = b$, then S forms a
group with the operation $\star$.

A3. $(49, 31, 13, \ldots, 16, 11, 25, 44)$ 49.2%

Let $f : [-1, 1] \to \mathbb{R}$ **be a continuous function such that**

(i) $f(x) = \frac{2 - x^2}{2} f\left(\frac{x^2}{2 - x^2}\right)$ **for every** x **in** $[-1, 1]$,

(ii) $f(0) = 1$, **and**

(iii) $\lim_{x \to 1^-} \frac{f(x)}{\sqrt{1 - x}}$ **exists and is finite.**

Prove that f is unique, and express $f(x)$ in closed form.

Answer. The only solution is $f(x) = \sqrt{1 - x^2}$.

Solution. Define the function $f_0 : [-1, 1] \to \mathbb{R}$ by $f_0(x) = \sqrt{1 - x^2}$. We first verify that f_0 is a solution. To check (i), write

$$\frac{2 - x^2}{2} \sqrt{1 - \left(\frac{x^2}{2 - x^2}\right)^2} = \frac{1}{2}\sqrt{(2 - x^2)^2 - x^4} = \sqrt{1 - x^2}.$$

From the definition of f_0, (ii) holds. To check (iii), write

$$\frac{f(x)}{\sqrt{1 - x}} = \sqrt{1 + x}$$

and note that this has the finite limit $\sqrt{2}$ as $x \to 1^-$.

We next verify that f_0 is the only possible solution. Define $g : (-1, 1) \to \mathbb{R}$ by $g(x) = f(x)/f_0(x)$. Dividing equation (i) for f by the same equation for f_0 yields

$$g(x) = g\left(\frac{x^2}{2 - x^2}\right) \tag{1}$$

for all $x \in (-1, 1)$. Now fix $x \in (-1, 1)$ and define a sequence $\{a_n\}_{n=1}^{\infty}$ by $a_1 = x$ and $a_{n+1} = \frac{a_n^2}{2 - a_n^2}$. Then $a_n \in (-1, 1)$ and thus $|a_{n+1}| \leq |a_n|^2$ for all n. It follows that $\{|a_n|\}$ is a decreasing sequence with $|a_n| \leq |x|^n$ for all n, and so $\lim_{n \to \infty} a_n = 0$. Since $g(a_n) = g(x)$ for all n by (1) and g is continuous at 0, $g(x) = g(0) = f(0) = 1$. This gives $f(x) = \sqrt{1 - x^2}$ for all $x \in (-1, 1)$ and thus for $x = \pm 1$ as well by continuity.

Remark. As pointed out by Noam Elkies, condition (iii) is unnecessary for this solution. However, one can use it to derive a slightly different solution by running the recursion in the opposite direction. To wit, (1) implies that g is an even function of x, so we need only check that g is constant on $(0, 1)$. Given $x \in (0, 1)$, define the sequence $\{b_n\}_{n=1}^{\infty}$ by $b_1 = x$ and $b_{n+1} = \sqrt{\frac{2b_n}{b_n + 1}}$. Then $b_n = \frac{b_{n+1}^2}{2 - b_{n+1}^2}$, so by (1), $g(b_n) = g(x)$ for all n. Given that $b_n \in (0, 1)$, $2b_n < b_n + 1 < 2$ and so $b_n < b_{n+1} < 1$. Since the sequence $\{b_n\}$ is monotone increasing with values in $(0, 1)$, it tends to a limit $L \in (0, 1]$ which must satisfy $L = \sqrt{\frac{2L}{L+1}}$; the only solution of this equation is $L = 1$. By (iii), g admits a limit as $x \to 1^-$, so $g(x)$ must be equal to this limit.

Remark. A key difficulty in finding this solution is making the identification of the function f_0. One way to do this is via a sequence of algebraic substitutions that makes the functional equation (i) progressively simpler. To begin with, one may eliminate the unwieldy multiplier $2 - x^2$ by setting $g(x) = xf(1/x)$. This puts (i) into the form

$$xg\left(\frac{1}{x}\right) = f(x) = \frac{x^2}{2}g\left(\frac{2 - x^2}{x^2}\right),$$

and substituting x for $1/x$ yields

$$2xg(x) = g(2x^2 - 1).$$

Noting that the factor $2x^2 - 1$ appears in the duplication formula for cosh, we set $h(x) = g(\cosh x)$ for $x \geq 0$. In this notation, (i) becomes

$$2h(x)\cosh x = h(2x).$$

Now recalling the duplication formula for sinh, we finally set $j(x) = h(x)\sinh x$ for $x > 0$. In this notation, (i) becomes

$$j(2x) = j(x)$$

and at this point one may guess (and then prove as above) that j is constant.

A4. $(5, 0, 0, \ldots, 0, 2, 97, 85)$ 2.6%

Let q and r be integers with $q > 0$, and let A and B be intervals on the real line. Let T be the set of all $b + mq$ where b and m are integers with b in B, and let S be the set of all integers a in A such that ra is in T. Show that if the product of the lengths of A and B is less than q, then S is the intersection of A with some arithmetic progression.

Remark. The problem phrasing is somewhat confusing: to say that "S is the intersection of [the interval] A with an arithmetic progression" is the same thing as saying that "S is the empty set or an arithmetic progression" unless it is implied that arithmetic progressions are necessarily infinite. Under that interpretation, however, the problem becomes false; for instance, for

$$q = 5, r = 1, A = [1, 3], B = [0, 2],$$

we have

$$T = \{\ldots, 0, 1, 2, 5, 6, 7, \ldots\}, S = \{1, 2\}.$$

Solution 1. We begin with a lemma.

Lemma. Let S be a nonempty finite set of integers with the following property:

For all $a, b, c \in S$ with $a \leq b \leq c$, we also have $a + c - b \in S$.   (2)

Then S is an arithmetic progression.

Proof. We may assume $\#S \geq 3$, as otherwise S is automatically empty or an arithmetic progression. Let a_1, a_2 be the smallest and second-smallest elements of S, respectively, and put $d = a_2 - a_1$. Let m be the smallest positive integer such that $a_1 + md \notin S$. Suppose that there exists an integer n in the set $S \setminus \{a_1, a_1 + d, \ldots, a_1 + (m-1)d\}$, and choose the least such n. By (2) applied with $(a, b, c) = (a_1, a_2, n)$, $n - d \in S \setminus \{a_1, a_1 + d, \ldots, a_1 + (m-1)d\}$, a contradiction. $\square$

Returning to the problem at hand, by dividing B, q, r by $\gcd(q, r)$ we may reduce to the case where $\gcd(q, r) = 1$. We may also assume $\#S \geq 3$, as otherwise S is automatically empty or an arithmetic progression. Let a_1, a_2, a_3 be elements of S for which $a_1 < a_2 < a_3$, and write $ra_i = b_i + m_i q$ with $b_i, m_i \in \mathbb{Z}$ and $b_i \in B$. Note that b_1, b_2, b_3 must also be distinct, so the differences $b_2 - b_1, b_3 - b_1, b_3 - b_2$ are all nonzero; consequently, two of them have the same sign. If $b_i - b_j$ and $b_k - b_l$ have the same sign, then

$$(a_i - a_j)(b_k - b_l) = (b_i - b_j)(a_k - a_l)$$

because both sides are of the same sign, of absolute value less than q, and congruent to each other modulo q. This means that the points $(a_1, b_1), (a_2, b_2), (a_3, b_3)$ in $\mathbb{R}^2$ are collinear. It follows that $a_4 = a_1 + a_3 - a_2$ also belongs to S (by taking $b_4 = b_1 + b_3 - b_2$), so S satisfies the conditions of the lemma. It is therefore an arithmetic progression.

Reinterpretation. One can also interpret this argument geometrically using cross products (suggested by Noam Elkies), or directly in terms of congruences (suggested by Karl Mahlburg).

Solution 2. Assume that the product of the lengths of A and B is less than q. Define the matrix

$$M = \begin{pmatrix} 1 & 0 \\ r & q \end{pmatrix}$$

and the lattice $\Lambda = M\mathbb{Z}^2$ in $\mathbb{Z}^2$. We show that the points of $\Lambda \cap (A \times B)$ are all collinear. Suppose the contrary; then there must be three points of $\Lambda \cap (A \times B)$ which are not collinear. The triangle with those vertices would have area at least $(1/2)\det(M) = q/2$. However, a triangle in a rectangle can have area at most half that of the rectangle, and the rectangle has area less than q, a contradiction.

Since the points of $\Lambda \cap (A \times B)$ are all collinear, they all lie on some line L. The lattice points on L form an arithmetic progression. Also, the rectangle $A \times B$ is convex, so the intersection of L with the rectangle is a line segment. The set S is just the set of x-coordinates of the lattice points on this segment, so they form a segment of an arithmetic progression.

A5. (8, 0, 1, ..., 3, 2, 60, 115) 4.8%

Let $\mathbb{F}_p$ denote the field of integers modulo a prime p, and let n be a positive integer. Let v be a fixed vector in $\mathbb{F}_p^n$, let M be an $n \times n$ matrix with entries in $\mathbb{F}_p$, and define $G : \mathbb{F}_p^n \to \mathbb{F}_p^n$ by $G(x) = v + Mx$. Let $G^{(k)}$ denote the k-fold composition of G with itself, that is, $G^{(1)}(x) = G(x)$ and $G^{(k+1)}(x) = G(G^{(k)}(x))$. Determine all pairs p, n for which there exist v and M such that the p^n vectors $G^{(k)}(0)$, $k = 1, 2, \ldots, p^n$ are distinct.

Answer. The pairs (p, n) with the specified property are those pairs with $n = 1$, together with the single pair $(2, 2)$.

Solution. We first check that these pairs do work. For $n = 1$, taking $v = (1)$ and $M = (1)$ has the desired effect. For $(p, n) = (2, 2)$, we take $v = \begin{pmatrix} 0 \\ 1 \end{pmatrix}$ and $M = \begin{pmatrix} 1 & 1 \\ 0 & 1 \end{pmatrix}$ and then observe that

$$G^{(k)}(0) = \begin{pmatrix} 0 \\ 1 \end{pmatrix}, \begin{pmatrix} 1 \\ 0 \end{pmatrix}, \begin{pmatrix} 1 \\ 1 \end{pmatrix}, \begin{pmatrix} 0 \\ 0 \end{pmatrix}, \quad k = 1, 2, 3, 4.$$

We next check that no other pairs work, keeping in mind that the desired condition means that G acts on $\mathbb{F}_p^n$ as a cyclic permutation. Assume by way of contradiction that (p, n) has the desired property but does not appear in our list. In particular, $n \geq 2$.

For every positive integer k, $G^{(k)}(0) = v + Mv + \cdots + M^{k-1}v$. In particular,

$$0 = G^{(p^n)}(0) = v + Mv + \cdots + M^{p^n-1}v.$$

Multiplying by M and combining the two expressions yields $M^{p^n}v = v$. But then, for all $k \geq 1$,

$$M^{p^n} G^{(k)}v = M^{p^n}(v + Mv + \cdots + M^k v)$$
$$= v + Mv + \cdots + M^k v = G^{(k)}v.$$

Since by hypothesis, the vectors $G^{(k)}v$ exhaust $\mathbb{F}_p^n$, we conclude that $M^{p^n} = I$ is the identity matrix. It follows that $N = M - I$ has the property that

$$N^{p^n} = M^{p^n} - I^{p^n} = 0.$$

Since N is a nilpotent $n \times n$ matrix, $N^n = 0$.

For any positive integer k,

$$G^{(k)}(0) = v + Mv + \cdots + M^{k-1}v$$

$$= \sum_{j=0}^{k-1} \sum_{i=0}^{n-1} \binom{j}{i} N^i v$$

$$= \sum_{i=0}^{n-1} \binom{k}{i+1} N^i v.$$

If $n \geq 2$ and $(p, n) \neq (2, 2)$, then $p^{n-1} > n$ and so $G^k(0) = 0$ for $k = p^{n-1}$ (because all of the binomial coefficients are divisible by p). This contradiction completes the proof.

A6. $(3, 3, 0, \ldots, 0, 0, 52, 131)$ 3.2%

Let $f(x, y)$ **be a continuous, real-valued function on** $\mathbb{R}^2$. **Suppose that, for every rectangular region** R **of area 1, the double integral of** $f(x, y)$ **over** R **equals 0. Must** $f(x, y)$ **be identically 0?**

Answer. Yes, f must be identically 0.

Solution 1. (Eric Larson, via Noam Elkies) In this solution, we fix coordinates and assume only that the double integral vanishes on each rectangular region of area 1 with sides parallel to the coordinate axes, and still conclude that f must be identically 0.

Lemma. Let R be a rectangular region of area 1 with sides parallel to the coordinate axes. Then the averages of f over any two adjacent sides of R are equal.

Proof. Without loss of generality, we may take R to have corners $(0, 0), (c, 0)$, $(c, 1/c), (0, 1/c)$ and consider the two sides adjacent to $(c, 1/c)$. Differentiate the equality

$$0 = \int_{x}^{x+c} \int_{y}^{y+1/c} f(u, v)\, du\, dv$$

with respect to c to obtain

$$0 = \int_{y}^{y+1/c} f(x + c, v)\, dv - \frac{1}{c^2} \int_{x}^{x+c} f(u, y + 1/c)\, du.$$

Rearranging yields

$$c \int_{y}^{y+1/c} f(x + c, v)\, dv = \frac{1}{c} \int_{x}^{x+c} f(u, y + 1/c)\, du,$$

which asserts the desired result. $\qquad\square$

Returning to the problem at hand, given $c > 0$, tile the plane with rectangles of area 1 whose vertices lie in the lattice $\{(mc, n/c) : m, n \in \mathbb{Z}\}$. By repeated application of the lemma, for any positive integer n,

$$\int_0^c f(u, 0)\, du = \int_{nc}^{(n+1)c} f(u, 0)\, du.$$

Replacing c with c/n, we obtain

$$\int_0^{c/n} f(u, 0)\, du = \int_c^{c+1/n} f(u, 0)\, du.$$

Fixing c and taking the limit as $n \to \infty$ yields $f(0, 0) = f(c, 0)$. By similar reasoning, f is constant on any horizontal line and on any vertical line, and so is constant. By integrating over any rectangle, the constant value is forced to be 0.

Solution 2. (Sergei Artamoshin) We retain the weaker hypothesis of the first solution. Assume by way of contradiction that f is not identically zero.

We first exhibit a vertical segment $\overline{PQ}$ with $f(P) > 0$ and $f(Q) < 0$. It cannot be the case that $f(P) \leq 0$ for all P, as otherwise the vanishing of the integral over any rectangle would force f to vanish identically. By continuity, there must exist an open disc U such that $f(P) > 0$ for all $P \in U$. Choose a rectangle R of area 1 with sides parallel to the coordinate axes with one horizontal edge contained in U. Since the integral of f over R is zero, there must exist a point $Q \in R$ such that $f(Q) < 0$. Take P to be the vertical projection of Q onto the edge of R contained in U.

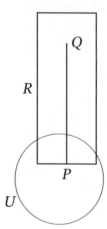

By translating coordinates, we may assume that $P = (0, 0)$ and $Q = (0, a)$ for some $a > 0$. For s sufficiently small, f is positive on the square of side length $2s$ centered at P, which we call S, and negative on the square of side length $2s$

centered at Q, which we call S'. Since the ratio $2s/(1 - 4s^2)$ tends to 0 as s does, we may choose s so that $2s/(1 - 4s^2) = a/n$ for some positive integer n.

For $j \in \mathbb{Z}$, let A_j be the rectangle

$$\left\{ (x,y) : s \leq x \leq s + \frac{1 - 4s^2}{2s}, -s + j\frac{2s}{1 - 4s^2} \leq y \leq s + j\frac{2s}{1 - 4s^2} \right\}$$

and let B_j be the rectangle

$$\left\{ (x,y) : s \leq x \leq s + \frac{1 - 4s^2}{2s}, s + j\frac{2s}{1 - 4s^2} \leq y \leq -s + (j+1)\frac{2s}{1 - 4s^2} \right\}.$$

Then for all $j \in \mathbb{Z}$,

$$S \cup A_0, A_n \cup S', A_j \cup B_j, B_j \cup A_{j+1}$$

are all rectangles of area 1 with sides parallel to the coordinate axes: the first two each have one side of length $2s$ and one of length $2s + \frac{1-4s^2}{2s}$, while the last two each have one side of length $\frac{1-4s^2}{2s}$ and one side of length $\frac{2s}{1-4s^2}$. By hypothesis, the integral over f over each of these rectangles is zero. Since the integral over S is positive, the integral over A_0 must be negative. By induction, for all $j \in \mathbb{Z}$ the integral over A_j is negative and the integral over B_j is positive. But this forces the integral over S' to be positive whereas f is negative everywhere on S', a contradiction.

B1. (174, 9, 0, ..., 3, 2, 0, 1) 96.8%

Let S be a class of functions from $[0, \infty)$ to $[0, \infty)$ that satisfies:

(i) The functions $f_1(x) = e^x - 1$ and $f_2(x) = \ln(x + 1)$ are in S;

(ii) If $f(x)$ and $g(x)$ are in S, the functions $f(x) + g(x)$ and $f(g(x))$ are in S;

(iii) If $f(x)$ and $g(x)$ are in S and $f(x) \geq g(x)$ for all $x \geq 0$, then the function $f(x) - g(x)$ is in S.

Prove that if $f(x)$ and $g(x)$ are in S, then the function $f(x)g(x)$ is also in S.

Solution. Each of the following functions belongs to S for the reasons indicated.

$f(x), g(x)$	given
$\log(x + 1)$	(i)
$\log(f(x) + 1), \log(g(x) + 1)$	(ii) plus two previous lines
$\log(f(x) + 1) + \log(g(x) + 1)$	(ii)
$e^x - 1$	(i)
$(f(x) + 1)(g(x) + 1) - 1$	(ii) plus two previous lines
$f(x)g(x) + f(x) + g(x)$	previous line
$f(x) + g(x)$	(ii) plus first line
$f(x)g(x)$	(iii) plus two previous lines

B2. (84, 14, 12, ..., 20, 17, 20, 22) 58.2%

Let P be a given (nondegenerate) polyhedron. Prove that there is a constant $c(P) > 0$ with the following property: If a collection of n balls whose volumes sum to V contains the entire surface of P, then $n > c(P)/V^2$.

Solution. Fix a face F of the polyhedron with area A. Suppose F is completely covered by balls of radii $r_1, \ldots, r_n$ whose volumes sum to V. Then on one hand,

$$\sum_{i=1}^{n} \frac{4}{3}\pi r_i^3 = V.$$

On the other hand, the intersection of a ball of radius r with the plane containing F is a disc of radius at most r, which covers a subset of F of area at most πr^2; therefore

$$\sum_{i=1}^{n} \pi r_i^2 \geq A.$$

By writing n as $\sum_{i=1}^{n} 1$ and applying Hölder's inequality, we obtain

$$nV^2 \geq \left(\sum_{i=1}^{n} \left(\frac{4}{3}\pi r_i^3 \right)^{2/3} \right)^3 \geq \frac{16}{9\pi} A^3.$$

Consequently, any value of $c(P)$ less than $\frac{16}{9\pi} A^3$ works.

B3. (44, 2, 3, ..., 4, 27, 48, 61) 25.9%

A round-robin tournament among $2n$ teams lasted for $2n - 1$ days, as follows. On each day, every team played one game against another team, with one team winning and one team losing in each of the n games. Over the course of the tournament, each team played every other team exactly once. Can one necessarily choose one winning team from each day without choosing any team more than once?

Answer. Yes, such a choice is always possible.

Solution. Note first that for any collection of m days with $1 \leq m \leq 2n-1$, there must be at least m distinct teams that won a game on at least one of those days. Namely, if this were not the case, then any of the teams that lost games on all of those days would in particular have lost to m other teams, a contradiction.

Now construct a bipartite graph whose vertices are the $2n$ teams and $2n - 1$ days, with an edge linking a day to a team if that team won their game on that day. In this graph, any collection of m days is connected to a total of at least m teams; it follows from Hall's marriage theorem that one can match the $2n - 1$ days with $2n - 1$ distinct teams that won on their respective days, as desired.

B4. (25, 3, 0, ..., 3, 1, 95, 62) 14.8%

Suppose that $a_0 = 1$ and that $a_{n+1} = a_n + e^{-a_n}$ for $n = 0, 1, 2, \ldots$. Does $a_n - \log n$ have a finite limit as $n \to \infty$? (Here $\log n = \log_e n = \ln n$.)

Answer. Yes, the limit exists.

Solution 1. For all real x, $e^x \geq 1 + x$; thus for all $x > -1$,

$$x \geq \log(1 + x). \tag{1}$$

We next check that $a_n > \log(n + 1)$ (and in particular that $a_n - \log n > 0$) for all n, by induction on n. For $n = 0$ this follows from $a_0 = 1$. Now suppose that $a_n > \log(n + 1)$, and define $f(x) = x + e^{-x}$, which is an increasing function in $x > 0$. We then have

$$a_{n+1} = f(a_n) > f(\log(n + 1))$$
$$= \log(n + 1) + 1/(n + 1) \geq \log(n + 2),$$

where the last inequality is (1) with $x = 1/(n + 1)$. This completes the induction step.

It follows that $a_n - \log n$ is a decreasing function in n, as

$$(a_{n+1} - \log(n + 1)) - (a_n - \log n) = e^{-a_n} + \log(n/(n + 1))$$
$$< 1/(n + 1) + \log(n/(n + 1)) \leq 0,$$

where the final inequality is (1) with $x = -1/(n + 1)$. Thus $\{a_n - \log n\}_{n=0}^{\infty}$ is a decreasing sequence of positive numbers, and so it has a limit as $n \to \infty$.

Solution 2. Put $b_n = e^{a_n}$, so that $b_{n+1} = b_n e^{1/b_n}$. In terms of the b_n, the problem is to prove that b_n/n has a limit as $n \to \infty$; we will show that the limit is in fact equal to 1.

Expanding e^{1/b_n} as a Taylor series in $1/b_n$ and using Taylor's theorem with remainder yields

$$b_{n+1} = b_n + 1 + R_n,$$

where $0 \leq R_n \leq c/b_n$ for some absolute constant $c > 0$. By writing

$$b_n = n + e + \sum_{i=0}^{n-1} R_i,$$

we obtain $b_n \geq n + e$ and then

$$0 \leq \frac{b_n}{n} - 1 \leq \frac{e}{n} + \sum_{i=0}^{n-1} \frac{R_i}{n}$$

$$\leq \frac{e}{n} + \sum_{i=0}^{n-1} \frac{c}{nb_i}$$

$$\leq \frac{e}{n} + \sum_{i=0}^{n-1} \frac{c}{n(i+e)} \leq \frac{e}{n} + \frac{c \log n}{n}.$$

It follows that $b_n/n \to 1$ as $n \to \infty$.

Remark. This problem is an example of the general principle (also seen in 2006B6) that one can often predict the asymptotic behavior of a recursive sequence by studying solutions of a similar differential equation. In this case, we start with the equation $a_{n+1} - a_n = e^{-a_n}$, then replace a_n with a function $y(x)$ and replace the difference $a_{n+1} - a_n$ with the derivative $y'(x)$ to obtain the differential equation $y' = e^{-y}$, which indeed has the solution $y = \log x$.

B5. $(2, 0, 1, \ldots, 0, 1, 18, 167)$ 1.6%
    Prove that, for any two bounded functions $g_1, g_2 : \mathbb{R} \to [1, \infty)$, there exist functions $h_1, h_2 : \mathbb{R} \to \mathbb{R}$ such that, for every $x \in \mathbb{R}$,

$$\sup_{s \in \mathbb{R}}(g_1(s)^x g_2(s)) = \max_{t \in \mathbb{R}}(x h_1(t) + h_2(t)).$$

Solution. Define the function

$$f(x) = \sup_{s \in \mathbb{R}}\{x \log g_1(s) + \log g_2(s)\}.$$

As a function of x, f is the supremum of a collection of affine functions, so it is convex. The function

$$e^{f(x)} = \sup_{s \in \mathbb{R}}\{g_1(s)^x g_2(s)\}$$

is then also convex, as may be checked directly from the definition: for $x_1, x_2 \in \mathbb{R}$ and $t \in [0, 1]$, by the weighted arithmetic mean/geometric mean inequality

$$t e^{f(x_1)} + (1 - t)e^{f(x_2)} \geq e^{tf(x_1) + (1-t)f(x_2)}$$

$$\geq e^{f(tx_1 + (1-t)x_2)}.$$

For each $t \in \mathbb{R}$, draw a *supporting line* to the graph of $e^{f(x)}$ at $x = t$. For example, the one-sided derivative $(e^f)'_-(t)$ exists, and by convexity, the supporting line $\ell_t(x) = (e^f)'_-(t) \cdot (x - t) + e^{f(t)}$ lies below the graph of $e^{f(x)}$ with equality for

$x = t$. Note that $\ell_t(x) = xh_1(t) + h_2(t)$ for some $h_1(t), h_2(t) \in \mathbb{R}$. For all x, we then have

$$\sup_{s \in \mathbb{R}} \{g_1(s)^x g_2(s)\} \geq xh_1(t) + h_2(t)$$

with equality for $x = t$. This proves the desired equality (including the fact that the maximum on the right side is achieved).

Reinterpretation. The function $f(x)$ is the *convex dual* of the pair of functions $\log g_1(s), \log g_2(s)$.

B6. $(15, 0, 0, \ldots, 3, 10, 33, 128)$ 7.9%

Let p **be an odd prime number such that** $p \equiv 2 \pmod 3$. **Define a permutation** π **of the residue classes modulo** p **by** $\pi(x) \equiv x^3 \pmod p$. **Show that** π **is an even permutation if and only if** $p \equiv 3 \pmod 4$.

Solution 1. Since fixed points do not affect the sign of a permutation, we may ignore the residue class of 0 and consider π as a permutation on the nonzero residue classes modulo p. These form a cyclic group of order $p - 1$, so the sign of π is also the sign of multiplication by 3 as a permutation σ of the residue classes modulo $p - 1$. If we identify these classes with the integers $0, \ldots, p - 2$, then the sign is given by the parity of the number of *inversions*: these are the pairs (i, j) with $0 \leq i < j \leq p - 2$ for which $\sigma(i) > \sigma(j)$. Write

$$\sigma(i) = 3i - (p - 1)q_i$$

where

$$q_i = \left\lfloor \frac{3i}{p - 1} \right\rfloor$$

is either 0, 1, or 2; then (i, j) cannot be an inversion unless $q_i < q_j$ (and, in particular, q_i is 0 or 1).

If $q_i = 0$, that is, $i < (p-1)/3$, the elements $j \in \{0, \ldots, p-2\}$ for which (i, j) is an inversion correspond to the elements $\sigma(j) \in \{0, \ldots, 3i\}$ which are not multiples of 3, which are $2i$ in number. This contributes a total of $0 + 2 + \cdots + 2(p-2)/3 = (p-2)(p+1)/9$ inversions.

If $q_i = 1$, that is, $(p-1)/3 < i < 2(p-1)/3$, the elements j of $\{0, \ldots, p-2\}$ for which (i, j) is an inversion correspond to the elements $\sigma(j) \in \{0, \ldots, 3i - p + 1\}$ congruent to 1 modulo 3, which are $(3i - p + 2)/3 = i - (p-2)/3$ in number. This contributes a total of $1 + 2 + \cdots + (p-2)/3 = (p-2)(p+1)/18$ inversions.

The total number of inversions is $(p-2)(p+1)/6$, which is even if and only if $p \equiv 3 \pmod 4$. This proves the claim.

Solution 2. (Mark van Hoeij) We compute the parity of π as the parity of the number of cycles of even length in the cycle decomposition of π. For any positive integer n, let $(\mathbb{Z}/n\mathbb{Z})^*$ denote the multiplicative group of nonzero residue classes modulo n (in other words, the group of units of the commutative ring $\mathbb{Z}/n\mathbb{Z}$).

For $x \in (\mathbb{Z}/p\mathbb{Z})^*$ of order d, the elements of the orbit of x under π also have order d (because d divides $p - 1$ and hence is coprime to 3). Since $(\mathbb{Z}/p\mathbb{Z})^*$ is cyclic of order $p - 1$, the elements of order d constitute $\varphi(d)/f(d)$ orbits under π, where φ is the Euler phi function and $f(d)$ is the order of 3 in $(\mathbb{Z}/d\mathbb{Z})^*$. The parity of π is then the parity of the sum of $\varphi(d)/f(d)$ over all divisors d of $p - 1$ for which $f(d)$ is even.

If d is odd, then $\varphi(d)/f(d) = \varphi(2d)/f(2d)$, so the summands corresponding to d and $2d$ coincide. It thus suffices to consider those d divisible by 4. If $p \equiv 3$ (mod 4), then there are no such summands, so the sum is vacuously even.

If $p \equiv 1$ (mod 4), then $d = 4$ contributes a summand of $\varphi(4)/f(4) = 2/2 = 1$. For each d which is a larger multiple of 4, $(\mathbb{Z}/d\mathbb{Z})^*$ is isomorphic to the product of $\mathbb{Z}/2\mathbb{Z}$ with another group of even order, so the maximal power of 2 dividing $f(d)$ is strictly smaller than the maximal power of 2 dividing d. Hence $\varphi(d)/f(d)$ is even, and so the overall sum is odd.

Solution 3. (Noam Elkies) Recall that the sign of π (which is $+1$ if π is even and -1 if π is odd) can be computed as

$$\operatorname{sgn} \pi = \prod_{0 \le x < y < p} \frac{\pi(x) - \pi(y)}{x - y}$$

(because composing π with a transposition changes the sign of the product). Modulo p, this is the same as

$$\prod_{0 \le x < y < p} \frac{x^3 - y^3}{x - y} = \prod_{0 \le x < y < p} (x^2 + xy + y^2).$$

It thus suffices to count the number of times each nonzero residue class modulo p occurs as the value of $x^2 + xy + y^2$ in the final product. The class c occurs $p + 1$ times with $0 \le x, y < p$ and hence $(p + \chi(c/3))/2$ times with $0 \le x < y < p$, where χ denotes the quadratic character modulo p. Since $p \equiv 2$ (mod 3), by the law of quadratic reciprocity $\chi(-3) = +1$, so $\chi(c/3) = \chi(-c)$. It thus remains to evaluate the product $\prod_{c=1}^{p-1} c^{(p+\chi(-c))/2}$ modulo p.

If $p \equiv 3$ (mod 4), then each factor is a quadratic residue (this is automatic if c is a residue, and otherwise $\chi(-c) = +1$ so $p + \chi(-c)$ is divisible by 4), so $\prod_{c=1}^{p-1} c^{(p+\chi(-c))/2} \equiv +1$ (mod p).

If $p \equiv 1$ (mod 4), we must do more work: we choose a generator g of $(\mathbb{Z}/p\mathbb{Z})^*$ (that is, a primitive root modulo p) and rewrite the product as

$$\prod_{i=0}^{p-2} g^{i(p+(-1)^i)/2}.$$

The sum of the exponents, split into sums over i odd and i even, gives

$$\sum_{j=0}^{(p-3)/2} \left(j(p+1) + \frac{(2j+1)(p-1)}{2} \right)$$

which simplifies to

$$\frac{(p-3)(p-1)(p+1)}{8} + \frac{(p-1)^3}{8} = \frac{p-1}{2}\left(\frac{p^2-1}{2} - p \right).$$

Hence $\prod_{c=1}^{p-1} c^{(p+\chi(-c))/2} \equiv g^{(p-1)/2} \equiv -1$ modulo p.

Remark. Note that the third proof uses quadratic reciprocity, whereas the first and second proofs are similar to several classical proofs of quadratic reciprocity. Abhinav Kumar notes that the problem itself is a special case of the Duke–Hopkins quadratic reciprocity law for abelian groups [**DH**] (see also [**Clar**]).

The Seventy-Fourth William Lowell Putnam
Mathematical Competition—December 7, 2013

A1. $(184, 3, 5, \ldots, 5, 0, 3, 1)$ 95.5%

   Recall that a regular icosahedron is a convex polyhedron having 12 vertices and 20 faces; the faces are congruent equilateral triangles. On each face of a regular icosahedron is written a nonnegative integer such that the sum of all 20 integers is 39. Show that there are two faces that share a vertex and have the same integer written on them.

Solution 1. Suppose otherwise. Then each vertex v is a vertex for five faces, all of which have different labels, and so the sum of the labels of the five faces incident to v is at least $0 + 1 + 2 + 3 + 4 = 10$. Adding this sum over all vertices v gives $3 \times 39 = 117$, since each face's label is counted three times. Since there are 12 vertices, we conclude that $10 \times 12 \leq 117$, a contradiction.

Solution 2. Suppose otherwise. Since there are just 12 vertices, any collection of five faces must contain two faces that share a vertex. It follows that each label can appear at most four times, and so the sum of all labels is at least $4(0+1+2+3+4) = 40 > 39$, a contradiction.

A2. $(153, 20, 8, \ldots, 2, 1, 9, 8)$ 90.0%

   Let S be the set of all positive integers that are *not* perfect squares. For n in S, consider choices of integers $a_1, a_2, \ldots, a_r$ such that $n < a_1 < a_2 < \cdots < a_r$ and $n \cdot a_1 \cdot a_2 \cdots a_r$ is a perfect square, and let $f(n)$ be the minimum of a_r over all such choices. For example, $2 \cdot 3 \cdot 6$ is a perfect square, while $2 \cdot 3, 2 \cdot 4, 2 \cdot 5, 2 \cdot 3 \cdot 4, 2 \cdot 3 \cdot 5, 2 \cdot 4 \cdot 5$, and $2 \cdot 3 \cdot 4 \cdot 5$ are not, and so $f(2) = 6$. Show that the function f from S to the integers is one-to-one.

Solution. Suppose to the contrary that $f(n) = f(m)$ with $n < m$, and let $n \cdot a_1 \cdots a_r$, $m \cdot b_1 \cdots b_s$ be perfect squares where $n < a_1 < \cdots < a_r$, $m < b_1 < \cdots < b_s$, a_r, b_s are minimal and $a_r = b_s$. Then $(n \cdot a_1 \cdots a_r) \cdot (m \cdot b_1 \cdots b_s)$ is also a perfect square. Now eliminate any factor in this product that appears twice by removing from the products any $a_i = b_j$ for some i, j. The product of what remains must also be a perfect square, but this is now a product of distinct integers, the smallest of which is n and the largest of which is strictly smaller than $a_r = b_s$. This contradicts the minimality of a_r.

Remark. Sequences whose product is a perfect square occur naturally in the *quadratic sieve* algorithm for factoring large integers. However, the behavior of the function $f(n)$ seems to be somewhat erratic. Karl Mahlburg points out the upper bound $f(n) \leq 2n$ for $n \geq 5$, which holds because the interval $(n, 2n)$ contains an integer of the form $2m^2$. A trivial lower bound is $f(n) \geq n + p$ where p is the least prime factor of n. For $n = p$ prime, the bounds agree and $f(p) = 2p$. For more discussion, see sequence A006255 in the OEIS.

A3. (61, 15, 9, ..., 1, 6, 53, 56) 42.3%

Suppose that the real numbers $a_0, a_1, \ldots, a_n$ and x, with $0 < x < 1$, satisfy

$$\frac{a_0}{1 - x} + \frac{a_1}{1 - x^2} + \cdots + \frac{a_n}{1 - x^{n+1}} = 0.$$

Prove that there exists a real number y with $0 < y < 1$ such that

$$a_0 + a_1 y + \cdots + a_n y^n = 0.$$

Solution. Suppose on the contrary that $a_0 + a_1 y + \cdots + a_n y^n$ is nonzero for $0 < y < 1$. By the intermediate value theorem, this is only possible if $a_0 + a_1 y + \cdots + a_n y^n$ has the same sign for $0 < y < 1$; without loss of generality, we may assume that $a_0 + a_1 y + \cdots + a_n y^n > 0$ for $0 < y < 1$. For the given value of x, we then have

$$a_0 x^m + a_1 x^{2m} + \cdots + a_n x^{(n+1)m} \geq 0$$

for $m = 0, 1, \ldots$, with strict inequality for $m > 0$. The sum of the left-hand side over all m is absolutely convergent, and hence we can group terms containing the same a_i. This yields

$$\frac{a_0}{1 - x} + \frac{a_1}{1 - x^2} + \cdots + \frac{a_n}{1 - x^{n+1}} > 0,$$

a contradiction.

A4. (53, 8, 5, ..., 4, 4, 41, 86) 32.8%

A finite collection of digits 0 and 1 is written around a circle. An *arc* of length $L \geq 0$ consists of L consecutive digits around the circle. For each arc w, let $Z(w)$ and $N(w)$ denote the number of 0's in w and the number of 1's in w, respectively. Assume that $|Z(w) - Z(w')| \leq 1$ for any two arcs w, w' of the same length. Suppose that some arcs $w_1, \ldots, w_k$ have the property that

$$Z = \frac{1}{k} \sum_{j=1}^{k} Z(w_j) \text{ and } N = \frac{1}{k} \sum_{j=1}^{k} N(w_j)$$

are both integers. Prove that there exists an arc w with $Z(w) = Z$ and $N(w) = N$.

Remark. It is unclear whether the problem statement was meant to include "arcs" that wrap all the way around the circle, including some digits more than once. This is allowed in the following solutions.

Solution 1. Define arcs $w'_1, \ldots, w'_k$ as follows: $w'_1 = w_1$, and w'_{j+1} $(1 \le j < k)$ is the arc with the same length as w_{j+1} that is adjacent to w'_j (that is, the last digit of w'_j immediately precedes the first digit of w'_{j+1}). Since w_j has length $Z(w_j) + N(w_j)$, the sum of the lengths of $w_1, \ldots, w_k$ is $k(Z + N)$, and so the concatenation of $w'_1, \ldots, w'_k$ is a string of $k(Z + N)$ consecutive digits around the circle. (This string may wrap around the circle, in which case some of these digits may appear more than once in the string.) Break this string into k arcs $w''_1, \ldots, w''_k$ each of length $Z + N$, each adjacent to the previous one. (If the number of digits around the circle is m, then $Z + N \le m$ since $Z(w_j) + N(w_j) \le m$ for all j, and thus each of $w''_1, \ldots, w''_k$ is indeed an arc.)

We claim that for some $j = 1, \ldots, k$, $Z(w''_j) = Z$ and $N(w''_j) = N$ (where the second equation follows from the first since $Z(w''_j) + N(w''_j) = Z + N$). Otherwise, since all of the $Z(w''_j)$ differ by at most 1, either $Z(w''_j) \le Z - 1$ for all j or $Z(w''_j) \ge Z + 1$ for all j. In either case, $|kZ - \sum_j Z(w''_j)| = |kZ - \sum_j Z(w''_j)| \ge k$. But since $w_1 = w'_1$,

$$\left| kZ - \sum_j Z(w'_j) \right| = \left| \sum_{j=1}^k (Z(w_j) - Z(w'_j)) \right|$$

$$= \left| \sum_{j=2}^k (Z(w_j) - Z(w'_j)) \right| \le \sum_{j=2}^k |Z(w_j) - Z(w'_j)| \le k - 1,$$

a contradiction.

Solution 2. Let m be the total number of digits around the circle, and let W denote the entire circle, considered as an arc of length m (its start and end point is immaterial).

Lemma. Let $\alpha = Z(W)/m$. If $L > 0$ is any integer, then there are arcs c_1, c_2 of length L with

$$Z(c_1) = \lfloor \alpha L \rfloor \quad \text{and} \quad Z(c_2) = \lceil \alpha L \rceil.$$

Proof. There are m distinct arcs of length L. The total number of zeros they contain is $L \cdot Z(W)$, so the average number of zeros they contain is $L \cdot Z(W)/m$. If this is not an integer, it follows that if w is an arc of length L then $Z(w)$ is either $\lfloor L \cdot Z(W)/m \rfloor$ or $\lceil L \cdot Z(W)/m \rceil$, and both possibilities occur. If $L \cdot Z(W)/m$ is an integer, then because $L \cdot Z(W)/m + 1$ and $L \cdot Z(W)/m - 1$ cannot both occur as $Z(w)$ for arcs w of length L, neither of them can actually occur, and $Z(w) = L \cdot Z(W)/m$ for all such w. $\qquad \square$

Under the assumption in the problem, let $L = N + Z \in \mathbb{Z}$. It is necessary and sufficient to show that there exists an arc of length L with Z zeros. Now consider the given family of arcs $w_1, \ldots, w_k$, of lengths $L_1, \ldots, L_k$, respectively, with average length $L \in \mathbb{Z}$ and average number of zeros $Z \in \mathbb{Z}$. Then for each j, $Z(w_j) = \lfloor \alpha L_j \rfloor$ or $Z(w_j) = \lceil \alpha L_j \rceil$. In particular, $|Z(w_j) - \alpha L_j| < 1$; thus $|Z - \alpha L| < 1$, and Z is either $\lfloor \alpha L \rfloor$ or $\lceil \alpha L \rceil$. The result follows from the lemma.

Remark. With a bit more work, one can show that for any $z, n \geq 0$, there is a unique way to arrange z zeros and n ones on a circle to satisfy the problem conditions. It is the sequence $d_0, \ldots, d_{m-1}$, where $m = z + n$, given by

$$d_i = \left\lfloor \frac{(i+1)n}{m} \right\rfloor - \left\lfloor \frac{in}{m} \right\rfloor,$$

the sequence of differences of a *Beatty sequence*.

A5. $(5, 6, 2, \ldots, 1, 0, 41, 146)$ 6.5%
  For $m \geq 3$, **a list of** $\binom{m}{3}$ **real numbers** a_{ijk} $(1 \leq i < j < k \leq m)$ **is said to be** *area definite* **for** $\mathbb{R}^n$ **if the inequality**

$$\sum_{1 \leq i < j < k \leq m} a_{ijk} \cdot \text{Area}(\triangle A_i A_j A_k) \geq 0$$

holds for every choice of m **points** $A_1, \ldots, A_m$ **in** $\mathbb{R}^n$. **For example, the list of four numbers** $a_{123} = a_{124} = a_{134} = 1$, $a_{234} = -1$ **is area definite for** $\mathbb{R}^2$. **Prove that if a list of** $\binom{m}{3}$ **numbers is area definite for** $\mathbb{R}^2$, **then it is area definite for** $\mathbb{R}^3$.

Solution. Let $A_1, \ldots, A_m$ be points in $\mathbb{R}^3$, and let $\mathbf{n}_{ijk}$ denote a unit vector normal to $\triangle A_i A_j A_k$ (unless A_i, A_j, A_k are collinear, there are two possible choices for $\mathbf{n}_{ijk}$). If $\mathbf{n}$ is a unit vector in $\mathbb{R}^3$, and $\Pi_\mathbf{n}$ is a plane perpendicular to $\mathbf{n}$, then the area of the orthogonal projection of $\triangle A_i A_j A_k$ onto $\Pi_\mathbf{n}$ is $\text{Area}(\triangle A_i A_j A_k)|\mathbf{n}_{ijk} \cdot \mathbf{n}|$. Thus if $\{a_{ijk}\}$ is area definite for $\mathbb{R}^2$, then for any $\mathbf{n}$,

$$\sum a_{ijk} \text{Area}(\triangle A_i A_j A_k)|\mathbf{n}_{ijk} \cdot \mathbf{n}| \geq 0. \tag{1}$$

We now let $\mathbf{n}$ vary over the whole unit sphere S^2 and integrate with respect to surface area. Note that

$$\iint_{\mathbf{n} \in S^2} |\mathbf{n}_{ijk} \cdot \mathbf{n}| \, dS$$

is a positive number c, which is independent of $\mathbf{n}_{ijk}$ by rotational symmetry. Thus integrating the inequality (1) over $\mathbf{n} \in S^2$ gives $c \sum a_{ijk} \text{Area}(\triangle A_i A_j A_k) \geq 0$. It follows that $\{a_{ijk}\}$ is area definite for $\mathbb{R}^3$, as desired.

Remark. It is not hard to check (say, by integration in spherical coordinates) that the constant c occurring above is equal to 2π. It follows that for any convex body C in $\mathbb{R}^3$, the average over $\mathbf{n}$ of the area of the projection of C onto $\Pi_\mathbf{n}$ equals $1/4$ of the surface area of C.

More generally, let C be a convex body in $\mathbb{R}^n$. For $\mathbf{n}$ a unit vector, let $\Pi_{\mathbf{n}}$ denote the hyperplane through the origin perpendicular to $\mathbf{n}$. Then the average over $\mathbf{n}$ of the volume of the projection of C onto $\Pi_{\mathbf{n}}$ equals a constant (depending only on n) times the $(n-1)$-dimensional surface area of C.

Statements of this form inhabit the field of *inverse problems*, in which one attempts to reconstruct information about a geometric object from low-dimensional samples. This field has important applications in imaging and tomography.

A6. $(1, 2, 0, \ldots, 1, 2, 33, 162)$ 1.5%

Define a function $w : \mathbb{Z} \times \mathbb{Z} \to \mathbb{Z}$ as follows. For $|a|, |b| \leq 2$, let $w(a, b)$ be as in the table shown; otherwise, let $w(a, b) = 0$.

$w(a,b)$		b			
	-2	-1	0	1	2
-2	-1	-2	2	-2	-1
-1	-2	4	-4	4	-2
a $\quad 0$	2	-4	12	-4	2
1	-2	4	-4	4	-2
2	-1	-2	2	-2	-1

For every finite subset S of $\mathbb{Z} \times \mathbb{Z}$, define

$$A(S) = \sum_{(\mathbf{s}, \mathbf{s}') \in S \times S} w(\mathbf{s} - \mathbf{s}').$$

Prove that if S is any finite nonempty subset of $\mathbb{Z} \times \mathbb{Z}$, then $A(S) > 0$. (For example, if $S = \{(0, 1), (0, 2), (2, 0), (3, 1)\}$, then the terms in $A(S)$ are $12, 12, 12, 12, 4, 4, 0, 0, 0, 0, -1, -1, -2, -2, -4, -4$.)

Solution. (Harm Derksen) Consider the generating functions

$$f(x, y) = \sum_{(a,b) \in S} x^a y^b,$$

$$g(x, y) = \sum_{(a,b) \in \mathbb{Z}^2} w(a, b) x^a y^b.$$

Then $A(S)$ is the constant term of the Laurent polynomial

$$h(x, y) = f(x, y) f(x^{-1}, y^{-1}) g(x, y).$$

We compute this coefficient using a standard trick in the theory of Fourier series. Note that, for integers a, b,

$$\frac{1}{2\pi} \int_0^{2\pi} \left(e^{is} \right)^a ds = \begin{cases} 1 & a = 0, \\ 0 & \text{otherwise,} \end{cases}$$

and hence

$$\frac{1}{(2\pi)^2} \int_0^{2\pi} \int_0^{2\pi} \left(e^{is}\right)^a \left(e^{it}\right)^b dt\,ds = \begin{cases} 1 & a = b = 0, \\ 0 & \text{otherwise.} \end{cases}$$

Accordingly, we can compute the constant term $A(S)$ of $h(x, y)$ by averaging over the unit torus $|x| = |y| = 1$:

$$A(S) = \frac{1}{(2\pi)^2} \int_0^{2\pi} \int_0^{2\pi} h(e^{is}, e^{it})\,dt\,ds$$

$$= \frac{1}{(2\pi)^2} \int_0^{2\pi} \int_0^{2\pi} \left|f(e^{is}, e^{it})\right|^2 g(e^{is}, e^{it})\,dt\,ds. \tag{1}$$

We claim that $g_1(s, t) = g(e^{is}, e^{it})$ is a nonnegative real number for all $s, t \in \mathbb{R}$. Note that g_1 is an even function of both s and t because of the symmetry of the table defining $w(a, b)$. This allows us to write g_1 in terms of their cosines, namely $g_1(s, t) = 16G(\cos s, \cos t)$ for

$$G(u, v) = uv + u^2 + v^2 - u^2 v - uv^2 - u^2 v^2.$$

If $u, v \in [-1, 1]$ and $uv \geq 0$, then

$$G(u, v) = uv(1 - uv) + u^2(1 - v) + v^2(1 - u) \geq 0.$$

If $u, v \in [-1, 1]$ and $uv \leq 0$, then

$$G(u, v) = (u + v)^2 - uv(1 + u)(1 + v) \geq 0.$$

Hence $g_1(s, t) \geq 0$ as desired. This establishes that $A(S) \geq 0$. To show that the inequality is strict, it suffices to show that the integrand of (1), which is clearly continuous, is not identically zero. Since $f(0, 0) = |S|^2 > 0$, and since $G(1, 1 - \epsilon) > 0$ for ϵ sufficiently small, the integrand of (1) is nonvanishing for pairs $(0, t)$ where t is sufficiently small.

B1. (166, 13, 3, ..., 6, 1, 10, 2) 90.5%
   For positive integers n, let the numbers $c(n)$ be determined by the rules $c(1) = 1$, $c(2n) = c(n)$, and $c(2n + 1) = (-1)^n c(n)$. Find the value of

$$\sum_{n=1}^{2013} c(n)c(n + 2).$$

Answer. The sum is -1.

Solution. Note that

$$c(2k + 1)c(2k + 3) = (-1)^k c(k)(-1)^{k+1} c(k + 1)$$
$$= -c(k)c(k + 1)$$
$$= -c(2k)c(2k + 2).$$

It follows that $\sum_{n=2}^{2013} c(n)c(n+2) = \sum_{k=1}^{1006}(c(2k)c(2k+2)+c(2k+1)c(2k+3)) = 0$, and so the desired sum is $c(1)c(3) = -1$.

Remark. Karl Mahlburg points out the general formula

$$c(n) = (-1)^{b_0 b_1 + b_1 b_2 + \cdots + b_{k-1} b_k}$$

for n having binary representation $b_k \cdots b_0$.

B2. (80, 3, 1, ..., 23, 0, 22, 72) 41.8%

Let $\mathcal{C} = \bigcup_{N=1}^{\infty} \mathcal{C}_N$, where $\mathcal{C}_N$ denotes the set of those 'cosine polynomials' of the form

$$f(x) = 1 + \sum_{n=1}^{N} a_n \cos(2\pi n x)$$

for which:

(i) $f(x) \geq 0$ for all real x, and

(ii) $a_n = 0$ whenever n is a multiple of 3.

Determine the maximum value of $f(0)$ as f ranges through $\mathcal{C}$, and prove that this maximum is attained.

Answer. The maximum value of $f(0)$ is 3.

Solution. The value 3 is attained for $N = 2$, $a_1 = \frac{4}{3}$, $a_2 = \frac{2}{3}$: in this case $f(x) = 1 + \frac{4}{3}\cos(2\pi x) + \frac{2}{3}\cos(4\pi x) = 1 + \frac{4}{3}\cos(2\pi x) + \frac{2}{3}(2\cos^2(2\pi x) - 1) = \frac{1}{3}(2\cos(2\pi x) + 1)^2$ is always nonnegative.

Now suppose that $f = 1 + \sum_{n=1}^{N} a_n \cos(2\pi n x) \in \mathcal{C}$. When n is an integer, $\cos(2\pi n/3)$ equals 1 if $3|n$ and $-1/2$ otherwise. Thus $a_n \cos(2\pi n/3) = -a_n/2$ for all n, and $f(1/3) = 1 - \sum_{n=1}^{N}(a_n/2)$. Since $f(1/3) \geq 0$, $\sum_{n=1}^{N} a_n \leq 2$, whence $f(0) = 1 + \sum_{n=1}^{N} a_n \leq 3$.

B3. (115, 16, 3, ..., 11, 4, 38, 14) 66.7%

Let $\mathcal{P}$ be a nonempty collection of subsets of $\{1, ..., n\}$ such that:

(i) if $S, S' \in \mathcal{P}$, then $S \cup S' \in \mathcal{P}$ and $S \cap S' \in \mathcal{P}$, and

(ii) if $S \in \mathcal{P}$ and $S \neq \emptyset$, then there is a subset $T \subset S$ such that $T \in \mathcal{P}$ and T contains exactly one fewer element than S.

Suppose that $f : \mathcal{P} \to \mathbb{R}$ is a function such that $f(\emptyset) = 0$ and

$$f(S \cup S') = f(S) + f(S') - f(S \cap S') \text{ for all } S, S' \in \mathcal{P}.$$

Must there exist real numbers $f_1, \ldots, f_n$ such that

$$f(S) = \sum_{i \in S} f_i$$

for every $S \in \mathcal{P}$?

Answer. Yes, such numbers f_i must exist.

Solution 1. To define the f_i, we make the following observations.

Lemma 1. For any $i \in \{1, \ldots, n\}$, if there exists any $S \in \mathcal{P}$ containing i, then there exist $S, T \in \mathcal{P}$ such that S is the disjoint union $T \cup \{i\}$.

Proof. Let S be an element of $\mathcal{P}$ containing i of minimum cardinality. By (ii), there must be a subset $T \subset S$ in $\mathcal{P}$ with exactly one fewer element than S. These sets have the desired form. $\qquad\square$

Lemma 2. Suppose $S_1, S_2, T_1, T_2 \in \mathcal{P}$ have the property that for some $i \in \{1, \ldots, n\}$, S_1 is the disjoint union $T_1 \cup \{i\}$ and S_2 is the disjoint union $T_2 \cup \{i\}$. Then

$$f(S_1) - f(T_1) = f(S_2) - f(T_2).$$

Proof. By (i),

$$f(T_1 \cup T_2 \cup \{i\}) = f(S_1) + f(T_2) - f(T_1 \cap T_2),$$
$$f(T_1 \cup T_2 \cup \{i\}) = f(T_1) + f(S_2) - f(T_1 \cap T_2),$$

from which the claim follows immediately. $\qquad\square$

We now define $f_1, \ldots, f_n$ as follows. If i does not appear in any element of $\mathcal{P}$, we put $f_i = 0$. Otherwise, by Lemma 1, we can find $S, T \in \mathcal{P}$ such that S is the disjoint union $T \cup \{i\}$. We then set $f_i = f(S) - f(T)$; by Lemma 2, this does not depend on the choice of S and T.

To check that $f(S) = \sum_{i \in S} f_i$ for $S \in \mathcal{P}$, note first that $\emptyset \in \mathcal{P}$ by repeated application of (ii) and that $f(\emptyset) = 0$ by hypothesis. This provides the base case for an induction on the cardinality of S; for any nonempty $S \in \mathcal{P}$, we may apply (ii) to find $T \subset S$ such that S is the disjoint union of T and some singleton $\{j\}$. By construction and the induction hypothesis, $f(S) = f(T) + f_j = f_j + \sum_{i \in T} f_i = \sum_{i \in S} f_i$, as desired.

Solution 2. View

$$\left\{ \sum_{i \in S} f_i = f(S) \right\}_{S \in \mathcal{P}}$$

as a system of linear equations in the unknowns f_i. Suppose by way of contradiction that this system is inconsistent. Then there exists a linear combination of the equations in which the coefficient of each f_i is zero, but the right-hand side is nonzero. Since the original system had integer coefficients, this linear combination can be taken with rational, hence integer, coefficients.

We thus obtain a pair of multisets $\{S_1, \ldots, S_m\}, \{T_1, \ldots, T_{m'}\}$ of subsets $S_i, T_i \in \mathcal{P}$ such that

(1) each $i \in \{1, \ldots, n\}$ belongs to the same number of S_i as T_i, but

(2) $\displaystyle\sum_i f(S_i) \neq \sum_i f(T_i)$.

We now transform the multiset $\{S_1, \ldots, S_m\}$ in the following way: as long as there is a pair of elements S_i and S_j, neither of which is contained in the other, we pick such a pair and replace them with $S_i \cup S_j$ and $S_i \cap S_j$. This operation preserves (1) and (2) but increases the monovariant $\sum_i |S_i|^2$, which is bounded in terms of n and m, implying that the operation can be performed only a finite number of times. At this point, the S_i form a chain (that is, $S_i \supseteq S_j$ or $S_i \subseteq S_j$ for every i, j) and can be ordered so that $S_1 \supseteq S_2 \supseteq \cdots \supseteq S_m$. We transform the multiset $\{T_i\}_i$ in the same way. By (1), the multisets $\{S_i\}_i$ and $\{T_i\}_i$ are the same except possibly for the number of occurrences of $\emptyset$, contradicting (2).

Remark. This solution shows that condition (ii) is actually unnecessary.

B4. $(11, 1, 0, \ldots, 1, 0, 68, 120)$ 6.0%
    For any continuous real-valued function f defined on the interval $[0, 1]$, let

$$\mu(f) = \int_0^1 f(x)\, dx,$$

$$\mathrm{Var}(f) = \int_0^1 \left(f(x) - \mu(f) \right)^2 dx,$$

$$M(f) = \max_{0 \leq x \leq 1} |f(x)|.$$

Show that if f and g are continuous real-valued functions defined on the interval $[0, 1]$, then

$$\mathrm{Var}(fg) \leq 2\mathrm{Var}(f)M(g)^2 + 2\mathrm{Var}(g)M(f)^2.$$

Solution. For any f, as $a \in \mathbb{R}$ varies, the integral

$$\int_0^1 \left(f(x) - a \right)^2 dx = \int_0^1 \left(f(x) \right)^2 dx - 2\mu(f)a + a^2$$

is a quadratic polynomial in a, which has its minimum when $a = \mu(f)$. Applying this to fg yields

$$\text{Var}(fg) = \int_0^1 \left(f(x)g(x) - \mu(fg) \right)^2 dx$$

$$\leq \int_0^1 \left(f(x)g(x) - \mu(f)\mu(g) \right)^2 dx.$$

Now note that

$$f(x)g(x) - \mu(f)\mu(g) = (f(x) - \mu(f))g(x) + (g(x) - \mu(g))\mu(f),$$

and that

$$\left((f(x) - \mu(f))g(x) + (g(x) - \mu(g))\mu(f) \right)^2$$

$$\leq 2\left((f(x) - \mu(f))g(x))^2 + ((g(x) - \mu(g))\mu(f))^2 \right).$$

Thus

$$\int_0^1 \left(f(x)g(x) - \mu(f)\mu(g) \right) dx$$

$$\leq 2 \int_0^1 \left((f(x) - \mu(f))g(x) \right)^2 dx + 2 \int_0^1 \left((g(x) - \mu(g))\mu(f) \right)^2 dx$$

$$\leq 2M(g)^2 \int_0^1 \left(f(x) - \mu(f) \right)^2 dx + 2M(f)^2 \int_0^1 \left(g(x) - \mu(g) \right)^2 dx,$$

proving the stated result.

B5. (13, 0, 2, ..., 4, 1, 76, 105) 7.5%

Let $X = \{1, 2, \ldots, n\}$, and let $k \in X$. **Show that there are exactly $k \cdot n^{n-1}$ functions $f : X \to X$ such that for every $x \in X$ there is a $j \geq 0$ such that $f^{(j)}(x) \leq k$. [Here $f^{(j)}$ denotes the jth iterate of f, so that $f^{(0)}(x) = x$ and $f^{(j+1)}(x) = f(f^{(j)}(x))$.]**

Solution 1. For T a set and S_1, S_2 two subsets of T, we say that a function $f : T \to T$ *iterates S_1 into S_2* if for each $x \in S_1$, there is a $j \geq 0$ such that $f^{(j)}(x) \in S_2$.

Lemma 3. Fix $k \in X$. Let $f, g : X \to X$ be two functions such that f iterates X into $\{1, \ldots, k\}$ and $f(x) = g(x)$ for $x \in \{k+1, \ldots, n\}$. Then g also iterates X into $\{1, \ldots, k\}$.

Proof. For $x \in X$, by hypothesis there exists a nonnegative integer j such that $f^{(j)}(x) \in \{1, \ldots, k\}$. Choose the integer j as small as possible; then $f^{(i)}(x) \in \{k+1, \ldots, n\}$ for $0 \leq i < j$. By induction on i, $f^{(i)}(x) = g^{(i)}(x)$ for $i = 0, \ldots, j$, so in particular $g^{(j)}(x) \in \{1, \ldots, k\}$. This proves the lemma. □

We proceed by induction on $n - k$, the case $n - k = 0$ being trivial. For the induction step, we need only confirm that the number x of functions $f : X \to X$ which iterate X into $\{1, \ldots, k+1\}$ but not into $\{1, \ldots, k\}$ is equal to n^{n-1}. These are precisely the functions f for which iterating f on $k+1$ yields a cycle C containing only numbers in $\{k + 1, \ldots, n\}$ and eventually returning to $k + 1$. Suppose C has length $\ell \in \{1, \ldots, n-k\}$. For a fixed choice of ℓ, we may choose the set of numbers in C in $\binom{n-k-1}{\ell-1}$ ways and the cycle structure (that is, the values of f on C) in $(\ell-1)!$ ways. Given C with its cycle structure, the functions f we want are the ones that act on C as specified and iterate X into $\{1, \ldots, k\} \cup C$. By Lemma 1, the number of such functions is $n^{-\ell}$ times the total number of functions that iterate X into $\{1, \ldots, k\} \cup C$, which is $(k + \ell)n^{n-1}$ by the induction hypothesis.

Thus the number of functions which iterate X into $\{1, \ldots, k + 1\}$ but not into $\{1, \ldots, k\}$ is

$$\sum_{\ell=1}^{n-k} \binom{n-k-1}{\ell-1}(\ell - 1)! \cdot n^{-\ell} \cdot (k + \ell)n^{n-1}$$

$$= \sum_{\ell=1}^{n-k} (n-k-1) \cdots (n-k-\ell+1)(k+\ell)n^{n-\ell-1}.$$

By rewriting this as a telescoping sum, we get

$$\sum_{\ell=1}^{n-k} (n-k-1) \cdots (n-k-\ell+1)(n)n^{n-\ell-1}$$

$$- \sum_{\ell=1}^{n-k} (n-k-1) \cdots (n-k-\ell+1)(n-k-\ell)n^{n-\ell-1}$$

$$= \sum_{\ell=0}^{n-k-1} (n-k-1) \cdots (n-k-\ell)n^{n-\ell-1}$$

$$- \sum_{\ell=1}^{n-k} (n-k-1) \cdots (n-k-\ell)n^{n-\ell-1}$$

$$= n^{n-1}.$$

as desired.

Solution 2. For T a set, $f : T \to T$ a function, and S a subset of T, we define the *contraction* of f at S as the function $g : \{*\} \cup (T - S) \to \{*\} \cup (T - S)$ (where $*$ is an arbitrary symbol not lying in $T - S$) given by

$$g(x) = \begin{cases} * & x = *, \\ * & x \neq *, f(x) \in S, \\ f(x) & x \neq *, f(x) \notin S. \end{cases}$$

Lemma 4. For $S \subseteq X$ of cardinality $\ell \geq 0$, there are $\ell n^{n-\ell-1}$ functions f : $\{*\} \cup X \to \{*\} \cup X$ with $f^{-1}(*) = \{*\} \cup S$ which iterate X into $\{*\}$.

Proof. We induct on n. If $\ell = n$ then there is nothing to check. Otherwise, put $T = f^{-1}(S)$, which must be nonempty. The contraction g of f at $\{*\} \cup S$ is then a function on $\{*\} \cup (X - S)$ with $f^{-1}(*) = \{*\} \cup T$ which iterates $X - S$ into $\{*\}$. Moreover, for given T, each such g arises from $\ell^{\#T}$ functions of the desired form. By summing over T and invoking the induction hypothesis, we see that the number of functions f is

$$\sum_{k=1}^{n-\ell} \binom{n-\ell}{k} \ell^k \cdot k(n-\ell)^{n-\ell-k-1}$$

$$= \sum_{k=1}^{n-\ell} \binom{n-\ell-1}{k-1} \ell^k (n-\ell)^{n-\ell-k} = \ell n^{n-\ell-1}$$

as claimed.   □

To finish the problem, if $f : X \to X$ is any function, let $h : \{*\} \cup X \to \{*\} \cup X$ be given by

$$h(x) = \begin{cases} * & x \in \{*\} \cup \{1, \dots, k\}, \\ f(x) & x \in \{k+1, \dots, n\}. \end{cases}$$

Note that f iterates X to $\{1, \dots, k\}$ if and only if h iterates $X \cup \{*\}$ to $\{*\}$, and $h^{-1}(*) = \{*, 1, \dots, k\}$. By Lemma 2, there are kn^{n-k-1} such functions h, and each corresponds to n^k functions f, yielding kn^{n-1} functions f as desired.

Remark. Functions of the sort counted in Lemma 2 can be identified with rooted trees on the vertex set $\{*\} \cup X$ with root $*$. Such trees can be counted using *Cayley's formula*, a special case of *Kirchhoff's matrix-tree theorem*. The matrix tree theorem can also be used to show directly that the number of rooted forests on n vertices with k fixed roots is kn^{n-k-1}; the desired count follows immediately from this formula plus Lemma 1. (One can also use Prüfer sequences for a more combinatorial interpretation.)

B6. $(0, 0, 0, \dots, 1, 5, 29, 166)$ 0.0%
    Let $n \geq 1$ be an odd integer. Alice and Bob play the following game, taking alternating turns, with Alice playing first. The playing area consists of n spaces, arranged in a line. Initially all spaces are empty. At each turn, a player either

- **places a stone in an empty space, or**

- **removes a stone from a nonempty space s, places a stone in the nearest empty space to the left of s (if such a space exists), and places a stone in the nearest empty space to the right of s (if such a space exists).**

Furthermore, a move is permitted only if the resulting position has not occurred previously in the game. A player loses if he or she is unable to move. Assuming that both players play optimally throughout the game, what moves may Alice make on her first turn?

Remark. To resolve a mild ambiguity in the problem statement, it should be clarified that the initial position (with no stones placed) should be treated as having occurred previously once the first move has been made. This only affects the case $n = 1$.

Answer. The only winning first move for Alice is to place a stone in the central space.

Solution. We start with some terminology. By a *block* of stones, we mean a (possibly empty) sequence of stones occupying consecutive spaces. By the *extremal blocks*, we mean the two (possibly empty) maximal blocks touching each end of the playing area.

We refer to a legal move consisting of placing a stone in an empty space as a move of *type 1*, and any other legal move as being of *type 2*. For $i = 0, \ldots, n$, let P_i be the collection of positions containing i stones. Define the *endgame* as the union $Z = P_{n-1} \cup P_n$. In this language, we make the following observations.

- Any move of type 1 from P_i ends in P_{i+1}.

- Any move of type 2 from P_n ends in P_{n-1}.

- For $i < n$, any move of type 2 from P_i ends in $P_i \cup P_{i+1}$.

- At this point, the number of stones cannot decrease until the endgame.

- For $i < n - 1$, if we start at a position in P_i where the extremal blocks have length a, b, then the only possible moves to P_i decrease one of a, b while leaving the other unchanged (because they are separated by at least two empty spaces). In particular, no repetition is possible within P_i, so the number of stones must eventually increase to $i + 1$.

- From any position in the endgame, the legal moves are precisely to the other positions in the endgame which have not previously occurred. Consequently, after the first move into the endgame, the rest of the game consists of enumerating all positions in the endgame in some order.

- At this point, we may change the rules without affecting the outcome by eliminating the rule on repetitions and declaring that the first player to move into the endgame loses (because $\#Z = n + 1$ is even).

To determine who wins in each position, label the spaces of the playing area $1, \ldots, n$ from left to right. Define the *weight* of a position to be the sum of the labels of the occupied spaces, reduced modulo $n + 1$. For any given position outside of the endgame and any given $s = 1, \ldots, n$, there is a unique move that adds s to the weight:

- if s is empty then a move of type 1 there does the job;

- otherwise, s inhabits a block running from $i + 1$ to $j - 1$ with i and j empty (or equal to 0 or $n + 1$), so the move at $i + j - s$ (which belongs to the same block) does the job.

We now verify that a position of weight s outside of the endgame is a win for the player to move if and only if $s \neq (n+1)/2$. We check this for positions in P_i for $i = n-2, \ldots, 0$ by descending induction. For positions in P_{n-2}, the only safe moves are in the extremal blocks; we may thus analyze these positions as two-pile Nim with pile sizes equal to the lengths of the extremal blocks. In particular, a position is a win for the player to move if and only if the extremal blocks are unequal, in which case the winning move is to equalize the blocks. In other words, a position is a win for the player to move unless the empty spaces are at s and $n + 1 - s$ for some $s \in \{1, \ldots, (n-1)/2\}$, and indeed these are precisely the positions for which the weight equals $(1 + \cdots + n) - (n + 1) \equiv (n + 1)/2 \pmod{n + 1}$. Given the analysis of positions in P_{i+1} for some i, if a position in P_i has weight $s \neq (n+1)/2$, there is a winning move of weight t where $s + t \equiv (n + 1)/2 \pmod{n}$, whereas if $s = (n + 1)/2$ then no move leads to a winning position.

It thus follows that the unique winning move for Alice at her first turn is to move at the central space, as claimed.

Remark. Despite the existence of a simple description of the winning positions, it is nonetheless necessary to go through the preliminary analysis in order to establish the nature of the endgame and to ensure that the repetition clause does not affect the availability of moves outside of the endgame. However, it is not strictly necessary to study P_{n-2} separately: none of the positions in P_{n-1} has weight $(n+1)/2$, so following the strategy of forcing the weight to equal $(n+1)/2$ cannot force a first move into the endgame.

Remark. It is easy to see that Alice's winning strategy is to ensure that after each of her moves, the stones are placed symmetrically and the central space is occupied. However, it is somewhat more complicated to describe Bob's winning strategy without the modular interpretation.

Remark. For the analogous problem with n even, David Savitt has conjectured (based on the cases $n = 2$ and $n = 4$) that Alice has a winning strategy, and her possible winning moves at her first turn are to place a stone in one of the two central spaces.

**The Seventy-Fifth William Lowell Putnam
Mathematical Competition—December 6, 2014**

A1. (129, 33, 11, ..., 13, 2, 2, 0) 91.1%
   Prove that every nonzero coefficient of the Taylor series of

$$(1 - x + x^2)e^x$$

**about $x = 0$ is a rational number whose numerator (in lowest terms) is
either 1 or a prime number.**

Solution. The coefficients of x^0, x^1, x^2 in the Taylor series of $(1 - x + x^2)e^x$ for
are $1, 0, \frac{1}{2}$, respectively. For $n \geq 3$, the coefficient of x^n is

$$\frac{1}{n!} - \frac{1}{(n-1)!} + \frac{1}{(n-2)!} = \frac{1 - n + n(n-1)}{n!}$$

$$= \frac{n-1}{n(n-2)!}.$$

   If $n - 1$ is prime, then the lowest-terms numerator is either 1 or the prime
$n - 1$ (and in fact the latter, since $n - 1$ is relatively prime to n and to $(n - 2)!$).
   If $n-1 = p^2$ for some prime p, then p appears in $(n-2)!$ and so the numerator
is either 1 or p. (In the latter case, the numerator is actually 1 unless $p = 2$, as in
all other cases both p and $2p$ appear in $(n - 2)!$.)
   Otherwise, $n - 1$ can be written as ab for some $a > b > 1$. Then both a and
b appear separately in $(n - 2)!$ and so the numerator is 1.

A2. (154, 18, 3, ..., 3, 0, 11, 1) 92.1%
   **Let A be the $n \times n$ matrix whose entry in the ith row and jth column
is**

$$\frac{1}{\min(i, j)}$$

for $1 \leq i, j \leq n$. Compute $\det(A)$.

Answer. The determinant is $\dfrac{(-1)^{n-1}}{(n-1)!\, n!}$.

Solution 1. Let $v_1, \ldots, v_n$ denote the rows of A. The determinant is unchanged if
we replace v_n by $v_n - v_{n-1}$, and then v_{n-1} by $v_{n-1} - v_{n-2}$, and so forth, eventually
replacing v_k by $v_k - v_{k-1}$ for $k \geq 2$. Since v_{k-1} and v_k agree in their first $k - 1$
entries, and the kth entry of $v_k - v_{k-1}$ is $\frac{1}{k} - \frac{1}{k-1}$, the result of these row operations
is an upper triangular matrix with diagonal entries $1, \frac{1}{2} - 1, \frac{1}{3} - \frac{1}{2}, \ldots, \frac{1}{n} - \frac{1}{n-1}$.

The determinant is then

$$\prod_{k=2}^{n}\left(\frac{1}{k}-\frac{1}{k-1}\right)=\prod_{k=2}^{n}\left(\frac{-1}{k(k-1)}\right)$$

$$=\frac{(-1)^{n-1}}{(n-1)!\,n!}.$$

Remark. A similar calculation can be made whenever A has the form $A_{ij} = a_{\min\{i,j\}}$ for any sequence $a_1, \ldots, a_n$. The standard Gaussian elimination algorithm leads to the same upper triangular matrix, but the nonstandard order of operations used here makes the computations somewhat easier.

Solution 2. The case $n = 1$ being trivially valid, we assume $n \geq 2$. In this case, we construct an explicit candidate for the inverse A^{-1} and compute its determinant instead.

Define the matrix B by

$$B_{ij} = \begin{cases} -1 & i = j = 1, \\ -2i^2 & 1 < i = j < n, \\ -(n-1)n & i = j = n, \\ ij & |i-j| = 1, \\ 0 & \text{otherwise.} \end{cases}$$

For example, for $n = 5$,

$$B = \begin{pmatrix} -1 & 2 & 0 & 0 & 0 \\ 2 & -8 & 6 & 0 & 0 \\ 0 & 6 & -18 & 12 & 0 \\ 0 & 0 & 12 & -32 & 20 \\ 0 & 0 & 0 & 20 & -20 \end{pmatrix}.$$

To confirm that $B = A^{-1}$, it suffices to verify that $AB = I_n$ is the identity matrix. To wit, we compute that the (i, j)-entry of AB equals

$$\begin{cases} -1 + \dfrac{2}{\min\{i,2\}} & j = 1, \\[2mm] j\left(\dfrac{j-1}{\min\{i,j-1\}} - \dfrac{2j}{\min\{i,j\}} + \dfrac{j+1}{\min\{i,j+1\}}\right) & 1 < j < n, \\[2mm] n\left(\dfrac{n-1}{\min\{i,n-1\}} - \dfrac{n-1}{i}\right) & j = n. \end{cases}$$

If $j = 1$, then we get $-1 + 1 = 0$ unless $i = 1$, in which case we get $-1 + 2 = 1$. If $j = n$, then we get $n\left(\frac{n-1}{i} - \frac{n-1}{i}\right) = 0$ unless $i = n$, in which case we get $n\left(1 - \frac{n-1}{n}\right) = 1$. If $1 < j < n$, then when $i \leq j-1$ the minima all equal i and the sum equals $j(j-1-2j+j+1) = 0$; when $i \geq j+1$ the minima equal $j-1, j, j+1$

and the sum equals $j(1 - 2 + 1) = 0$; and when $i = j$ the sum equals

$$j\left(\frac{j-1}{j-1} - \frac{2j}{j} + \frac{j+1}{j}\right) = \frac{j}{j} = 1.$$

We conclude that $B = A^{-1}$.

Let C denote the matrix obtained from B by replacing the bottom-right entry with $-2n^2$ (for consistency with the rest of the diagonal). Expanding by minors about the bottom row produces a second-order recursion for $\det(C)$ solving to $\det(C) = (-1)^n (n!)^2$. A similar expansion then yields

$$\det(B) = (-1)^{n-1} n! (n-1)!.$$

Remark. The statement appears in the comments on sequence A010790 in the OEIS (that is, the sequence $(n-1)! \, n!$), attributed to Benoît Cloitre in 2002.

A3. (95, 10, 5, ..., 1, 46, 4, 29) 57.9%
   Let $a_0 = 5/2$ and $a_k = a_{k-1}^2 - 2$ for $k \geq 1$. Compute

$$\prod_{k=0}^{\infty}\left(1 - \frac{1}{a_k}\right)$$

in closed form.

Answer. The product is 3/7.

Solution 1. Using the identity

$$(x + x^{-1})^2 - 2 = x^2 + x^{-2},$$

we may check by induction on k that $a_k = 2^{2^k} + 2^{-2^k}$; in particular, the product is absolutely convergent. Using the identities

$$\frac{x^2 + 1 + x^{-2}}{x + 1 + x^{-1}} = x - 1 + x^{-1},$$

$$\frac{x^2 - x^{-2}}{x - x^{-1}} = x + x^{-1},$$

we may telescope the product to obtain

$$\prod_{k=0}^{\infty}\left(1 - \frac{1}{a_k}\right) = \prod_{k=0}^{\infty}\frac{2^{2^k} - 1 + 2^{-2^k}}{2^{2^k} + 2^{-2^k}}$$

$$= \prod_{k=0}^{\infty}\frac{2^{2^{k+1}} + 1 + 2^{-2^{k+1}}}{2^{2^k} + 1 + 2^{-2^k}} \cdot \frac{2^{2^k} - 2^{-2^k}}{2^{2^{k+1}} - 2^{-2^{k-1}}}$$

$$= \frac{2^{2^0} - 2^{-2^0}}{2^{2^0} + 1 + 2^{-2^0}} = \frac{3}{7}.$$

Solution 2. (Catalin Zara) In this solution, we do not use the explicit formula for a_k. We instead note first that the a_k form an increasing sequence which cannot approach a finite limit (since the equation $L = L^2 - 2$ has no real solution $L > 2$), and is thus unbounded. Using the identity

$$a_{k+1} + 1 = (a_k - 1)(a_k + 1),$$

one checks by induction on n that

$$\prod_{k=0}^{n} \left(1 - \frac{1}{a_k} \right) = \frac{2}{7} \frac{a_{n+1} + 1}{a_0 a_1 \cdots a_n}.$$

Using the identity

$$a_{n+1}^2 - 4 = a_n^4 - 4a_n^2,$$

one also checks by induction on n that

$$a_0 a_1 \cdots a_n = \frac{2}{3} \sqrt{a_{n+1}^2 - 4}.$$

Hence

$$\prod_{k=0}^{n} \left(1 - \frac{1}{a_k} \right) = \frac{3}{7} \frac{a_{n+1} + 1}{\sqrt{a_{n+1}^2 - 4}}$$

tends to $\frac{3}{7}$ as a_{n+1} tends to infinity, hence as n tends to infinity.

A4. (64, 6, 2, ..., 1, 1, 61, 55) 37.9%
 Suppose X is a random variable that takes on only nonnegative integer values, with $E[X] = 1$, $E[X^2] = 2$, and $E[X^3] = 5$. (Here $E[Y]$ denotes the expectation of the random variable Y.) Determine the smallest possible value of the probability of the event $X = 0$.

Answer. The smallest possible value is $\frac{1}{3}$.

Solution 1. Let $a_n = P(X = n)$; we want the minimum value of a_0. For $k \geq 1$, write

$$E_k = E[X^k] = \sum_{n=1}^{\infty} n^k a_n.$$

Let $f(n) = (1 - n)(2 - n)(3 - n)$, noting that $f(0) = 6$ and $f(n) \leq 0$ for $n > 0$, with equality for $n = 1, 2$, and 3. By the linearity of expectation,

$$6a_0 \geq E[f(X)]$$
$$= 6 - 11E[X] + 6E[X^2] - E[X^3]$$
$$= 6 - 11 \cdot 1 + 6 \cdot 2 - 5 = 2.$$

Thus $a_0 \geq \frac{1}{3}$. Equality can hold only if the values that X takes with positive probability are contained in $\{0, 1, 2, 3\}$. In fact, equality is achieved when $a_0 = \frac{1}{3}$, $a_1 = \frac{1}{2}$, $a_3 = \frac{1}{6}$, and $a_n = 0$ for all other n, and so the answer is $\frac{1}{3}$.

Solution 2. (Tony Qiao) Define the *probability generating function* of X as the power series

$$G(z) = \sum_{n=0}^{\infty} P(X = n)z^n.$$

We compute that $G(1) = G'(1) = G''(1) = G'''(1) = 1$. By Taylor's theorem with remainder, for any $x \in [0, 1]$, there exists $c \in [x, 1]$ such that

$$G(x) = 1 + (x - 1) + \frac{(x-1)^2}{2!} + \frac{(x-1)^3}{3!} + \frac{G''''(c)}{4!}(x - 1)^4.$$

In particular, $G(0) = \frac{1}{3} + \frac{1}{24}G''''(c)$ for some $c \in [0, 1]$. However, since G has nonnegative coefficients and $c \geq 0$, we must have $G''''(c) \geq 0$, and so $G(0) \geq \frac{1}{3}$. As in the first solution, this bound is best possible.

Remark. It can be shown that the possible values of a_0 are exactly the numbers in the interval $[1/3, 1/2]$.

A5. $(0, 0, 0, \ldots, 0, 6, 79, 105)$ 0.0%
    Let

$$P_n(x) = 1 + 2x + 3x^2 + \cdots + nx^{n-1}.$$

Prove that the polynomials $P_j(x)$ and $P_k(x)$ are relatively prime for all positive integers j and k with $j \neq k$.

Solution 1. Suppose to the contrary that there exist positive integers $i \neq j$ and a complex number z such that $P_i(z) = P_j(z) = 0$. Note that z cannot be a nonnegative real number or else $P_i(z), P_j(z) > 0$; we may put $w = z^{-1} \neq 0, 1$. For $n \in \{i + 1, j + 1\}$ we compute that

$$w^n = nw - n + 1;$$

note crucially that this equation also holds for $n \in \{0, 1\}$. Therefore the function $f : [0, +\infty) \to \mathbb{R}$ given by

$$f(t) = |w|^{2t} - |tw - t + 1|^2$$
$$= |w|^{2t} - t^2|w - 1|^2 + 2t\text{Re}(w - 1) - 1$$

has four zeros at $t \in \{0, 1, i + 1, j + 1\}$. By Rolle's theorem, this implies that

$$f'''(t) = (2\log|w|)^3|w|^{2t}$$

has a positive root. This is impossible unless $|w| = 1$. But in this case, f itself is a quadratic polynomial, the t^2 coefficient being nonzero since $w \neq 1$. Since a nonzero quadratic polynomial has at most two roots, this is a contradiction.

Remark. By similar reasoning, an equation of the form $e^x = P(x)$ in which P is a real polynomial of degree d has at most $d + 1$ real solutions. This turns out to be closely related to a concept in mathematical logic known as *o-minimality*, which in turn has deep consequences for the solution of Diophantine equations.

Solution 2. (by David Feldman) Note that

$$P_n(x)(1 - x) = 1 + x + \cdots + x^{n-1} - nx^n.$$

If $|z| \geq 1$, then

$$n|z|^n \geq |z|^{n-1} + \cdots + 1 \geq |z^{n-1} + \cdots + 1|,$$

with the first equality occurring only if $|z| = 1$ and the second equality occurring only if z is a positive real number. Hence the equation $P_n(z)(1 - z) = 0$ has no solutions with $|z| \geq 1$ other than the trivial solution $z = 1$. Since

$$P_n(x)(1 - x)^2 = 1 - (n + 1)x^n + nx^{n+1},$$

it now suffices to check that the curves

$$C_n = \{z \in \mathbb{C} : 0 < |z| < 1, |z|^n |n + 1 - zn| = 1\}$$

are pairwise disjoint as n varies over positive integers.

Write $z = u + iv$; we may assume without loss of generality that $v \geq 0$. Define the function

$$E_z(n) = n \log |z| + \log |n + 1 - zn|.$$

One computes that for $n \in \mathbb{R}$, $E_z''(n) < 0$ if and only if

$$\frac{u - v - 1}{(1 - u)^2 + v^2} < n < \frac{u + v - 1}{(1 - u)^2 + v^2}.$$

In addition, $E_z(0) = 0$ and

$$E_z'(0) = \frac{1}{2} \log(u^2 + v^2) + (1 - u) \geq \log(u) + 1 - u \geq 0$$

since $\log(u)$ is concave. From this, it follows that the equation $E_z(n) = 0$ can have at most one solution with $n > 0$.

Remark. The reader may notice a strong similarity between this solution and the first solution. The primary difference is we compute that $E_z'(0) \geq 0$ instead of discovering that $E_z(-1) = 0$.

Solution 3. (Noam Elkies) We recall a result commonly known as the *Eneström-Kakeya theorem.*

Lemma. Let

$$f(x) = a_0 + a_1 x + \cdots + a_n x^n$$

be a polynomial with real coefficients such that $0 < a_0 \leq a_1 \leq \cdots \leq a_n$. Then every root $z \in \mathbb{C}$ of f satisfies $|z| \leq 1$.

Proof. If $f(z) = 0$, then we may rearrange the equality $0 = f(z)(z - 1)$ to obtain

$$a_n z^{n+1} = (a_n - a_{n-1})z^n + \cdots + (a_1 - a_0)z + a_0.$$

But if $|z| > 1$, then

$$|a_n z^{n+1}| \leq (|a_n - a_{n-1}| + \cdots + |a_1 - a_0|)|z|^n \leq |a_n z^n|,$$

a contradiction.   □

Corollary. Let

$$f(x) = a_0 + a_1 x + \cdots + a_n x^n$$

be a polynomial with positive real coefficients. Then every root $z \in \mathbb{C}$ of f satisfies $r \leq |z| \leq R$ for

$$r = \min\{a_0/a_1, \ldots, a_{n-1}/a_n\},$$
$$R = \max\{a_0/a_1, \ldots, a_{n-1}/a_n\}.$$

Proof. The bound $|z| \leq R$ follows by applying the lemma to the polynomial $f(x/R)$. The bound $|z| \geq r$ follows by applying the lemma to the reverse of the polynomial $f(x/r)$.   □

Suppose now that $P_i(z) = P_j(z) = 0$ for some $z \in \mathbb{C}$ and some integers $i < j$. We cannot have $j = i + 1$, as then $P_i(0) \neq 0$ and so $P_j(z) - P_i(z) = (i + 1)z^i \neq 0$; thus $j - i \geq 2$. By applying the corollary to $P_i(x)$, $|z| \leq 1 - \frac{1}{i}$. On the other hand, by applying the corollary to $(P_j(x) - P_i(x))/x^i$, $|z| \geq 1 - \frac{1}{i+2}$, a contradiction.

Remark. Elkies reports that this problem arises in work of Joe Harris. It dates back even further to [**Kaji**, Example 3.7], in which the third solution is given.

Elkies also points out a mild generalization which may be treated using the first solution but not the third: for integers $a < b < c < d$ and $z \in \mathbb{C}$ which is neither zero nor a root of unity, the matrix

$$\begin{pmatrix} 1 & 1 & 1 & 1 \\ a & b & c & d \\ z^a & z^b & z^c & z^d \end{pmatrix}$$

has rank 3. (The problem at hand is the case $a = 0, b = 1, c = i + 1, d = j + 1$.)

Remark. It is also possible to solve this problem using a p-adic valuation on the field of algebraic numbers in place of the complex absolute value; however, this leads to a substantially more complicated solution. In lieu of including such a solution here, we refer to the approach described by Victor Wang at AoPS (topic c7t127334f7h616731).

Remark. It seems likely that the individual polynomials $P_k(x)$ are all irreducible, but this appears difficult to prove.

A6. $(3, 2, 2, \ldots, 1, 0, 31, 151)$ 3.7%
    Let n be a positive integer. What is the largest k for which there exist $n \times n$ matrices $M_1, \ldots, M_k$ and $N_1, \ldots, N_k$ with real entries such that for all i and j, the matrix product $M_i N_j$ has a zero entry somewhere on its diagonal if and only if $i \neq j$?

Answer. The largest such k is n^n.

Solution. We first show that this value can be achieved by an explicit construction. Let $e_1, \ldots, e_n$ be the standard basis of $\mathbb{R}^n$. For $i_1, \ldots, i_n \in \{1, \ldots, n\}$, let $M_{i_1, \ldots, i_n}$ be the matrix with row vectors $e_{i_1}, \ldots, e_{i_n}$, and let $N_{i_1, \ldots, i_n}$ be the transpose of $M_{i_1, \ldots, i_n}$. Then $M_{i_1, \ldots, i_n} N_{j_1, \ldots, j_n}$ has kth diagonal entry $e_{i_k} \cdot e_{j_k}$, proving the claim.

We next show that for any families of matrices M_i, N_j as described, we must have $k \leq n^n$. Let V be the n-fold *tensor product* of $\mathbb{R}^n$, that is, the vector space with orthonormal basis $e_{i_1} \otimes \cdots \otimes e_{i_n}$ for $i_1, \ldots, i_n \in \{1, \ldots, n\}$. Let m_i be the tensor product of the rows of M_i; that is,

$$m_i = \sum_{i_1, \ldots, i_n = 1}^{n} (M_i)_{1, i_1} \cdots (M_i)_{n, i_n} e_{i_1} \otimes \cdots \otimes e_{i_n}.$$

Similarly, let n_j be the tensor product of the columns of N_j. One computes that $m_i \cdot n_j$ equals the product of the diagonal entries of $M_i N_j$, and so vanishes if and only if $i \neq j$. For any $c_i \in \mathbb{R}$ such that $\sum_i c_i m_i = 0$, for each j

$$0 = \left(\sum_i c_i m_i \right) \cdot n_j = \sum_i c_i (m_i \cdot n_j) = c_j (m_j \cdot n_j),$$

yielding $c_j = 0$. Therefore the vectors $m_1, \ldots, m_k$ in V are linearly independent, implying $k \leq n^n$ as desired.

Remark. Noam Elkies points out that a similar argument yields the answer n^m in the case that the M_i are $m \times n$ matrices and the N_j are $n \times m$ matrices.

B1. (131, 36, 6, ..., 12, 0, 5, 0) 91.1%

　　A *base*-10 *over-expansion* **of a positive integer** N **is an expression of the form**

$$N = d_k 10^k + d_{k-1} 10^{k-1} + \cdots + d_0 10^0$$

with $d_k \neq 0$ **and** $d_i \in \{0, 1, 2, \ldots, 10\}$ **for all** i. **For instance, the integer** $N = 10$ **has two base-10 over-expansions:** $10 = 10 \cdot 10^0$ **and the usual base-10 expansion** $10 = 1 \cdot 10^1 + 0 \cdot 10^0$. **Which positive integers have a unique base-10 over-expansion?**

Answer. These are the integers with no 0's in their usual base-10 expansion.

Solution. If the usual base-10 expansion of N is $d_k 10^k + \cdots + d_0 10^0$ and one of the digits is 0, then there exists an $i \leq k - 1$ such that $d_i = 0$ and $d_{i+1} > 0$; then we can replace $d_{i+1} 10^{i+1} + (0)10^i$ by $(d_{i+1} - 1)10^{i+1} + (10)10^i$ to obtain a second base-10 over-expansion.

　　We claim conversely that if N has no 0's in its usual base-10 expansion, then this standard form is the unique base-10 over-expansion for N. This holds by induction on the number of digits of N: if $1 \leq N \leq 9$, then the result is clear. Otherwise, any base-10 over-expansion $N = d_k 10^k + \cdots + d_1 10 + d_0 10^0$ must have $d_0 \equiv N \pmod{10}$, which uniquely determines d_0 since N is not a multiple of 10; then $(N - d_0)/10$ inherits the base-10 over-expansion $d_k 10^{k-1} + \cdots + d_1 10^0$, which must be unique by the induction hypothesis.

Remark. (Shawn Williams, via Karl Mahlburg) For an alternate proof of uniqueness, write the usual expansion $N = d_k 10^k + \cdots + d_0 10^0$ and suppose $d_i \neq 0$ for all i. Let $M = c_l 10^l + \cdots + c_0 10^0$ be an over-expansion with at least one 10. To have $M = N$, we must have $l \leq k$; we may pad the expansion of M with zeros to force $l = k$. Now define $e_i = c_i - d_i$; since $1 \leq d_i \leq 9$ and $0 \leq c_i \leq 10$, $0 \leq |e_i| \leq 9$. Moreover, there exists at least one index i with $e_i \neq 0$, since any index for which $c_i = 10$ has this property. But if i is the largest such index, then

$$10^i \leq |e_i 10^i| = \left| -\sum_{j=0}^{i-1} e_j 10^j \right|$$

$$\leq \sum_{j=0}^{i-1} |e_j 10^j| \leq 9 \cdot 10^{i-1} + \cdots + 9 \cdot 10^0,$$

a contradiction.

B2. (91, 5, 0, ..., 0, 59, 18, 17) 50.5%

　　Suppose that f **is a function on the interval** $[1, 3]$ **such that** $-1 \leq f(x) \leq 1$ **for all** x **and** $\int_1^3 f(x)\, dx = 0$. **How large can** $\int_1^3 \frac{f(x)}{x}\, dx$ **be?**

Answer. The maximum value of the integral is $\log \frac{4}{3}$.

Solution 1. Let

$$g(x) = \begin{cases} 1 & 1 \le x \le 2, \\ -1 & 2 < x \le 3, \end{cases}$$

and define $h(x) = g(x) - f(x)$. Then

$$h(x) \ge 0, \quad 1 \le x \le 2,$$
$$h(x) \le 0, \quad 2 < x \le 3,$$

$$\int_1^3 h(x)\,dx = 0.$$

Now

$$\int_1^3 \frac{h(x)}{x}\,dx = \int_1^2 \frac{|h(x)|}{x}\,dx - \int_2^3 \frac{|h(x)|}{x}\,dx$$
$$\ge \int_1^2 \frac{|h(x)|}{2}\,dx - \int_2^3 \frac{|h(x)|}{2}\,dx = 0,$$

and thus $\int_1^3 \frac{f(x)}{x}\,dx \le \int_1^3 \frac{g(x)}{x}\,dx = 2\log 2 - \log 3 = \log \frac{4}{3}$. The bound is achieved for $h = 0$, that is, $f = g$.

Solution 2. (Zilin Jiang, via AoPS) Define the function $F(x) = \int_1^x f(t)\,dt$ for $1 \le x \le 3$; then $F(1) = F(3) = 0$ and $F(x) \le \min\{x - 1, 3 - x\}$. Using integration by parts, we obtain

$$\int_1^3 \frac{f(x)}{x}\,dx = \int_1^3 \frac{F(x)}{x^2}\,dx$$
$$\le \int_1^2 \frac{x-1}{x^2}\,dx + \int_2^3 \frac{3-x}{x^2}\,dx$$
$$= \log \frac{4}{3}.$$

(To make this completely rigorous, one can approximate F by continuously differentiable functions.)

B3. (86, 22, 11, ..., 6, 5, 39, 21) 62.6%

   Let A be an $m \times n$ **matrix with rational entries. Suppose that there are at least $m + n$ distinct prime numbers among the absolute values of the entries of A. Show that the rank of A is at least 2.**

Solution 1. Assume by way of contradiction that A has rank at most 1. In this case, every column of A is a multiple of some fixed column vector; that is, we can find rational numbers $a_1, \ldots, a_m, b_1, \ldots, b_n$ such that $A_{ij} = a_i b_j$ for all i, j. By deleting rows or columns, we may reduce to the case where $a_i, b_j \neq 0$ for all i, j.

Recall that any nonzero rational number q has a unique prime factorization

$$q = \pm 2^{c_1} 3^{c_2} 5^{c_3} \cdots$$

with exponents in $\mathbb{Z}$. Set

$$c(q) = (c_1, c_2, c_3, \ldots).$$

Note that $|a_i b_j|$ is prime if and only if $c(a_i) + c(b_j)$ has one entry equal to 1 and all others equal to 0. The condition that $m + n$ distinct primes appear among the $|a_i b_j|$ implies that the vector space

$$V = \left\{ \sum_i x_i c(a_i) + \sum_j y_j c(b_j) : x_i, y_j \in \mathbb{R}, \sum_i x_i = \sum_j y_j \right\}$$

contains a linearly independent set of size $m + n$. But V is evidently spanned by $m + n - 1$ vectors, so $\dim V \leq m + n - 1$, a contradiction.

Solution 2. In this solution, we use standard terminology of graph theory, considering only simple undirected graphs (with no self-loops or multiple edges). We first recall a standard lemma in graph theory.

Lemma. A graph on k vertices with no cycles contains at most $k - 1$ edges.

Proof. We induct on k. For $k = 1$, the claim is trivially true because there can be no edges. Assume that $k > 1$. If there are no edges, we are done, so suppose e: a—b is an edge of the given graph $\mathcal{G}$. Removing e from $\mathcal{G}$ yields a graph $\mathcal{G}'$ with no paths from a to b. Hence $\mathcal{G}'$ can be decomposed (not necessarily uniquely) into a disjoint union $\mathcal{G}_1 \sqcup \mathcal{G}_2$ of two nonempty graphs. Let $\mathcal{G}_i$ have k_i vertices. By induction, $\mathcal{G}$ has at most

$$(k_1 - 1) + (k_2 - 1) + 1 = k - 1$$

edges, as desired.   □

Returning to the original problem, suppose that A has rank at most 1. Draw a bipartite graph $\mathcal{G}$ whose vertices R_i ($1 \leq i \leq m$), C_j ($1 \leq j \leq n$) correspond to the rows and columns of A, and for each prime occurring among the $|A_{ij}|$, draw an edge between R_i and C_j (only one such edge for each prime). By hypothesis, $\mathcal{G}$ has at least $m + n$ edges. By the lemma, $\mathcal{G}$ must contain a cycle. Since $\mathcal{G}$ is bipartite, this cycle must be of length $2k$ for some integer $k \geq 2$ (we cannot have $k = 1$ because the graph has no multiple edges). Without loss of generality, we may assume that the cycle is R_1—C_1—R_2—C_2—$\cdots$—C_k—R_1. There must then exist distinct prime numbers $p_1, \ldots, p_{2k}$ such that

$$|A_{11}| = p_1, |A_{21}| = p_2, |A_{22}| = p_3, \ldots, |A_{kk}| = p_{2k-1}, |A_{1k}| = p_{2k}.$$

However, since A has rank at most 1, we can write $A_{ij} = a_i b_j$ for some rational numbers a_i and b_j. We get

$$
\begin{aligned}
p_1 \cdot p_3 \cdots p_{2k-1} &= (a_1 b_1)(a_2 b_2) \cdots (a_k b_k) \\
&= (a_2 b_1) \cdots (a_n b_{n-1})(a_1 b_n) \\
&= p_2 \cdot p_4 \cdots p_{2k},
\end{aligned}
$$

a contradiction since the p_i are distinct.

B4. (14, 4, 3, ..., 2, 10, 41, 116) 11.1%
   Show that for each positive integer n, all the roots of the polynomial

$$
\sum_{k=0}^{n} 2^{k(n-k)} x^k
$$

are real numbers.

Solution. (based on a suggestion of Karl Mahlburg) Define the polynomial $f_n(x) = \sum_{k=0}^{n} 2^{k(n-k)} x^k$. Since

$$
f_1(x) = 1 + x, \quad f_2(x) = 1 + 2x + x^2 = (1 + x)^2,
$$

the claim holds for $n \le 2$. For $n \ge 3$, we show that the quantities

$$
f_n(-2^{-n}), f_n(-2^{-n+2}), \ldots, f_n(-2^n)
$$

alternate in sign. By the intermediate value theorem, this will imply that f_n has a root in each of the n intervals $(-2^{-n}, -2^{-n+2}), \ldots, (-2^{n-2}, -2^n)$, forcing f_n to have as many distinct real roots as its degree.
   For $j \in \{0, \ldots, n\}$,

$$
\begin{aligned}
f_n(-2^{-n+2j}) &= \sum_{k=0}^{n} (-1)^k 2^{2jk-k^2} \\
&= 2^{j^2} \sum_{k=0}^{n} (-1)^k 2^{-(j-k)^2} \\
&= (-1)^j 2^{j^2} \sum_{k=-j}^{n-j} (-1)^k 2^{-k^2}.
\end{aligned}
$$

To show that these values alternate in sign, it suffices to prove that the sum

$$
s_{n,j} = \sum_{k=-j}^{n-j} (-1)^k 2^{-k^2}
$$

is always positive.

If $0 < j < n$, the terms of this sum for $k = -1, 0, 1$ are

$$-\frac{1}{2} + 1 - \frac{1}{2} = 0,$$

so these terms cancel. The remaining terms

$$\sum_{k=2}^{j}(-1)^k 2^{-k^2} + \sum_{k=2}^{n-j}(-1)^k 2^{-k^2}$$

form two alternating series whose terms strictly decrease in absolute value. Each sum (if nonempty) is therefore dominated by its first term $2^{-2^2} > 0$. Since $n \geq 3$, at least one of the sums is nonempty.

Finally, if $j = 0$ or $j = n$, then

$$s_{n,j} = \sum_{k=0}^{n}(-1)^k 2^{-k^2}$$

is itself an alternating series whose terms strictly decrease in absolute value, and thus is positive.

B5. (3, 0, 0, ..., 2, 21, 35, 129) 1.6%

In the 75th annual Putnam Games, participants compete at mathematical games. Patniss and Keeta play a game in which they take turns choosing an element from the group of invertible $n \times n$ matrices with entries in the field $\mathbb{Z}/p\mathbb{Z}$ of integers modulo p, where n is a fixed positive integer and p is a fixed prime number. The rules of the game are:

(1) **A player cannot choose an element that has been chosen by either player on any previous turn.**

(2) **A player can only choose an element that commutes with all previously chosen elements.**

(3) **A player who cannot choose an element on his/her turn loses the game.**

Patniss takes the first turn. Which player has a winning strategy? (Your answer may depend on n and p.)

Answer. For all n, Patniss has a winning strategy if $p = 2$ and Keeta has a winning strategy if $p > 2$.

Solution. We first analyze the analogous game played using an arbitrary finite group G. Recall that for any subset S of G, the set of elements $g \in G$ which commute with all elements of S forms a subgroup $Z(S)$ of G, called the *centralizer* (or *commutant*) of S. At any given point in the game, the set S of previously chosen elements is contained in $Z(S)$. Initially $S = \emptyset$ and $Z(S) = G$; after each turn, S is increased by one element and $Z(S)$ is replaced by a subgroup. In particular, if the order of $Z(S)$ is odd at some point, it remains odd thereafter; conversely, if S contains an element of even order, then the order of $Z(S)$ remains even thereafter. Therefore any element $g \in G$ for which $Z(\{g\})$ has odd order is a winning first move for Patniss, while any other first move by Patniss loses if Keeta responds with some $h \in Z(\{g\})$ of even order (for example, a nontrivial element of a 2-Sylow subgroup of $Z(\{g\})$). In both cases, the win is guaranteed no matter what moves follow.

Now let G be the group of invertible $n \times n$ matrices with entries in $\mathbb{Z}/p\mathbb{Z}$. If $p > 2$, then $Z(S)$ will always contain the scalar matrix -1 of order 2, so the win for Keeta is guaranteed. (An explicit winning strategy is to answer any move g with the move $-g$.)

If $p = 2$, we establish the existence of $g \in G$ such that $Z(\{g\})$ has odd order using the existence of an irreducible polynomial $P(x)$ of degree n over $\mathbb{Z}/p\mathbb{Z}$ (see remark). We construct an $n \times n$ matrix over $\mathbb{Z}/p\mathbb{Z}$ with characteristic polynomial $P(x)$ by taking the *companion matrix* of $P(x)$: write $P(x) = x^n + P_{n-1}x^{n-1} + \cdots + P_0$ and set

$$g = \begin{pmatrix} 0 & 0 & \cdots & 0 & -P_0 \\ 1 & 0 & \cdots & 0 & -P_1 \\ 0 & 1 & \cdots & 0 & -P_2 \\ \vdots & \vdots & \ddots & \vdots & \vdots \\ 0 & 0 & \cdots & 1 & -P_{n-1} \end{pmatrix}.$$

In particular, $\det(g) = (-1)^n P_0 \neq 0$, so $g \in G$. Over an algebraic closure of $\mathbb{Z}/p\mathbb{Z}$, g becomes diagonalizable with distinct eigenvalues, so any matrix commuting with g must also be diagonalizable, and hence of odd order. In particular, $Z(\{g\})$ is of odd order, so Patniss has a winning strategy.

Remark. It can be shown that in the case $p = 2$, the only elements $g \in G$ for which $Z(\{g\})$ has odd order are those for which g has distinct eigenvalues.

Remark. We sketch two ways to verify the standard fact that there exists an irreducible polynomial of degree n over $\mathbb{Z}/p\mathbb{Z}$ for any positive integer n and any prime number p. One is to use Möbius inversion to count the number of irreducible polynomials of degree n over $\mathbb{Z}/p\mathbb{Z}$ and then give a positive lower bound for this count; this approach is taken in [**Berl**, Theorem 3.36]. The other is to first establish the existence of a finite field $\mathbb{F}$ of cardinality p^n, for instance by taking the set of roots of the polynomial $x^{p^n} - x$ inside a splitting field, and then take the minimal polynomial over $\mathbb{Z}/p\mathbb{Z}$ of a primitive $(p^n - 1)$st root of unity in $\mathbb{F}$ (which exists because the multiplicative group of $\mathbb{F}$ contains at most one cyclic subgroup of any given order). One might be tempted to apply the primitive element theorem for $\mathbb{F}$ over $\mathbb{Z}/p\mathbb{Z}$, but in fact one of the preceding techniques is needed in order to verify this result for finite fields, as the standard argument that "most" elements of the upper field are primitive breaks down for finite fields.

One may also describe the preceding analysis for $p = 2$ in terms of an identification of $\mathbb{F}$ as a $\mathbb{Z}/2\mathbb{Z}$-vector space with the space of column vectors of length n. Under such an identification, if we take g to be an element of $\mathbb{F} - \{0\}$ generating this group, then any element of $Z(\{g\})$ commutes with all of $\mathbb{F} - \{0\}$ and hence must define an $\mathbb{F}$-linear endomorphism of $\mathbb{F}$. Any such endomorphism is itself multiplication by an element of $\mathbb{F}$, so $Z(\{g\})$ is identified with the multiplicative group of $\mathbb{F}$, whose order is the odd number $2^n - 1$.

B6. (1, 1, 0, ..., 1, 3, 37, 147) 1.1%

Let $f : [0, 1] \to \mathbb{R}$ be a function for which there exists a constant $K > 0$ such that $|f(x) - f(y)| \le K|x - y|$ for all $x, y \in [0, 1]$. Suppose also that for each rational number $r \in [0, 1]$, there exist integers a and b such that $f(r) = a + br$. Prove that there exist finitely many intervals $I_1, \ldots, I_n$ such that f is a linear function on each I_i and $[0, 1] = \bigcup_{i=1}^{n} I_i$.

Solution. Let us say that a linear function g on an interval is *integral* if it has the form $g(x) = a + bx$ for some $a, b \in \mathbb{Z}$, and that a piecewise linear function is *integral* if on every interval where it is linear, it is also integral.

For each positive integer n, define the nth *Farey sequence* F_n as the sequence of rational numbers in $[0, 1]$ with denominators at most n. We show by induction on n that any two consecutive elements $\frac{r}{s}, \frac{r'}{s'}$ of F_n, written in lowest terms, satisfy $\gcd(s, s') = 1$, $s + s' > n$, and $r's - rs' = 1$. The base case $n = 1$ holds because $F_1 = \left(\frac{0}{1}, \frac{1}{1}\right)$. To deduce the claim for F_n from the claim for F_{n-1}, let $\frac{r}{s}, \frac{r'}{s'}$ be consecutive elements of F_{n-1}. If $s + s' = n$, then for $m = r + r'$, $\frac{r}{s} < \frac{m}{n} < \frac{r'}{s'}$ and the pairs $\frac{r}{s}, \frac{m}{n}$ and $\frac{m}{n}, \frac{r'}{s'}$ satisfy the desired conditions. Conversely, if $s + s' > n$, then we cannot have $\frac{r}{s} < \frac{m}{n} < \frac{r'}{s'}$ for $a \in \mathbb{Z}$, as this yields the contradiction

$$n = (ms - nr)s' + (r'n - ms')s \ge s + s' > n.$$

Hence $\frac{r}{s}, \frac{r'}{s'}$ remain consecutive in F_n.

Let $f_n : [0, 1] \to \mathbb{R}$ be the continuous, piecewise linear function which agrees with f at each element of F_n and is linear between any two consecutive elements of F_n. Between any two consecutive elements $\frac{r}{s}, \frac{r'}{s'}$ of F_n, f_n coincides with some linear function $a + bx$. Since $sf\left(\frac{r}{s}\right), s'f\left(\frac{r'}{s'}\right) \in \mathbb{Z}$, we deduce that

$$a = r'sf\left(\frac{r}{s}\right) - rs'f\left(\frac{r'}{s'}\right)$$

and

$$b = ss'\left(f\left(\frac{r'}{s'}\right) - f\left(\frac{r}{s}\right)\right)$$

are integers. It follows that f_n is integral.

We now check that if $n > 2K$, then $f_n = f_{n-1}$. For this, it suffices to check that for any consecutive elements $\frac{r}{s}, \frac{m}{n}, \frac{r'}{s'}$ in F_n, the linear function $a_0 + b_0 x$ coinciding with f_{n-1} on the interval $\left[\frac{r}{s}, \frac{r'}{s'}\right]$ has the property that $f(\frac{m}{n}) = a_0 + b_0 \frac{m}{n}$. Define the integer $t = nf(\frac{m}{n}) - a_0 n - b_0 m$. We then compute that the slope of f_n from $\frac{r}{s}$ to $\frac{m}{n}$ is $b_0 + st$, while the slope of f_n from $\frac{m}{n}$ to $\frac{r'}{s'}$ is $b_0 - s't$. In order to have $|b_0 + st|, |b_0 - s't| \le K$, we must have $(s + s')|t| \le 2K$; since $s + s' = n > 2K$, this is only possible if $t = 0$. Hence $f_n = f_{n-1}$, as claimed.

It follows that for any $n > 2K$, we must have $f_n = f_{n+1} = \cdots$. Since the condition on f and K implies that f is continuous, we must also have $f_n = f$, completing the proof.

Remark. An alternate approach is to prove that for each $x \in [0, 1)$, there exists $\epsilon \in (0, 1 - x)$ such that the restriction of f to $[x, x + \epsilon]$ is linear; one may then deduce the claim using the compactness of $[0, 1]$. In this approach, the role of the Farey sequence may also be played by the convergents of the continued fraction of x (at least in the case where x is irrational).

Remark. The condition on f and K is called *Lipschitz continuity*. Some related results can be proved with the Lipschitz continuity condition replaced by suitable convexity conditions; see for example [**KT**]. Such results arise in the theory of p-adic differential equations; see for example [**KX**].

The Seventy-Sixth William Lowell Putnam
Mathematical Competition—December 5, 2015

A1. $(165, 17, 7, \ldots, 3, 0, 5, 2)$ 95.0%

Let A and B be points on the same branch of the hyperbola $xy = 1$. Suppose that P is a point lying between A and B on this hyperbola, such that the area of the triangle APB is as large as possible. Show that the region bounded by the hyperbola and the chord AP has the same area as the region bounded by the hyperbola and the chord PB.

Solution 1. Without loss of generality, assume that A and B lie in the first quadrant with $A = (a, 1/a)$, $B = (b, 1/b)$, and $a < b$. If $P = (t, 1/t)$ with $a \le t \le b$, then the area of $\triangle APB$ is

$$\frac{1}{2}\begin{vmatrix} 1 & 1 & 1 \\ a & t & b \\ 1/a & 1/t & 1/b \end{vmatrix} = \frac{b-a}{2ab}(a+b-t-ab/t).$$

When a and b are fixed, this is maximized when $t + ab/t$ is minimized, which by the arithmetic mean/geometric mean inequality exactly holds when $t = \sqrt{ab}$.

The line $\overleftrightarrow{AP}$ is given by $y = \frac{a+t-x}{ta}$, and so the area of the region bounded by the hyperbola and $\overleftrightarrow{AP}$ is

$$\int_a^t \left(\frac{a+t-x}{ta} - \frac{1}{x} \right) dx = \frac{t}{2a} - \frac{a}{2t} - \log\left(\frac{t}{a}\right),$$

which at $t = \sqrt{ab}$ is equal to $\frac{b-a}{2\sqrt{ab}} - \log(\sqrt{b/a})$. Similarly, the area of the region bounded by the hyperbola and $\overleftrightarrow{PB}$ is $\frac{b}{2t} - \frac{t}{2b} - \log\frac{b}{t}$, which at $t = \sqrt{ab}$ is also $\frac{b-a}{2\sqrt{ab}} - \log(\sqrt{b/a})$, as desired.

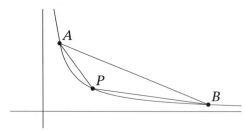

Solution 2. For any $\lambda > 0$, the map $(x, y) \mapsto (\lambda x, \lambda^{-1} y)$ preserves all areas and the hyperbola $xy = 1$. We may thus rescale the picture so that A, B are symmetric across the line $y = x$, with A above the line. As P moves from A to B, the area of $\triangle APB$ increases until P passes through the point $(1, 1)$, then decreases.

Consequently, $P = (1, 1)$ achieves the maximum area, and the desired equality holds by symmetry. Alternatively, since the hyperbola is convex, the maximum is uniquely achieved at the point where the tangent line is parallel to $\overleftrightarrow{AB}$, and by symmetry that point is $(1, 1)$.

A2. $(109, 8, 3, \ldots, 12, 2, 45, 20)$ 60.3%
   Let $a_0 = 1$, $a_1 = 2$, and $a_n = 4a_{n-1} - a_{n-2}$ for $n \geq 2$. **Find an odd prime factor of** a_{2015}.

Answer. One such prime factor is 181.

Solution 1. By induction, $a_n = ((2 + \sqrt{3})^n + (2 - \sqrt{3})^n)/2 = (\alpha^n + \beta^n)/2$ for all n, where $\alpha = 2 + \sqrt{3}$ and $\beta = 2 - \sqrt{3}$. Now note that if k is an odd positive integer and $a_n \neq 0$, then $\frac{a_{kn}}{a_n} = \frac{\alpha^{kn} + \beta^{kn}}{\alpha^n + \beta^n} = \alpha^{(k-1)n} - \alpha^{(k-2)n}\beta^n + \cdots - \alpha^n \beta^{(k-2)n} + \beta^{(k-1)n}$. This expression is both rational (because a_n and a_{kn} are integers) and of the form $a + b\sqrt{3}$ for some integers a and b by the expressions for α and β; it follows that it must be an integer, and so a_{kn} is divisible by a_n. Applying this to $n = 5$ and $k = 403$, we find that a_{2015} is divisible by $a_5 = 362$ and thus by 181.

Solution 2. By rewriting the formula for a_n as $a_{n-2} = 4a_{n-1} - a_n$, we may extend the sequence backwards to define a_n for all integers n. Since $a_{-1} = 2$, by induction $a_{-n} = a_n$ for all n. For any integer m and any prime p dividing a_m, p also divides a_{-m}; on the other hand, p cannot divide a_{-m+1}, as otherwise p would also divide $a_{-m+2}, \ldots, a_0 = 1$, a contradiction. We can thus find an integer k such that $a_{m+1} \equiv ka_{-m+1} \pmod{p}$; by induction on n, $a_n \equiv ka_{n-2m} \pmod{p}$ for all n. In particular, if k is odd, then p also divides a_{km}; we thus conclude that a_{2015} is divisible by $a_5 = 362$ and thus by 181.

Remark. Similar arguments show that if $a_n \equiv 0 \pmod{p}$, then $a_{2n+k} \equiv -a_k \pmod{p}$ for all k.

Remark. One can find other prime factors of a_{2015} in the same manner. For example, a_{2015} is divisible by each of the following quantities.

$a_{13} = 2 \times 6811741$,

$a_{31} = 2 \times 373 \times 360250962984637$,

$a_{5 \cdot 13} = 2 \times 181 \times 6811741$
$\qquad \times 30450462746793166654761356161$,

$a_{5 \cdot 31} = 1215497709121 \times 28572709494917432101$
$\qquad \times 1327736055550617981699782712 6375881581$,

$a_{13 \cdot 31} = 2 \times 373 \times 193441 \times 6811741 \times 360250962984637$
$\qquad \times 16866100753000669 \times 79988387992470656916594531961 \times p_{156}$.

(The prime factorizations were computed using the *Magma* computer algebra system. The quantity p_{156} is a prime of 156 decimal digits.) Dividing a_{2015} by the product of the primes appearing in this list yields a number N of 824 decimal digits whose prime factorization we have been unable to establish. One thing we can show is that each prime factor of N is congruent to 1 modulo $2^2 \times 3 \times 2015 = 24180$. Using *Magma*'s implementation of the Pollard $p-1$ method (which looks for prime factors p of N for which $p-1$ has relatively small prime factors), we found that there is an integer N_1 such that

$$N = 150719356321 \times 12750650139609721 \times N_1.$$

We can check that N_1 is itself not prime using the *Fermat test*, by computing that $2^{N_1} \not\equiv 2 \pmod{N_1}$. We were unable to factor N_1 using *Magma*; this is not surprising, as N_1 is larger than a 2048-bit RSA modulus. The best known approach to factor numbers appearing in linear recurrence relations is the *special number field sieve*, but even this is infeasible for numbers as large as N_1.

A3. (99, 22, 1, ..., 13, 6, 23, 35) 61.3%
   Compute

$$\log_2\left(\prod_{a=1}^{2015}\prod_{b=1}^{2015}(1+e^{2\pi iab/2015})\right)$$

Here i is the imaginary unit (that is, $i^2 = -1$).

Answer. The answer is 13725.

Solution. We begin with a lemma.

Lemma. If n is odd, then $\prod_{b=1}^{n}(1+e^{2\pi iab/n}) = 2^{\gcd(a,n)}$.

Proof. Write $d = \gcd(a,n)$ and $a = da_1$, $n = dn_1$ with $\gcd(a_1,n_1) = 1$. Then $a_1, 2a_1, \ldots, n_1a_1$ modulo n_1 is a permutation of $1, 2, \ldots, n_1$ modulo n_1, and so $\omega^{a_1}, \omega^{2a_1}, \ldots, \omega^{n_1a_1}$ is a permutation of $\omega, \omega^2, \ldots, \omega^{n_1}$; it follows that for $\omega = e^{2\pi i/n_1}$,

$$\prod_{b=1}^{n_1}(1+e^{2\pi iab/n}) = \prod_{b=1}^{n_1}(1+e^{2\pi ia_1b/n_1}) = \prod_{b=1}^{n_1}(1+\omega^b).$$

Since the roots of $z^{n_1}-1$ are $\omega, \omega^2, \ldots, \omega^{n_1}$, it follows that $z^{n_1}-1 = \prod_{b=1}^{n_1}(z-\omega^b)$. Setting $z = -1$ and using the fact that n_1 is odd gives $\prod_{b=1}^{n_1}(1+\omega^b) = 2$.
   Finally, $\prod_{b=1}^{n}(1+e^{2\pi iab/n}) = (\prod_{b=1}^{n_1}(1+e^{2\pi iab/n}))^d = 2^d$, as desired. □

From the lemma,

$$\log_2 \left(\prod_{a=1}^{2015} \prod_{b=1}^{2015} (1 + e^{2\pi i a b/2015}) \right)$$

$$= \sum_{a=1}^{2015} \log_2 \left(\prod_{b=1}^{2015} (1 + e^{2\pi i a b/2015}) \right)$$

$$= \sum_{a=1}^{2015} \gcd(a, 2015).$$

Now for each divisor d of 2015, there are $\phi(2015/d)$ integers between 1 and 2015 inclusive whose gcd with 2015 is d. Thus

$$\sum_{a=1}^{2015} \gcd(a, 2015) = \sum_{d|2015} d \cdot \phi(2015/d).$$

We factor $2015 = pqr$ with $p = 5, q = 13, r = 31$. Since ϕ is multiplicative,

$$\sum_{d|pqr} d \cdot \phi(pqr/d) = \sum_{d|p} d \cdot \phi(p/d) \cdot \sum_{d|q} d \cdot \phi(q/d) \cdot \sum_{d|r} d \cdot \phi(r/d)$$

$$= (2p - 1)(2q - 1)(2r - 1)$$

$$= 9 \cdot 25 \cdot 61$$

$$= 13725.$$

Remark. Noam Elkies suggests the following similar but shorter derivation of the equality $\prod_{b=1}^{n_1}(1 + \omega^b) = 2$: write

$$\prod_{b=1}^{n_1-1} (1 + \omega^b) = \frac{\prod_{b=1}^{n_1-1}(1 - \omega^{2b})}{\prod_{b=1}^{n_1-1}(1 - \omega^b)}$$

and note (as above) that $\omega^2, \omega^4, \ldots, \omega^{2(n_1-1)}$ is a permutation of $\omega, \ldots, \omega^{n_1-1}$, so the two products in the fraction are equal.

Remark. The function $f(n) = \sum_{d|n} d \cdot \phi(n/d)$ is multiplicative: for any two co-prime positive integers m, n, $f(mn) = f(m)f(n)$. This follows from the fact that $f(n)$ is the convolution of the two multiplicative functions $n \mapsto n$ and $n \mapsto \phi(n)$; it can also be seen directly using the Chinese remainder theorem.

A4. (52, 21, 4, ..., 15, 20, 33, 54) 38.7%
   For each real number x, let

$$f(x) = \sum_{n \in S_x} \frac{1}{2^n},$$

where S_x is the set of positive integers n for which $\lfloor nx \rfloor$ is even. What is the largest real number L such that $f(x) \geq L$ for all $x \in [0, 1)$? (As usual, $\lfloor z \rfloor$ denotes the greatest integer less than or equal to z.)

Answer. The largest such real number is $L = 4/7$.

Solution. For $S \subset \mathbb{N}$, let $F(S) = \sum_{n \in S} 1/2^n$, so that $f(x) = F(S_x)$. Note that for $T = \{1, 4, 7, 10, \ldots\}$, $F(T) = 4/7$.

We first show by contradiction that for any $x \in [0, 1)$, $f(x) \geq 4/7$. Since each term in the geometric series $\sum_n 1/2^n$ is equal to the sum of all subsequent terms, if S, S' are different subsets of $\mathbb{N}$ and the smallest positive integer in one of S, S' but not in the other is in S, then $F(S) \geq F(S')$. Assume $f(x) < 4/7$; then the smallest integer in one of S_x, T but not in the other is in T. Now $1 \in S_x$ for any $x \in [0, 1)$, and we conclude that there are three consecutive integers $n, n+1, n+2$ that are not in S_x: that is, $\lfloor nx \rfloor$, $\lfloor (n+1)x \rfloor$, $\lfloor (n+2)x \rfloor$ are all odd. Since the difference between consecutive terms in nx, $(n+1)x$, $(n+2)x$ is $x < 1$, we conclude that $\lfloor nx \rfloor = \lfloor (n+1)x \rfloor = \lfloor (n+2)x \rfloor$ and so $x < 1/2$. But then $2 \in S_x$ and so $f(x) \geq 3/4$, contradicting our assumption.

It remains to show that $4/7$ is the greatest lower bound for $f(x)$, $x \in [0, 1)$. For each n, choose $x = 2/3 - \epsilon$ with $0 < \epsilon < 1/(9n)$. Then for $1 \leq k \leq n$, we have $0 < 3k\epsilon < 1/3$, and so

$$\lfloor (3k-2)x \rfloor = \lfloor (2k-2) + 2/3 - (3k-2)\epsilon \rfloor = 2k - 2,$$
$$\lfloor (3k-1)x \rfloor = \lfloor (2k-1) + 1/3 - (3k-1)\epsilon \rfloor = 2k - 1,$$
$$\lfloor (3k)x \rfloor = \lfloor (2k-1) + 1 - 3k\epsilon \rfloor = 2k - 1.$$

It follows that S_x is a subset of $S = \{1, 4, 7, \ldots, 3n-2, 3n+1, 3n+2, 3n+3, \ldots\}$, and so $f(x) = F(S_x) \leq F(S) = (1/2 + 1/2^4 + \cdots + 1/2^{3n+1}) + 1/2^{3n+1}$. This last expression tends to $4/7$ as $n \to \infty$. Hence no number greater than $4/7$ can be a lower bound for $f(x)$ for all $x \in [0, 1)$.

Remark. One can equivalently give the argument in terms of binary expansions of real numbers. In this language, the inequality $F(S) \geq F(S')$ amounts to the usual fact that two real numbers can be compared using the leftmost position where their binary expansions differ, except for the equality between 1 and $0.111 \cdots_2$.

A5. (13, 1, 6, ..., 22, 4, 26, 127) 10.1%

Let q be an odd positive integer, and let N_q denote the number of integers a such that $0 < a < q/4$ and $\gcd(a, q) = 1$. Show that N_q is odd if and only if q is of the form p^k with k a positive integer and p a prime congruent to 5 or 7 modulo 8.

Solution 1. By the inclusion/exclusion principle,

$$N_q = \sum_{d|q} \mu(d) \left\lfloor \frac{\lfloor q/4 \rfloor}{d} \right\rfloor$$

$$= \sum_{d|q} \mu(d) \left\lfloor \frac{q/d}{4} \right\rfloor$$

$$\equiv \sum_{\substack{d|q \text{ squarefree}}} \left\lfloor \frac{q/d}{4} \right\rfloor \quad (\text{mod } 2),$$

where μ is the Möbius function. Now

$$\left\lfloor \frac{q/d}{4} \right\rfloor \equiv \begin{cases} 0 \quad (\text{mod } 2) & \text{if } q/d \equiv 1, 3 \quad (\text{mod } 8), \\ 1 \quad (\text{mod } 2) & \text{if } q/d \equiv 5, 7 \quad (\text{mod } 8). \end{cases}$$

So N_q is odd if and only if q has an odd number of squarefree factors q/d congruent to 5 or 7 modulo 8.

If q has a prime factor p congruent to 1 or 3 modulo 8, then the squarefree factors d of q occur in pairs $\{c, pc\}$, which are either both 1 or 3 modulo 8 or both 5 or 7 modulo 8. Hence q must have an even number of factors that are congruent to 5 or 7 modulo 8, and so N_q is even in this case.

If q has two prime factors p_1, p_2, each congruent to either 5 or 7 modulo 8, then the squarefree factors d of q occur in quadruples $\{d, p_1d, q_1d, p_1q_1d\}$, which are then congruent respectively to some permutation of $\{1, 3, 5, 7\}$ modulo 8 (if p_1 and p_2 are distinct modulo 8) or are congruent respectively to $\{d, p_1d, p_1d, d\}$ modulo 8. Either way, exactly two of the four residues are congruent to 5 or 7 modulo 8. Thus again q must have an even number of factors that are 5 or 7 modulo 8, and so N_q is even in this case as well.

If $q = 1$, then $N_q = 0$ is even. The only case that remains is that $q = p^k$ is a positive power of a prime p congruent to 5 or 7 modulo 8. In this case, q has two squarefree factors, 1 and p, of which exactly one is congruent to 5 or 7 modulo 8. We conclude that N_q is odd in this case, as desired.

Remark. The case analysis may be shortened using the *Dirichlet character*

$$\chi(n) = \begin{cases} 1 & \text{if } n \equiv 1, 3 \quad (\text{mod } 8), \\ -1 & \text{if } n \equiv 5, 7 \quad (\text{mod } 8). \end{cases}$$

Then χ is a multiplicative function on the positive odd integers, and

$$2N_q \equiv \sum_{\substack{d|q \text{ squarefree}}} (1 - \chi(d)) \equiv \prod_{p|n} 2 - \prod_{p|n} (1 + \chi(p)) \quad (\text{mod } 4).$$

It is then easy to see that the last two products are congruent modulo 4 unless n has only one prime divisor p and $\chi(p) = -1$.

Solution 2. Consider the set S of all integers in $\{1, \ldots, q-1\}$ that are even and relatively prime to q. Then the product of all elements in S is

$$2^{\phi(q)/2} \prod_{\substack{1 \leq a \leq (q-1)/2 \\ (a,q)=1}} a.$$

On the other hand, we can rewrite the set of elements in S modulo q as a set T of residues in the interval $[-(q-1)/2, (q-1)/2]$. Then for each $1 \leq a \leq (q-1)/2$ with $(a, q) = 1$, T contains exactly one element from $\{a, -a\}$: if $-2r \equiv 2s \pmod{q}$ for some $r, s \in \{1, \ldots, (q-1)/2\}$, then $r \equiv -s \pmod{q}$, which is impossible given the ranges of r and s. Thus the product of all elements in T is

$$(-1)^n \prod_{\substack{1 \leq a \leq (q-1)/2 \\ (a,q)=1}} a,$$

where n denotes the number of elements of S greater than $(q-1)/2$. We conclude that $(-1)^n \equiv 2^{\phi(q)/2} \pmod{q}$.

However, the number of elements of S less than $(q-1)/2$ is equal to N_q, since dividing these numbers by 2 gives exactly the numbers counted by N_q. Hence the total cardinality of S is $N_q + n$. However, this cardinality also equals $\phi(q)/2$ because the numbers in $\{1, \ldots, q-1\}$ relatively prime to q come in pairs $\{a, q-a\}$ in each of which exactly one member is even. We thus obtain

$$(-1)^{N_q} = (-1)^{\phi(q)/2+n}$$

$$\equiv (-1)^{\phi(q)/2} 2^{\phi(q)/2} = (-2)^{\phi(q)/2} \pmod{q}.$$

If $q = 1$, then N_q is even. If q has more than one prime factor, then the group $(\mathbb{Z}/q\mathbb{Z})^\times$ has exponent dividing $\phi(q)/2$, so $(-1)^{N_q} \equiv (-2)^{\phi(q)/2} \equiv 1 \pmod{q}$, and thus N_q must be even in this case as well. Finally, suppose that q is a prime power p^k with p odd and k positive. Since $(\mathbb{Z}/q\mathbb{Z})^\times$ is a cyclic group of order $\phi(q) = p^{k-1}(p-1)$, in which the only square roots of unity are ± 1, it follows that $(-2)^{\phi(q)/2} \equiv \pm 1 \pmod{q}$ in accordance with whether $(-2)^{(p-1)/2} \equiv \pm 1 \pmod{p}$, or in other words whether -2 is a quadratic residue or nonresidue. But recall that -2 is a quadratic residue modulo p if and only if $p \equiv 1$ or $3 \pmod 8$. Thus N_q is odd in this case if and only if $p \equiv 5$ or $7 \pmod 8$.

We conclude that for any odd integer $q \geq 1$, the quantity N_q is odd if and only if $q = p^k$ with k positive and p a prime that is 5 or 7 modulo 8.

Remark. The combination of the two solutions recovers Gauss's criterion for when -2 is a quadratic residue modulo p, with essentially the original proof.

A6. (4, 3, 1, $\ldots$, 2, 0, 53, 136) 4.0%

Let n be a positive integer. Suppose that A, B, and M are $n \times n$ matrices with real entries such that $AM = MB$, and such that A and B have the

same characteristic polynomial. Prove that $\det(A - MX) = \det(B - XM)$ **for every** $n \times n$ **matrix** X **with real entries.**

Solution 1. (Noam Elkies) Using row and column operations, we may construct invertible matrices U, V such that $U^{-1}MV$ is a block diagonal matrix of the form

$$\begin{pmatrix} I & 0 \\ 0 & 0 \end{pmatrix}.$$

Put $A' = U^{-1}AU, M' = U^{-1}MV, B' = V^{-1}BV, X' = V^{-1}XU$, so that $A'M' = M'B'$, $\det(A - MX) = \det(U^{-1}(A - MX)U) = \det(A' - M'X')$, and $\det(B - XM) = \det(V^{-1}(B - XM)V) = \det(B' - X'M')$. Form the corresponding block decompositions

$$A' = \begin{pmatrix} A_{11} & A_{12} \\ A_{21} & A_{22} \end{pmatrix}, B' = \begin{pmatrix} B_{11} & B_{12} \\ B_{21} & B_{22} \end{pmatrix}, X' = \begin{pmatrix} X_{11} & X_{12} \\ X_{21} & X_{22} \end{pmatrix}.$$

We then have

$$A'M' = \begin{pmatrix} A_{11} & 0 \\ A_{21} & 0 \end{pmatrix}, \qquad M'B' = \begin{pmatrix} B_{11} & B_{12} \\ 0 & 0 \end{pmatrix},$$

so $A_{11} = B_{11}$ and $A_{21} = B_{12} = 0$. In particular, the characteristic polynomial of A is the product of the characteristic polynomials of A_{11} and A_{22}, and the characteristic polynomial of B is the product of the characteristic polynomials of B_{11} and B_{22}. Since $A_{11} = B_{11}$, it follows that A_{22} and B_{22} have the same characteristic polynomial. Since

$$X'M' = \begin{pmatrix} X_{11} & 0 \\ X_{21} & 0 \end{pmatrix}, \qquad M'X' = \begin{pmatrix} X_{11} & X_{12} \\ 0 & 0 \end{pmatrix},$$

we conclude that

$$\det(A - MX) = \det(A' - M'X')$$
$$= \det\begin{pmatrix} A_{11} - X_{11} & A_{12} - X_{12} \\ 0 & A_{22} \end{pmatrix}$$
$$= \det(A_{11} - X_{11})\det(A_{22})$$
$$= \det(B_{11} - X_{11})\det(B_{22})$$
$$= \det\begin{pmatrix} B_{11} - X_{11} & 0 \\ B_{21} - X_{21} & B_{22} \end{pmatrix}$$
$$= \det(B' - X'M')$$
$$= \det(B - XM),$$

as desired. (By similar arguments, $A - MX$ and $B - XM$ have the same characteristic polynomial.)

Solution 2. We prove directly that $A - MX$ and $B - XM$ have the same characteristic polynomial; in other words, for any $t \in \mathbb{R}$, writing $A_t = A - tI$, $B_t = B - tI$,

$$\det(A_t - MX) = \det(B_t - XM).$$

For fixed A, B, M, the stated result is a polynomial identity in t and the entries of X. It thus suffices to check it assuming that A_t, B_t, X are all invertible. Since $AM = MB$, we also have $A_t M = MB_t$, so $A_t MB_t^{-1} = M$. Since $\det(A_t) = \det(B_t)$ by hypothesis,

$$\begin{aligned}
\det(A_t - MX) &= \det(A_t - A_t MB_t^{-1}X) \\
&= \det(A_t)\det(1 - MB_t^{-1}X) \\
&= \det(A_t)\det(X)\det(B_t)^{-1}\det(X^{-1}B_t - M) \\
&= \det(X)\det(X^{-1}B_t - M) \\
&= \det(B_t - XM).
\end{aligned}$$

Remark. One can also note directly that $\det(1 - MB_t^{-1}X) = \det(1 - XMB_t^{-1})$ using the fact that for any square matrices U and V, UV and VU have the same characteristic polynomial. The latter (commonly known as *Sylvester's determinant identity*) is again proved by reducing to the case where one of the two matrices is invertible, in which case the two matrices are similar.

Solution 3. (Lev Borisov) We will check that for each positive integer k,

$$\text{Trace}((A - MX)^k) = \text{Trace}((B - XM)^k).$$

This will imply that $A - MX$ and $B - XM$ have the same characteristic polynomial, yielding the desired result.

We establish the claim by expanding both sides and comparing individual terms. By hypothesis, A^k and B^k have the same characteristic polynomial, so $\text{Trace}(A^k) = \text{Trace}(B^k)$. To compare the other terms, it suffices to check that for any sequence $i_1, i_2, \ldots, i_m$ of nonnegative integers,

$$\text{Trace}(A^{i_1}MXA^{i_2}MX \cdots A^{i_{m-1}}MXA^{i_m})$$
$$= \text{Trace}(B^{i_1}XMB^{i_2}XM \cdots B^{i_{m-1}}XMB^{i_m}).$$

To establish this equality, first apply the remark following the previous solution to write

$$\text{Trace}(A^{i_1}MXA^{i_2}MX \cdots A^{i_{m-1}}MXA^{i_m})$$
$$= \text{Trace}(A^{i_m + i_1}MXA^{i_2}MX \cdots A^{i_{m-1}}MX).$$

Then apply the relation $AM = MB$ repeatedly to commute M past A, to obtain

$$\text{Trace}(MB^{i_m + i_1}XMB^{i_2}XM \cdots XMB^{i_{m-1}}X).$$

Finally, apply the remark again to shift MB^{i_m} from the left end to the right end.

Remark. The conclusion holds with $\mathbb{R}$ replaced by an arbitrary field. In the second solution, one must reduce to the case of an infinite field, for instance by replacing the original field with an algebraic closure. The third solution only applies to fields of characteristic 0 or positive characteristic greater than n.

Remark. It is tempting to try to reduce to the case where M is invertible, as in this case $A - MX$ and $B - XM$ are in fact similar. However, it is not clear how to make such an argument work.

B1. (61, 27, 7, ..., 41, 32, 10, 21) 47.7%
   Let f be a three times differentiable function (defined on $\mathbb{R}$ and real-valued) such that f has at least five distinct real zeros. Prove that $f + 6f' + 12f'' + 8f'''$ has at least two distinct real zeros.

Solution. Let $g(x) = e^{x/2} f(x)$. Then g has at least 5 distinct real zeros, and by repeated applications of Rolle's theorem, g', g'', g''' have at least 4, 3, 2 distinct real zeros, respectively. But

$$g'''(x) = \frac{1}{8} e^{x/2} (f(x) + 6f'(x) + 12f''(x) + 8f'''(x))$$

and $e^{x/2}$ is never zero, so we obtain the desired result.

B2. (62, 10, 3, ..., 3, 8, 60, 53) 37.7%
   Given a list of the positive integers $1, 2, 3, 4, \ldots$, take the first three numbers $1, 2, 3$ and their sum 6 and cross all four numbers off the list. Repeat with the three smallest remaining numbers $4, 5, 7$ and their sum 16. Continue in this way, crossing off the three smallest remaining numbers and their sum, and consider the sequence of sums produced: $6, 16, 27, 36, \ldots$. Prove or disprove that there is some number in the sequence whose base 10 representation ends with 2015.

Answer. We prove the assertion.

Solution. It suffices to show that 42015 appears in the sequence. Label the sequence of sums $s_0, s_1, \ldots$, and let a_n, b_n, c_n be the summands of s_n in ascending order. We prove the following two statements for each nonnegative integer n:

(a)$_n$ The sequence

$$a_{3n}, b_{3n}, c_{3n}, a_{3n+1}, b_{3n+1}, c_{3n+1}, a_{3n+2}, b_{3n+2}, c_{3n+2}$$

is obtained from the sequence $10n + 1, \ldots, 10n + 10$ by removing one of $10n + 5, 10n + 6, 10n + 7$.

(b)$_n$ We have

$$s_{3n} = 30n + 6,$$
$$s_{3n+1} \in \{30n + 15, 30n + 16, 30n + 17\},$$
$$s_{3n+2} = 30n + 27.$$

These statements follow by induction from the following simple observations:

- by computing the table of values

n	a_n	b_n	c_n	s_n
0	1	2	3	6
1	4	5	7	16
2	8	9	10	27

  we see that (a)$_0$ and (b)$_0$ hold;

- (a)$_n$ implies (b)$_n$;

- (a)$_n$ and (b)$_1, \ldots,$ (b)$_n$ together imply (a)$_{n+1}$.

To produce a value of n for which $s_n \equiv 2015 \pmod{10000}$, we take $n = 3m + 1$ for some nonnegative integer m for which $s_{3m+1} = 30m + 15$. We must also have $30m \equiv 2000 \pmod{10000}$, or equivalently $m \equiv 400 \pmod{1000}$. By taking $m = 1400$, we ensure that $m \equiv 2 \pmod 3$, so $s_m = 10m + 7$; this ensures that s_n does indeed equal $30m + 15 = 42015$, as desired.

Remark. With a bit more work, we can give a complete description of s_n, and in particular find the first term in the sequence whose decimal expansion ends in 2015. Define a function f on the nonnegative integers by

$$f(n) = s_{3n+1} - (30n + 16),$$

which takes values in $\{-1, 0, 1\}$. We then have

$$f(n) = \begin{cases} 0 & n \equiv 0 \pmod 3, \\ -f((n-1)/3) & n \equiv 1 \pmod 3, \\ -1 & n \equiv 2 \pmod 3. \end{cases}$$

Consequently, $f(n) = 0$ unless the base-3 expansion of n ends with 2 followed by a string of 1's of length $k \geq 0$, in which case $f(n) = (-1)^{k+1}$.

In this notation, $s_n \equiv 2015 \pmod{10000}$ if and only if $n = 3m + 1$ for some nonnegative integer m for which $m \equiv 400 \pmod{1000}$ and $f(m) = -1$. Since $400 = 112211_3$, the first such term in the sequence is in fact $s_{1201} = 12015$.

B3. $(32, 1, 6, \ldots, 18, 6, 81, 55)$ 19.6%

Let S be the set of all 2×2 real matrices

$$M = \begin{pmatrix} a & b \\ c & d \end{pmatrix}$$

whose entries a, b, c, d (in that order) form an arithmetic progression. Find all matrices M in S for which there is some integer $k > 1$ such that M^k is also in S.

Answer. The matrices in question are the scalar multiples of the matrices

$$A = \begin{pmatrix} 1 & 1 \\ 1 & 1 \end{pmatrix}, B = \begin{pmatrix} -3 & -1 \\ 1 & 3 \end{pmatrix}.$$

Solution 1. Any element of S can be written as $M = \alpha A + \beta B$ with $\alpha, \beta \in \mathbb{R}$. Note that $A^2 = \begin{pmatrix} 4 & 4 \\ 4 & 4 \end{pmatrix}$ and $B^3 = \begin{pmatrix} -24 & -8 \\ 8 & 24 \end{pmatrix}$ are both in S, and so any matrix of the form αA or βB, $\alpha, \beta \in \mathbb{R}$, satisfies the given condition.

We claim that these are also the only matrices in S satisfying the given condition. Indeed, suppose $M = \alpha A + \beta B$ where $\alpha, \beta \neq 0$. Let $C = \begin{pmatrix} 1 & 1/\sqrt{2} \\ -1 & 1/\sqrt{2} \end{pmatrix}$ with inverse $C^{-1} = \begin{pmatrix} 1/2 & -1/2 \\ 1/\sqrt{2} & 1/\sqrt{2} \end{pmatrix}$. If we define $D = C^{-1}MC$, then $D = 2\alpha \begin{pmatrix} 0 & \gamma \\ \gamma & 1 \end{pmatrix}$ where $\gamma = -\frac{\beta\sqrt{2}}{\alpha}$. Now suppose that M^k is in S with $k \geq 2$. The equalities $(1 \ {-1}) A \begin{pmatrix} 1 \\ -1 \end{pmatrix} = (1 \ {-1}) B \begin{pmatrix} 1 \\ -1 \end{pmatrix} = 0$ imply $(1 \ {-1}) M^k \begin{pmatrix} 1 \\ -1 \end{pmatrix} = 0$, and so the upper left entry of $C^{-1}M^kC = D^k$ is 0. On the other hand, from the expression for D, by induction on k we have $D^k = (2\alpha)^k \begin{pmatrix} \gamma^2 p_{k-1} & \gamma p_k \\ \gamma p_k & p_{k+1} \end{pmatrix}$, where p_k is defined recursively by $p_0 = 0$, $p_1 = 1$, $p_{k+2} = \gamma^2 p_k + p_{k+1}$. In particular, it follows from the recursive definition that $p_k > 0$ when $k \geq 1$, whence the upper left entry of D^k is nonzero when $k \geq 2$, a contradiction.

Remark. A variant of this solution can be obtained by diagonalizing the matrix M.

Solution 2. If a, b, c, d are in arithmetic progression, then

$$a = r - 3s, b = r - s, c = r + s, d = r + 3s$$

for some r, s. If $s = 0$, then clearly all powers of M are in S. Also, if $r = 0$, then one checks directly that M^3 is in S.

We now assume $rs \neq 0$, and show that in that case M cannot be in S. The characteristic polynomial of M is $x^2 - 2rx - 8s^2$, and since M is not a scalar matrix (as $s \neq 0$), this is also the minimal polynomial of M by the Cayley-Hamilton theorem. By repeatedly using the relation $M^2 = 2rM + 8s^2I$, we see for each positive integer k, $M^k = t_kM + u_kI$ for unique real constants t_k, u_k (uniqueness follows from the independence of M and I). Since M is in S, M^k lies in S only if $u_k = 0$.

On the other hand, we claim that if $k > 1$, then $rt_k > 0$ and $u_k > 0$ if k is even, and $t_k > 0$ and $ru_k > 0$ if k is odd (in particular, u_k can never be zero). The claim is true for $k = 2$ by the relation $M^2 = 2rM + 8s^2I$. Assuming the claim for k, and multiplying both sides of the relation $M^k = t_k M + u_k I$ by M, yields

$$M^{k+1} = t_k(2rM + 8s^2I) + u_k M = (2rt_k + u_k)M + 8s^2 t_k I,$$

implying the claim for $k + 1$.

B4. $(70, 10, 3, \ldots, 5, 17, 39, 55)$ 41.7%

Let T be the set of all triples (a, b, c) of positive integers for which there exist triangles with side lengths a, b, c. Express

$$\sum_{(a,b,c) \in T} \frac{2^a}{3^b 5^c}$$

as a rational number in lowest terms.

Answer. The sum is 17/21.

Solution 1. For fixed b and c, there is a triangle of side lengths a, b, c if and only if a satisfies the triangle inequality $|b - c| < a < b + c$. It follows that the desired sum is

$$S = \sum_{b,c} \frac{1}{3^b 5^c} \left(\sum_{a=|b-c|+1}^{b+c-1} 2^a \right) = \sum_{b,c} \frac{2^{b+c} - 2^{|b-c|+1}}{3^b 5^c}.$$

Write this as $S = S_1 + S_2$ where S_1 sums over positive integers b, c with $b \leq c$ and S_2 sums over $b > c$. Then

$$S_1 = \sum_{b=1}^{\infty} \sum_{c=b}^{\infty} \frac{2^{b+c} - 2^{c-b+1}}{3^b 5^c}$$

$$= \sum_{b=1}^{\infty} \left(\left(\left(\frac{2}{3}\right)^b - \frac{2}{6^b} \right) \sum_{c=b}^{\infty} \left(\frac{2}{5}\right)^c \right)$$

$$= \sum_{b=1}^{\infty} \left(\left(\frac{2}{3}\right)^b - \frac{2}{6^b} \right) \frac{5}{3} \left(\frac{2}{5}\right)^b$$

$$= \sum_{b=1}^{\infty} \left(\frac{5}{3} \left(\frac{4}{15}\right)^b - \frac{10}{3} \left(\frac{1}{15}\right)^b \right)$$

$$= \frac{5}{3} \cdot \frac{4}{11} - \frac{10}{3} \cdot \frac{1}{14} = \frac{85}{231}.$$

Similarly,

$$S_2 = \sum_{c=1}^{\infty} \sum_{b=c+1}^{\infty} \frac{2^{b+c} - 2^{b-c+1}}{3^b 5^c}$$

$$= \sum_{c=1}^{\infty} \left(\left(\left(\frac{2}{5}\right)^c - \frac{2}{10^c} \right) \sum_{b=c+1}^{\infty} \left(\frac{2}{3}\right)^b \right)$$

$$= \sum_{c=1}^{\infty} \left(\left(\frac{2}{5}\right)^c - \frac{2}{10^c} \right) 3 \left(\frac{2}{3}\right)^{c+1}$$

$$= \sum_{c=1}^{\infty} \left(2\left(\frac{4}{15}\right)^c - 4\left(\frac{1}{15}\right)^c \right)$$

$$= 2 \cdot \frac{4}{11} - 4 \cdot \frac{1}{14} = \frac{34}{77}.$$

We conclude that $S = S_1 + S_2 = \frac{17}{21}$.

Solution 2. Recall that the real numbers a, b, c form the side lengths of a triangle if and only if

$$s - a, s - b, s - c > 0, \qquad s = \frac{a + b + c}{2},$$

and that if we put $x = 2(s - a), y = 2(s - b), z = 2(s - c)$, then

$$a = \frac{y + z}{2}, \qquad b = \frac{z + x}{2}, \qquad c = \frac{x + y}{2}.$$

To generate all *integer* triples (a, b, c) which form the side lengths of a triangle, we must also assume that x, y, z are either all even or all odd. We may therefore write the original sum as

$$\sum_{x,y,z>0 \text{ odd}} \frac{2^{(y+z)/2}}{3^{(z+x)/2} 5^{(x+y)/2}} + \sum_{x,y,z>0 \text{ even}} \frac{2^{(y+z)/2}}{3^{(z+x)/2} 5^{(x+y)/2}}.$$

To unify the two sums, we substitute in the first case $x = 2u + 1, y = 2v + 1, z = 2w + 1$ and in the second case $x = 2u + 2, y = 2v + 2, z = 2w + 2$ to obtain

$$\sum_{(a,b,c) \in T} \frac{2^a}{3^b 5^c} = \sum_{u,v,w=1}^{\infty} \frac{2^{v+w}}{3^{w+u} 5^{u+v}} \left(1 + \frac{2^{-1}}{3^{-1} 5^{-1}} \right)$$

$$= \frac{17}{2} \sum_{u=1}^{\infty} \left(\frac{1}{15}\right)^u \sum_{v=1}^{\infty} \left(\frac{2}{5}\right)^v \sum_{w=1}^{\infty} \left(\frac{2}{3}\right)^w$$

$$= \frac{17}{2} \frac{1/15}{1 - 1/15} \frac{2/5}{1 - 2/5} \frac{2/3}{1 - 2/3}$$

$$= \frac{17}{21}.$$

B5. $(16, 8, 4, \ldots, 7, 8, 30, 126)$ 14.1%

Let P_n be the number of permutations π of $\{1, 2, \ldots, n\}$ such that

$$|i - j| = 1 \text{ implies } |\pi(i) - \pi(j)| \le 2$$

for all i, j in $\{1, 2, \ldots, n\}$. Show that for $n \ge 2$, the quantity

$$P_{n+5} - P_{n+4} - P_{n+3} + P_n$$

does not depend on n, and find its value.

Answer. The value is 4.

Solution. Let $\mathcal{P}_n$ be the set of permutations counted by P_n. We write permutations π in $\mathcal{P}_n$ as sequences $\pi(1), \pi(2), \ldots, \pi(n)$. Wherever n appears in the sequence, its only possible neighbors are $n - 1$ and $n - 2$. For $n \ge 3$, we may partition $\mathcal{P}_n$ as follows:

- Let $\mathcal{U}_n$ be the sequences that end with $n - 1, n$.

- Let $\mathcal{V}_n$ be the sequences that end with $n, n - 1$.

- Let $\mathcal{W}_n$ be the sequences that start with $n - 1$ and end with $n - 2, n$.

- Let $\mathcal{T}_n$ be the sequences that do not start with $n - 1$ but end with $n - 2, n$.

- Let $\mathcal{S}_n$ be the sequences that have $n-1, n$ consecutively in that order, but not at the beginning or end.

- Let $\mathcal{U}'_n, \ldots, \mathcal{S}'_n$ be the sets of sequences which, when reversed, lie in $\mathcal{U}_n, \ldots, \mathcal{S}_n$, respectively.

These ten subsets partition $\mathcal{P}_n$, and by symmetry, the primed subsets have the same cardinality as their unprimed counterparts. Therefore letting $U_n = |\mathcal{U}_n| = |\mathcal{U}'_n|$ and so forth,

$$P_n = 2(U_n + V_n + W_n + T_n + S_n). \tag{1}$$

Now suppose that $\pi \in \mathcal{P}_{n+1}$ for some $n \ge 3$.

- If π is in $\mathcal{U}_{n+1}$, then it must end with $n-1, n, n+1$ or $n-2, n, n+1$. Removing $n + 1$ yields a permutation in one of $\mathcal{U}_n, \mathcal{W}_n$, or $\mathcal{T}_n$.

- If π is in $\mathcal{V}_{n+1}$, then it must end with $n - 1, n + 1, n$. Removing $n + 1$ yields a permutation in $\mathcal{U}_n$.

- If π is in $\mathcal{W}_{n+1}$, then it must start with $n, n - 2$ and end with $n - 1, n + 1$. Removing $n + 1$ yields a permutation in $\mathcal{W}'_n$.

- If π is in $\mathcal{T}_{n+1}$, then it must end with $n, n-1, n+1$ because n must be adjacent to both $n - 1$ and $n - 2$. Removing $n + 1$ yields a permutation in $\mathcal{V}_n$.

- If π is in $\mathcal{S}_{n+1}$, it must have $n-1, n, n+1$ consecutively in that order, but not at the end. Removing $n+1$ yields a permutation in $\mathcal{S}_n$ unless $n-1$ occurs at the beginning, in which case it yields a permutation in $\mathcal{V}'_n$.

Conversely, inserting $n+1$ into permutations in $\mathcal{P}_n$ in the above ways yields only permutations in $\mathcal{P}_{n+1}$. We deduce the recurrence relations

$$
\begin{aligned}
U_{n+1} &= U_n + W_n + T_n, \\
V_{n+1} &= U_n, \\
W_{n+1} &= W_n, \\
T_{n+1} &= V_n, \\
S_{n+1} &= S_n + V_n
\end{aligned}
\tag{2}
$$

for $n \geq 3$. Since

$$(U_3, V_3, W_3, T_3, S_3) = (1, 1, 1, 0, 0),$$

we may maintain the recurrences (2) and the formula (1) by setting

$$(U_2, V_2, W_2, T_2, S_2) = (1, 0, 1, -1, 0).$$

It is clear that $W_n = 1$ for all $n \geq 2$. Therefore

$$
\begin{aligned}
P_{n+5} &= 2(U_{n+5} + V_{n+5} + W_{n+5} + T_{n+5} + S_{n+5}) \\
&= 2((U_{n+4} + W_{n+4} + T_{n+4}) + U_{n+4} \\
&\quad + W_{n+4} + V_{n+4} + (S_{n+4} + V_{n+4})) \\
&= P_{n+4} + 2(U_{n+4} + W_{n+4} + V_{n+4}) \\
&= P_{n+4} + 2((U_{n+3} + W_{n+3} + T_{n+3}) + W_{n+3} + U_{n+3}) \\
&= P_{n+4} + P_{n+3} + 2(U_{n+3} - V_{n+3} + W_{n+3} - S_{n+3}) \\
&= P_{n+4} + P_{n+3} + 2((U_{n+2} + W_{n+2} + T_{n+2}) - U_{n+2} \\
&\quad + W_{n+2} - (S_{n+2} + V_{n+2})) \\
&= P_{n+4} + P_{n+3} + 2(-V_{n+2} + 2W_{n+2} + T_{n+2} - S_{n+2}) \\
&= P_{n+4} + P_{n+3} + 2(-U_{n+1} + 2W_{n+1} + V_{n+1} - (S_{n+1} + V_{n+1})) \\
&= P_{n+4} + P_{n+3} + 2(-U_{n+1} + 2W_{n+1} - S_{n+1}) \\
&= P_{n+4} + P_{n+3} + 2(-(U_n + W_n + T_n) + 2W_n - (S_n + V_n)) \\
&= P_{n+4} + P_{n+3} - P_n + 4,
\end{aligned}
$$

as desired.

Remark. There are many possible variants of the above solution obtained by dividing the permutations up according to different features. For example, Karl Mahlburg suggests writing

$$P_n = 2P'_n, \qquad P'_n = Q'_n + R'_n$$

where P'_n counts the sequences in $\mathcal{P}_n$ in which 1 occurs before 2, and Q'_n counts the sequences in $\mathcal{P}_n$ that start with 1. One then has the recursion

$$Q'_n = Q'_{n-1} + Q'_{n-3} + 1$$

by separating the sequences starting with $1, 2$, with $1, 3, 2$, and the exceptional sequence $1, 3, 5, \ldots, 6, 4, 2$. Meanwhile, one has

$$R'_n = R'_{n-1} + Q'_{n-2}$$

corresponding to the cases containing $3, 1, 2, 4$ (where removing 1 and reversing gives a permutation counted by R'_{n-1}); and where 4 occurs before $3, 1, 2$ (where removing $1, 2$ and reversing gives a permutation counted by Q'_{n-2}).

Remark. The permutations $\mathcal{P}_n$ are known as *key permutations*, and have been studied by E.S. Page [**Page**]. We have used the same notation for consistency with the literature. The sequence $\{P_n\}$ also appears as entry A003274 in the OEIS.

B6. $(0, 0, 3, \ldots, 1, 0, 27, 168)$ 1.5%
   For each positive integer k, let $A(k)$ be the number of odd divisors of k in the interval $[1, \sqrt{2k})$. Evaluate

$$\sum_{k=1}^{\infty} (-1)^{k-1} \frac{A(k)}{k}.$$

Answer. The sum is $\pi^2/16$.

Solution. (adapted from work of Rodrigo Angelo, via AoPS)
   The elements of the set counted by $A(k)$ are those odd positive integers d for which $m = k/d$ is also an integer and $d < \sqrt{2dm}$; if we write $d = 2\ell - 1$, then the condition on m reduces to $m \geq \ell$. In other words, the given sum equals

$$S_1 = \sum_{k=1}^{\infty} \sum_{\substack{m \geq \ell \geq 1, \\ m(2\ell-1)=k}} \frac{(-1)^{m-1}}{m(2\ell - 1)}.$$

We would like to rearrange this to

$$S_2 = \sum_{\ell=1}^{\infty} \frac{1}{2\ell - 1} \sum_{m=\ell}^{\infty} \frac{(-1)^{m-1}}{m}.$$

Note that S_2 converges: the inner sum converges by the alternating series test, and since

$$\left| \sum_{m=\ell}^{\infty} \frac{(-1)^{m-1}}{m} \right| < \frac{1}{\ell},$$

the outer sum converges absolutely. In particular, S_2 is the limit of the truncated sums

$$S_{2,n} = \sum_{\ell(2\ell-1)\leq n} \frac{1}{2\ell-1} \sum_{m=\ell}^{\infty} \frac{(-1)^{m-1}}{m}.$$

To see that S_1 converges and equals S_2, let

$$S_{1,n} = \sum_{k=1}^{n} \sum_{\substack{m\geq\ell\geq 1, \\ m(2\ell-1)=k}} \frac{(-1)^{m-1}}{m(2\ell-1)}$$

be the nth partial sum of S_1 and note that

$$|S_{2,n} - S_{1,n}| = \left| \sum_{\ell(2\ell-1)\leq n} \frac{1}{2\ell-1} \sum_{m=\lfloor \frac{n}{2\ell-1}+1\rfloor}^{\infty} \frac{(-1)^{m-1}}{m} \right|$$

$$\leq \sum_{\ell(2\ell-1)\leq n} \frac{1}{2\ell-1} \cdot \frac{2\ell-1}{n}$$

$$= \frac{1}{n} \sum_{\ell(2\ell-1)\leq n} 1$$

$$\leq \frac{1}{\sqrt{n}}.$$

Hence $|S_{2,n} - S_{1,n}| \to 0$ as $n \to \infty$; that is, S_1 converges and equals S_2.

We may thus focus hereafter on computing S_2. We begin by writing

$$S_2 = \sum_{\ell=1}^{\infty} \frac{1}{2\ell-1} \sum_{m=\ell}^{\infty} (-1)^{m-1} \int_0^1 t^{m-1}\, dt.$$

Our next step will be to interchange the inner sum and the integral, but again this requires some justification.

Lemma. Let $f_0, f_1, \ldots$ be a sequence of continuous functions on $[0,1]$ such that for each $x \in [0,1]$,

$$f_0(x) \geq f_1(x) \geq \cdots \geq 0.$$

Then

$$\sum_{n=0}^{\infty} (-1)^n \int_0^1 f_n(t)\, dt = \int_0^1 \left(\sum_{n=0}^{\infty} (-1)^n f_n(t) \right) dt$$

provided that both sums converge.

Proof. Put $g_n(t) = f_{2n}(t) - f_{2n+1}(t) \geq 0$. We may then rewrite the desired equality as

$$\sum_{n=0}^{\infty} \int_0^1 g_n(t)\, dt = \int_0^1 \left(\sum_{n=0}^{\infty} g_n(t) \right) dt,$$

which is a case of the (Lebesgue) monotone convergence theorem. $\qquad\square$

By the lemma,

$$S_2 = \sum_{\ell=1}^{\infty} \frac{1}{2\ell-1} \int_0^1 \left(\sum_{m=\ell}^{\infty} (-1)^{m-1} t^{m-1} \right) dt$$

$$= \sum_{\ell=1}^{\infty} \frac{1}{2\ell-1} \int_0^1 \frac{(-t)^{\ell-1}}{1+t} \, dt.$$

Since the sum is absolutely convergent, we may freely interchange it with the integral:

$$S_2 = \int_0^1 \left(\sum_{\ell=1}^{\infty} \frac{1}{2\ell-1} \frac{(-t)^{\ell-1}}{1+t} \right) dt$$

$$= \int_0^1 \frac{1}{\sqrt{t}(1+t)} \left(\sum_{\ell=1}^{\infty} \frac{(-1)^{\ell-1} t^{\ell-1/2}}{2\ell-1} \right) dt$$

$$= \int_0^1 \frac{1}{\sqrt{t}(1+t)} \arctan(\sqrt{t}) \, dt$$

$$= \int_0^1 \frac{2}{1+u^2} \arctan(u) \, du \qquad (u = \sqrt{t})$$

$$= \arctan(1)^2 - \arctan(0)^2 = \frac{\pi^2}{16}.$$

Remark. Beware that the original sum does not converge absolutely, so we are not free to rearrange it arbitrarily. For that matter, the standard alternating series test does not apply because the absolute values of the terms are not monotonically decreasing, so even the convergence of the sum is far from obvious.

The Seventy-Seventh William Lowell Putnam
Mathematical Competition—December 3, 2016

A1. (123, 55, 1, ..., 3, 0, 5, 0) 95.7%
   Find the smallest positive integer j such that for every polynomial $p(x)$ with integer coefficients and for every integer k, the integer

$$p^{(j)}(k) = \frac{d^j}{dx^j} p(x)\Big|_{x=k}$$

(the jth derivative of $p(x)$ at k) is divisible by 2016.

Answer. The smallest such integer is $j = 8$.

Solution. First suppose that j satisfies the given condition. For $p(x) = x^j$, $p^{(j)}(x) = j!$ and thus $j!$ is divisible by 2016. Since 2016 is divisible by 2^5 and $7!$ is not, it follows that $j \geq 8$. Conversely, we claim that $j = 8$ works. Indeed, let $p(x) = \sum_{m=0}^{n} a_m x^m$ be a polynomial with integer coefficients. If k is any integer,

$$p^{(8)}(k) = \sum_{m=8}^{n} m(m-1)\cdots(m-7)a_m k^{m-8}$$

$$= \sum_{m=8}^{n} \binom{m}{8} 8! \, a_m k^{m-8}$$

is divisible by $8! = 20 \cdot 2016$, and so $p^{(8)}(k)$ is divisible by 2016.

Remark. By the same reasoning, if one replaces 2016 in the problem by a general integer N, then the minimum value of j is the smallest one for which N divides $j!$. This can be deduced from Pólya's observation that the set of integer-valued polynomials is the free $\mathbb{Z}$-module generated by the binomial polynomials $\binom{x}{n}$ for $n = 0, 1, \ldots$. That statement can be extended to polynomials evaluated on a subset of a Dedekind domain using Bhargava's method of *P-orderings* [**Bhar**]; we do not know if this generalization can be adapted to the analogue of this problem, where one considers polynomials whose jth derivatives take integral values on a prescribed subset.

A2. (49, 66, 49, ..., 13, 7, 3, 0) 87.7%
   Given a positive integer n, let $M(n)$ be the largest integer m such that

$$\binom{m}{n-1} > \binom{m-1}{n}.$$

Evaluate

$$\lim_{n \to \infty} \frac{M(n)}{n}.$$

Answer. The limit is $\frac{3+\sqrt{5}}{2}$.

Solution. For $m > n+1$, both binomial coefficients are nonzero and their ratio is

$$\binom{m}{n-1} \Big/ \binom{m-1}{n} = \frac{m! \, n! \, (m-n-1)!}{(m-1)! \, (n-1)! \, (m-n+1)!}$$

$$= \frac{mn}{(m-n+1)(m-n)}.$$

Thus the condition $\binom{m}{n-1} > \binom{m-1}{n}$ is equivalent to $(m-n+1)(m-n) - mn < 0$. The left-hand side of this last inequality is a quadratic function of m with roots

$$\alpha(n) = \frac{3n - 1 + \sqrt{5n^2 - 2n + 1}}{2},$$

$$\beta(n) = \frac{3n - 1 - \sqrt{5n^2 - 2n + 1}}{2},$$

both of which are real since $5n^2 - 2n + 1 = 4n^2 + (n-1)^2 > 0$. It follows that m satisfies the given inequality if and only if $\beta(n) < m < \alpha(n)$. (Note in particular that since $\alpha(n) - \beta(n) = \sqrt{5n^2 - 2n + 1} > 1$, there is always some integer m between $\beta(n)$ and $\alpha(n)$.)

We conclude that $M(n)$ is the greatest integer strictly less than $\alpha(n)$, and thus that $\alpha(n) - 1 \le M(n) < \alpha(n)$. Now

$$\lim_{n\to\infty} \frac{\alpha(n)}{n} = \lim_{n\to\infty} \frac{3 - \frac{1}{n} + \sqrt{5 - \frac{2}{n} + \frac{1}{n^2}}}{2} = \frac{3 + \sqrt{5}}{2}$$

and similarly $\lim_{n\to\infty} \frac{\alpha(n)-1}{n} = \frac{3+\sqrt{5}}{2}$, and so by the sandwich theorem, $\lim_{n\to\infty} \frac{M(n)}{n} = \frac{3+\sqrt{5}}{2}$.

A3. (15, 6, 47, ..., 12, 37, 45, 25) 36.4%
   Suppose that f is a function from $\mathbb{R}$ to $\mathbb{R}$ such that

$$f(x) + f\left(1 - \frac{1}{x}\right) = \arctan x$$

for all real $x \neq 0$. (As usual, $y = \arctan x$ means $-\pi/2 < y < \pi/2$ and $\tan y = x$.) Find

$$\int_0^1 f(x)\, dx.$$

Answer. The integral is $3\pi/8$.

Solution. The given functional equation, along with the same equation but with x replaced by $\frac{x-1}{x}$ and $\frac{1}{1-x}$, respectively, yields, for all $x \neq 0, 1$,

$$f(x) + f\left(1 - \frac{1}{x}\right) = \arctan(x),$$

$$f\left(\frac{x-1}{x}\right) + f\left(\frac{1}{1-x}\right) = \arctan\left(\frac{x-1}{x}\right),$$

$$f\left(\frac{1}{1-x}\right) + f(x) = \arctan\left(\frac{1}{1-x}\right).$$

Adding the first and third equations and subtracting the second gives:

$$2f(x) = \arctan(x) + \arctan\left(\frac{1}{1-x}\right) - \arctan\left(\frac{x-1}{x}\right).$$

Now $\arctan(t) + \arctan(1/t)$ is equal to $\pi/2$ if $t > 0$ and $-\pi/2$ if $t < 0$. It follows that for $x \in (0, 1)$,

$$2(f(x) + f(1 - x)) = (\arctan(x) + \arctan(1/x))$$
$$+ \left(\arctan(1 - x) + \arctan\left(\frac{1}{1-x}\right)\right)$$
$$- \left(\arctan\left(\frac{x-1}{x}\right) + \arctan\left(\frac{x}{x-1}\right)\right)$$
$$= \frac{\pi}{2} + \frac{\pi}{2} + \frac{\pi}{2}$$
$$= \frac{3\pi}{2}.$$

Thus

$$4\int_0^1 f(x)\,dx = 2\int_0^1 (f(x) + f(1-x))\,dx = \frac{3\pi}{2}$$

and finally $\int_0^1 f(x)\,dx = \frac{3\pi}{8}$.

Remark. Once one has the formula for $f(x)$, one can also (with some effort) directly evaluate the integral of each summand over $[0, 1]$ to obtain the same result. A much cleaner variant of this approach (from Henrik Boecken, via AoPS) is to write

$$\arctan(x) = \int_0^y \frac{1}{1 + y^2}\,dy$$

and do a change of variable on the resulting double integral.

A4. (45, 16, 4, ..., 12, 5, 31, 74) 34.8%

Consider a $(2m - 1) \times (2n - 1)$ **rectangular region, where m and n are integers such that $m, n \geq 4$. This region is to be tiled using tiles of the two**

types shown:

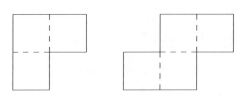

(The dotted lines divide the tiles into 1×1 squares.) The tiles may be rotated and reflected, as long as their sides are parallel to the sides of the rectangular region. They must all fit within the region, and they must cover it completely without overlapping. What is the minimum number of tiles required to tile the region?

Answer. The minimum number of tiles is mn.

Solution. To see that at least mn tiles are required, label the squares (i, j) with $1 \leq i \leq 2m - 1$ and $1 \leq j \leq 2n - 1$, and for each square with i, j both odd, color the square red. Then no tile can cover more than one red square, and there are mn red squares.

It remains to show that any $(2m - 1) \times (2n - 1)$ rectangle can be tiled with mn tiles when $m, n \geq 4$. First, any $2 \times (2k - 1)$ rectangle can be tiled with $k \geq 3$ by k tiles: one of the first type, then $k - 2$ of the second type, and finally one of the first type. Thus assuming that a 7×7 square can be tiled with 16 tiles, the general $(2m - 1) \times (2n - 1)$ rectangle can be tiled by separately tiling a 7×7 square in the lower left corner, $(m - 4)$-many (2×7) rectangles to the right of the square, and $n - 4$ $((2m - 1) \times 2)$ rectangles above the square, using a total of $16 + 4(m - 4) + m(n - 4) = mn$ tiles.

To tile the 7×7 square, note that the tiling must consist of 15 tiles of the first type and 1 of the second type, and that any 2×3 rectangle can be tiled using 2 tiles of the first type. We may thus construct a suitable tiling by covering all but the center square with eight 2×3 rectangles, in such a way that attaching the center square to one of these rectangles yields a shape that can be covered by two tiles. An example of such a tiling, with the remaining 2×3 rectangles left intact for visual clarity, is depicted below. (Many other solutions are possible.)

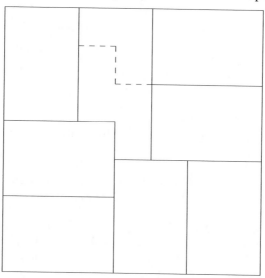

A5. (28, 4, 1, …, 10, 8, 27, 109) 17.6%

Suppose that G is a finite group generated by the two elements g and h, where the order of g is odd. Show that every element of G can be written in the form

$$g^{m_1} h^{n_1} g^{m_2} h^{n_2} \cdots g^{m_r} h^{n_r}$$

with $1 \leq r \leq |G|$ and $m_1, n_1, m_2, n_2, \ldots, m_r, n_r \in \{-1, 1\}$. **(Here $|G|$ is the number of elements of G.)**

Solution 1. For $s \in G$ and r a positive integer, define a *representation of s of length r* to be a sequence of values $m_1, n_1, \ldots, m_r, n_r \in \{-1, 1\}$ for which

$$s = g^{m_1} h^{n_1} \cdots g^{m_r} h^{n_r}.$$

We first check that every $s \in G$ admits at least one representation of some length; this is equivalent to saying that the set S of $s \in G$ which admit representations of some length is equal to G itself. Since S is closed under the group operation and G is finite, S is also closed under formation of inverses and contains the identity element; that is, S is a subgroup of G. In particular, S contains not only gh but also its inverse $h^{-1}g^{-1}$; since S also contains $g^{-1}h$, we deduce that S contains g^{-2}. Since g is of odd order in G, g^{-2} is also a generator of the cyclic subgroup containing g; it follows that $g \in S$ and hence $h \in S$. Since we assumed that g, h generate G, we now conclude that $S = G$, as claimed.

To complete the proof, we must now check that for each $s \in G$, the smallest possible length of a representation of s cannot exceed $|G|$. Suppose the contrary,

and let
$$s = g^{m_1} h^{n_1} \cdots g^{m_r} h^{n_r}$$
be a representation of the smallest possible length. Set
$$s_i = g^{m_1} h^{n_1} \cdots g^{m_i} h^{n_i} \qquad (i = 0, \ldots, r-1),$$
interpreting s_0 as e; since $r > |G|$ by hypothesis, by the pigeonhole principle there must exist indices $0 \le i < j \le r-1$ such that $s_i = s_j$. Then
$$s = g^{m_1} h^{n_1} \cdots g^{m_i} h^{n_i} g^{m_{j+1}} h^{n_{j+1}} \cdots g^{m_r} h^{n_r}$$
is another representation of s of length strictly less than r, a contradiction.

Remark. If one considers $s_0, \ldots, s_r$ instead of $s_0, \ldots, s_{r-1}$, then the case $s = e$ must be handled separately: otherwise, one might end up with a representation of length 0 which is disallowed by the problem statement.

Reinterpretation. The elements $gh, gh^{-1}, g^{-1}h, g^{-1}h^{-1}$ generate the product $gh(g^{-1}h)^{-1} = g^2$ and hence all of G (again using the hypothesis that g has odd order, as above). Form the *Cayley digraph* on the set G, that is, the directed graph with an edge from s_1 to s_2 whenever $s_2 = s_1 *$ for $* \in \{gh, gh^{-1}, g^{-1}h, g^{-1}h^{-1}\}$. Since G is finite, this digraph is strongly connected: there exists at least one path from any vertex to any other vertex (traveling all edges in the correct direction). The shortest such path cannot repeat any vertices (except the starting and ending vertices in case they coincide), and so has length at most $|G|$.

Solution 2. For r a positive integer, let S_r be the set of $s \in G$ which admit a representation of length at most r (terminology as in the first solution), so that $S_r \subseteq S_{r+1}$. We will show that $S_r \ne S_{r+1}$ unless $S_r = G$; this will imply by induction on r that $\#S_r \ge \min\{r, |G|\}$ and hence that $S_r = G$ for some $r \le |G|$.

Suppose that $S_r = S_{r+1}$. Then the map $s \mapsto sgh$ defines an injective map $S_r \to S_{r+1} = S_r$, so S_r is closed under right multiplication by gh. By the same token, S_r is closed under right multiplication by each of $gh^{-1}, g^{-1}h, g^{-1}h^{-1}$. Since $gh, gh^{-1}, g^{-1}h, g^{-1}h^{-1}$ generate G as in the first solution, it follows that $S_r = G$ as claimed.

Remark. The condition on the order of g is needed to rule out the case where G admits a (necessarily normal) subgroup H of index 2 not containing either g or h; in this case, all products of the indicated form belong to H. On the other hand, if one assumes that both g and h have odd order, then one can say a bit more: there exists some positive integer r with $1 \le r \le |G|$ such that every element of G has a representation of length exactly r. (Namely, the set of such elements for a given r strictly increases in size until it is stable under right multiplication by both $gh(g^{-1}h)^{-1} = g^2$ and $gh(gh^{-1})^{-1} = gh^2g^{-1}$, but under the present hypotheses these generate G.)

A6. $(2, 0, 0, \ldots, 1, 1, 69, 114)$ 1.1%

Find the smallest constant C such that for every real polynomial $P(x)$ of degree 3 that has a root in the interval $[0, 1]$,

$$\int_0^1 |P(x)| \, dx \leq C \max_{x \in [0,1]} |P(x)|.$$

Answer. The smallest such value of C is $5/6$.

Solution 1. We first reduce to the case where P is nonnegative in $[0, 1]$ and $P(0) = 0$. To achieve this reduction, suppose that a given value C obeys the inequality for such P. For general P, divide the interval $[0, 1]$ into subintervals $I_1, \ldots, I_k$ at the roots of P. Write $\ell(I_i)$ for the length of the interval I_i. Since each interval is bounded by a root of P, we may make a linear change of variable to see that

$$\int_{I_i} |P(x)| \, dx \leq C\ell(I_i) \max_{x \in I_i} |P(x)| \quad (i = 1, \ldots, k).$$

Summing over i yields the desired inequality.

Suppose now that P takes nonnegative values on $[0, 1]$, $P(0) = 0$, and that $\max_{x \in [0,1]} P(x) = 1$. Write $P(x) = ax^3 + bx^2 + cx$ for some $a, b, c \in \mathbb{R}$; then

$$\int_0^1 P(x) \, dx = \frac{1}{4}a + \frac{1}{3}b + \frac{1}{2}c$$

$$= \frac{2}{3}\left(\frac{1}{8}a + \frac{1}{4}b + \frac{1}{2}c\right) + \frac{1}{6}(a + b + c)$$

$$= \frac{2}{3}P\left(\frac{1}{2}\right) + \frac{1}{6}P(1)$$

$$\leq \frac{2}{3} + \frac{1}{6} = \frac{5}{6}.$$

Consequently, the originally claimed inequality holds with $C = 5/6$. To prove that this value is best possible, it suffices to exhibit a polynomial P as above with $\int_0^1 P(x) \, dx = 5/6$; we will verify that

$$P(x) = 4x^3 - 8x^2 + 5x$$

has this property. It is apparent that $\int_0^1 P(x) \, dx = 5/6$. Since $P'(x) = (2x - 1)(6x - 5)$ and

$$P(0) = 0, \ P\left(\frac{1}{2}\right) = 1, \ P\left(\frac{5}{6}\right) = \frac{25}{27}, P(1) = 1,$$

it follows that P increases from 0 at $x = 0$ to 1 at $x = 1/2$, then decreases to a positive value at $x = 5/6$, then increases to 1 at $x = 1$. Hence P has the desired form.

Remark. Here is some conceptual motivation for the preceding solution. Let V be the set of polynomials of degree at most 3 vanishing at 0, viewed as a three-dimensional vector space over $\mathbb{R}$. Let S be the subset of V consisting of those polynomials $P(x)$ for which $0 \leq P(x) \leq 1$ for all $x \in [0, 1]$; this set is convex and compact. We may then compute the minimal C as the maximum value of $\int_0^1 P(x)\,dx$ over all $P \in S$, provided that the maximum is achieved for some polynomial of degree exactly 3. (Any extremal polynomial must satisfy $\max_{x \in [0,1]} P(x) = 1$, as otherwise we could multiply it by some constant $c > 1$ so as to increase $\int_0^1 P(x)\,dx$.)

Let $f : V \to \mathbb{R}$ be the function taking $P(x)$ to $\int_0^1 P(x)\,dx$. This function is linear, so we can characterize its extrema on S as follows: there exist exactly two level surfaces for f which are supporting planes for S, and the intersections of these two planes with S are the minima and the maxima. The unique minimum is achieved by the zero polynomial, so this accounts for one of the planes.

It thus suffices to exhibit a single polynomial $P(x) \in S$ such that the level plane of f through P is a supporting plane for S. The calculation made in the solution amounts to verifying that

$$P(x) = 4x^3 - 8x^2 + 5x$$

has this property, by interpolating between the constraints $P(1/2) \leq 1$ and $P(1) \leq 1$.

This still leaves the matter of correctly guessing the optimal polynomial. If one supposes that it should be extremized both at $x = 1$ and at an interior point of the interval, it is forced to have the form $P(x) = 1 + (x - 1)(cx - 1)^2$ for some $c > 0$; the interpolation property then pins down c uniquely.

Solution 2. (James Merryfield, via AoPS) As in the first solution, we may assume that P is nonnegative on $[0, 1]$ and $P(0) = 0$. Since P has degree at most 3, Simpson's rule for approximating $\int_0^1 P(x)\,dx$ is an exact formula:

$$\int_0^1 P(x)\,dx = \frac{1}{6}\left(P(0) + 4P\left(\frac{1}{2}\right) + P(1)\right).$$

This immediately yields the claimed inequality for $C = 5/6$. Again as in the first solution, we obtain an example showing that this value is best possible.

B1. (110, 18, 22, ..., 17, 8, 10, 2) 80.2%

   Let $x_0, x_1, x_2, \ldots$ **be the sequence such that** $x_0 = 1$ **and for** $n \geq 0$,

$$x_{n+1} = \ln(e^{x_n} - x_n)$$

(as usual, the function ln is the natural logarithm). Show that the infinite series

$$x_0 + x_1 + x_2 + \cdots$$

converges and find its sum.

Answer. The sum is $e - 1$.

Solution. The function $e^x - x$ is strictly increasing for $x > 0$ (because its derivative is $e^x - 1$, which is positive because e^x is strictly increasing), and its value at 0 is 1. By induction on n, $x_n > 0$ for all n.

By exponentiating the two sides of the equation defining x_{n+1}, we obtain the expression

$$x_n = e^{x_n} - e^{x_{n+1}}.$$

We use this equation repeatedly to acquire increasingly precise information about the sequence $\{x_n\}$.

- Since $x_n > 0$, $e^{x_n} > e^{x_{n+1}}$ and so $x_n > x_{n+1}$.

- Since the sequence $\{x_n\}$ is decreasing and bounded below by 0, it converges to some limit L.

- Taking limits in the equation yields $L = e^L - e^L$, whence $L = 0$.

- Since $L = 0$, the sequence $\{e^{x_n}\}$ converges to 1.

We now have a telescoping sum:

$$x_0 + \cdots + x_n = (e^{x_0} - e^{x_1}) + \cdots + (e^{x_n} - e^{x_{n+1}})$$
$$= e^{x_0} - e^{x_{n+1}} = e - e^{x_{n+1}}.$$

By taking limits, the sum $x_0 + x_1 + \cdots$ converges to the value $e - 1$.

B2. (94, 18, 39, ..., 23, 8, 5, 0) 80.7%
Define a positive integer n to be *squarish* if either n is itself a perfect square or the distance from n to the nearest perfect square is a perfect square. For example, 2016 is squarish, because the nearest perfect square to 2016 is $45^2 = 2025$ and $2025 - 2016 = 9$ is a perfect square. (Of the positive integers between 1 and 10, only 6 and 7 are not squarish.)

For a positive integer N, let $S(N)$ be the number of squarish integers between 1 and N, inclusive. Find positive constants α and β such that

$$\lim_{N \to \infty} \frac{S(N)}{N^\alpha} = \beta,$$

or show that no such constants exist.

Answer. The limit exists for $\alpha = \frac{3}{4}$, $\beta = \frac{4}{3}$.

Solution. For any given positive integer n, the integers which are closer to n^2 than to any other perfect square are the ones in the interval $[n^2 - n + 1, n^2 + n]$.

The number of squarish numbers in this interval is $1+\lfloor\sqrt{n-1}\rfloor+\lfloor\sqrt{n}\rfloor$. Roughly speaking, this means that

$$S(N) \sim \int_0^{\sqrt{N}} 2\sqrt{x}\,dx = \frac{4}{3}N^{3/4}.$$

To make this precise, we use the bounds $x-1 \le \lfloor x\rfloor \le x$, and the upper and lower Riemann sum estimates for the integral of $\sqrt{x}$, to derive upper and lower bounds for $S(N)$:

$$S(N) \ge \sum_{n=1}^{\lfloor\sqrt{N}\rfloor-1} (2\sqrt{n-1}-1)$$

$$\ge \int_0^{\lfloor\sqrt{N}\rfloor-2} 2\sqrt{x}\,dx - \sqrt{N}$$

$$\ge \frac{4}{3}(\sqrt{N}-3)^{3/2} - \sqrt{N},$$

$$S(N) \le \sum_{n=1}^{\lceil\sqrt{N}\rceil} (2\sqrt{n}+1)$$

$$\le \int_0^{\lceil\sqrt{N}\rceil+1} 2\sqrt{x}\,dx + \sqrt{N} + 1$$

$$\le \frac{4}{3}(\sqrt{N}+2)^{3/2} + \sqrt{N} + 1.$$

Remark. John Rickert points out that when $N = n^4$, one can turn the previous estimates into exact calculations to obtain the formula

$$S(N) = \frac{4}{3}\left(n^3 + \frac{n}{2}\right) = \frac{4}{3}N^{3/4} + \frac{2}{3}N^{1/4}.$$

For general N, one can then use the estimates

$$S(\lfloor N^{1/4}\rfloor^4) \le S(N) \le S(\lceil N^{1/4}\rceil^4)$$

to obtain the desired limit.

B3. (28, 124, 13, ..., 3, 1, 6, 12) 88.2%
    Suppose that S is a finite set of points in the plane such that the area of triangle $\triangle ABC$ is at most 1 whenever A, B, and C are in S. Show that there exists a triangle of area 4 that (together with its interior) covers the set S.

Solution. Since S is finite, we can choose three points A, B, C in S so as to maximize the area of the triangle $\triangle ABC$. If this area is 0, then the points of S all lie on a line and are easy to cover by a triangle of any positive area, so we assume that $\triangle ABC$ has positive area. Let A', B', C' be the points in the plane such that A, B, C are the midpoints of the segments $\overline{B'C'}, \overline{C'A'}, \overline{A'B'}$. The triangle $\triangle A'B'C'$ is similar to $\triangle ABC$ with sides twice as long, so its area is 4 times that of $\triangle ABC$ and hence no greater than 4.

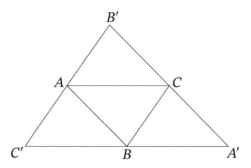

We claim that this triangle has the desired effect; that is, every point P of S is contained within $\triangle A'B'C'$. (If $\triangle A'B'C'$ has area less than 4, we can scale up by a homothety to produce a triangle of area exactly 4 containing it.) To see this, note that since the area of the triangle $\triangle PBC$ is no more than that of $\triangle ABC$, P must lie in the half-plane bounded by $\overleftrightarrow{B'C'}$ containing B and C. Similarly, P must lie in the half-plane bounded by $\overleftrightarrow{C'A'}$ containing C and A, and the half-plane bounded by $\overleftrightarrow{A'B'}$ containing A and B. These three half-planes intersect precisely in the region bounded by the triangle $\triangle A'B'C'$, proving the claim.

B4. $(62, 32, 16, \ldots, 3, 9, 27, 38)$ 58.8%
   Let A be a $2n \times 2n$ matrix, with entries chosen independently at random. Every entry is chosen to be 0 or 1, each with probability $1/2$. Find the expected value of $\det(A - A^t)$ (as a function of n), where A^t is the transpose of A.

Answer. The expected value is $(2n)! / (4^n n!)$.

Solution 1. Write the determinant of $A - A^t$ as the sum over permutations σ of $\{1, \ldots, 2n\}$ of $\mathrm{sgn}(\sigma)P_\sigma$, where

$$P_\sigma = \prod_{i=1}^{2n} (A - A^t)_{i\sigma(i)} = \prod_{i=1}^{2n} (A_{i\sigma(i)} - A_{\sigma(i)i}).$$

then the expected value of the determinant is the sum over σ of the expected value $\mathrm{sgn}(\sigma) \cdot E[P_\sigma]$.
   Decompose σ into disjoint cycles (that is, orbits for the action of σ on $\{1, 2, \ldots, 2n\}$), and define a *cycle-factor* to be the portion of P_σ whose indices i belong

to a given cycle. Since no entry of A appears in more than one cycle-factor, the cycle-factors are independent random variables, and we can compute $E[P_\sigma]$ as the product of the expected values of the individual cycle-factors.

Any 1-cycle in σ yields a cycle-factor that is identically zero. For a cycle of order $m \geq 3$, the corresponding cycle-factor contains $2m$ distinct entries of A, so again we may compute the expected value of the cycle-factor as the product of the expected values of the individual factors $A_{i\sigma(i)} - A_{\sigma(i)i}$. However, the distribution of this factor is symmetric about 0, so its expected value is 0.

We conclude that $E[P_\sigma] = 0$ unless σ consists of n cycles of order 2. To compute $E[P_\sigma]$ in this case, assume without loss of generality that the cycles of σ are $(1,2),\ldots,(2n-1,2n)$. Note that $\mathrm{sgn}(\sigma) = (-1)^n$. Then $E[P_\sigma]$ is the expected value of $\prod_{i=1}^n -(A_{(2i-1)2i} - A_{2i(2i-1)})^2$, which is $(-1)^n$ times the nth power of the expected value of $(A_{12}-A_{21})^2$. Since $A_{12}-A_{21}$ takes the values $-1,0,1$ with probabilities $\frac{1}{4},\frac{1}{2},\frac{1}{4}$, respectively, its square takes the values $0,1$ with probabilities $\frac{1}{2},\frac{1}{2}$, respectively. We conclude that

$$\mathrm{sgn}(\sigma) \cdot E[P_\sigma] = \frac{1}{2^n}.$$

The permutations σ of this form correspond to unordered partitions of the set $\{1,\ldots,2n\}$ into n sets of size 2, so there are

$$\frac{(2n)!}{n!\,(2!\,)^n}$$

such permutations. Putting this all together yields the claimed result.

Solution 2. The matrix $A - A^t$ is skew-symmetric:

$$(A - A^t)^t = A^t - A = -(A - A^t).$$

The determinant of a $2n \times 2n$ skew-symmetric matrix M is the square of the *Pfaffian* of M, which is a polynomial of degree n in the entries of M defined as follows. Define a *perfect matching* of $\{1,\ldots,2n\}$ to be a permutation of $\{1,\ldots,2n\}$ that is the product of n disjoint transpositions. Then the Pfaffian of M is given by

$$\sum_\alpha \mathrm{sgn}(\alpha)M_{i_1,j_1} \cdots M_{i_n,j_n} \qquad (1)$$

where the sum is over perfect matchings $\alpha = (i_1, j_1) \cdots (i_n, j_n)$, and $\mathrm{sgn}(\alpha)$ denotes the sign of the permutation $\begin{pmatrix} 1 & 2 & 3 & 4 & \cdots & (2n-1) & 2n \\ i_1 & j_1 & i_2 & j_2 & \cdots & i_n & j_n \end{pmatrix}$. The determinant of M is then the square of (1):

$$\det(M) = \sum_{\alpha,\beta} \mathrm{sgn}(\alpha)\,\mathrm{sgn}(\beta)M_{i_1,j_1} \cdots M_{i_n,j_n}M_{i'_1,j'_1} \cdots M_{i'_n,j'_n} \qquad (2)$$

where the sum is now over ordered pairs

$$(\alpha = (i_1, j_1) \cdots (i_n, j_n), \beta = (i'_1, j'_1) \cdots (i'_n, j'_n))$$

of perfect matchings.

Taking $M = A - A^t$, so that $M_{ij} = A_{ij} - A_{ji}$, we wish to find the expected value of (2); again, this is the sum of the expected values of each summand in (2). Each M_{ij} with $i < j$ is an independent random variable taking the values $-1, 0, 1$ with probabilities $\frac{1}{4}, \frac{1}{2}, \frac{1}{4}$, respectively.

Consider first a summand in (2) with $\alpha \neq \beta$. Then some factor M_{ij} occurs with exponent 1; since the distribution of M_{ij} is symmetric about 0, any such summand has expected value 0.

Consider next a summand in (2) with $\alpha = \beta$. This summand is a product of distinct factors of the form M_{ij}^2; from the distributions of the M_{ij}, the expected value of each of these terms is $1/2^n$.

Since the total number of perfect matchings α is $(2n)! / (2^n n!)$, the expected value of (2) is therefore $(2n)! / (2^n n!) \cdot 1/2^n = (2n)! / (4^n n!)$, as desired.

B5. (21, 12, 5, ..., 6, 5, 62, 76) 20.3%

Find all functions f from the interval $(1, \infty)$ to $(1, \infty)$ with the following property: if $x, y \in (1, \infty)$ and $x^2 \leq y \leq x^3$, then $f(x)^2 \leq f(y) \leq f(x)^3$.

Answer. The functions satisfying the condition are those of the form $f(x) = x^c$ for some $c > 0$.

Solution. The functions $f(x) = x^c$ do indeed have the desired property. Conversely, let f be a function having the desired property. Define the function $g : (0, \infty) \to (0, \infty)$ given by $g(x) = \log f(e^x)$; this function has the property that if $x, y \in (0, \infty)$ and $2x \leq y \leq 3x$, then $2g(x) \leq g(y) \leq 3g(x)$. It will suffice to show that there exists $c > 0$ such that $g(x) = cx$ for all $x > 0$.

Similarly, define the function $h : \mathbb{R} \to \mathbb{R}$ given by $h(x) = \log g(e^x) = \log g(e^x)$. This function has the property that if $x, y \in \mathbb{R}$ and $x + \kappa \leq y \leq x + \lambda$, then $h(x) + \kappa \leq h(y) \leq h(x) + \lambda$, where $\kappa = \log 2$ and $\lambda = \log 3$. It will suffice to show that there exists $c > 0$ such that $h(x) = x + c$ for all $x \in \mathbb{R}$ (as then $g(x) = e^c x$ for all $x > 0$).

By interchanging the roles of x and y, we may restate the condition on h as follows: if $x - \lambda \leq y \leq x - \kappa$, then $h(x) - \lambda \leq h(y) \leq h(x) - \kappa$. We now claim that if a and b are nonnegative integers, then for all $x, y \in \mathbb{R}$ such that

$$x + a\kappa - b\lambda \leq y \leq x + a\lambda - b\kappa,$$

we have

$$h(x) + a\kappa - b\lambda \leq h(y) \leq h(x) + a\lambda - b\kappa.$$

We proceed by induction on $a + b$. The base cases $a + b = 0, 1$ follow from the given condition on h. Suppose that $a + b > 1$ and that the claim is known for all smaller values of $a + b$. In particular, either $a > 0$ or $b > 0$; the two cases are similar, so we treat only the first one. Define the function

$$j(t) = \frac{(a+b-1)t - b(\kappa+\lambda)}{a+b},$$

so that

$$j(a\kappa - b\lambda) = (a-1)\kappa - b\lambda,$$
$$j(a\lambda - b\kappa) = (a-1)\lambda - b\kappa.$$

For $t \in [a\kappa - b\lambda, a\lambda - b\kappa]$ and $y = x + t, \kappa \leq t - j(t) \leq \lambda$ and hence

$$(a-1)\kappa - b\lambda \leq h(x+j(t)) - h(x) \leq (a-1)\lambda - b\kappa,$$
$$\kappa \leq h(y) - h(x+j(t)) \leq \lambda;$$

this completes the induction.

Now fix two values $x, y \in \mathbb{R}$ with $x \leq y$. Since κ and λ are linearly independent over $\mathbb{Q}$, the fractional parts of the nonnegative integer multiples of λ/κ are dense in $[0, 1)$. (This result is due to Kronecker; a stronger result of Weyl shows that the fractional parts are uniformly distributed in $[0, 1)$.) In particular, for any $\epsilon > 0$ and any $N > 0$, we can find integers $a, b > N$ such that

$$y - x < a\lambda - b\kappa < y - x + \epsilon.$$

As $N \to \infty$,

$$a\kappa - b\lambda = (a\lambda - b\kappa) - (\lambda - \kappa)(a+b) \to -\infty;$$

in particular, for N sufficiently large, $a\kappa - b\lambda < y - x$. Thus $h(y) - h(x) \leq a\kappa - b\lambda < y - x + \epsilon$; since $\epsilon > 0$ was chosen arbitrarily, we deduce that $h(y) - h(x) \leq y - x$. A similar argument shows that $h(y) - h(x) \geq y - x$; we deduce that $h(y) - h(x) = y - x$, or equivalently $h(y) - y = h(x) - x$. In other words, the function $x \mapsto h(x) - x$ is constant, as desired.

B6. (20, 11, 7, ..., 4, 2, 35, 108) 20.3%

Evaluate

$$\sum_{k=1}^{\infty} \frac{(-1)^{k-1}}{k} \sum_{n=0}^{\infty} \frac{1}{k2^n + 1}.$$

Answer. The sum is 1.

Solution 1. Write

$$\sum_{n=0}^{\infty} \frac{1}{k2^n + 1} = \frac{1}{k+1} + \sum_{n=1}^{\infty} \frac{1}{k2^n + 1};$$

then the desired sum is $S = S_1 + S_2$ where

$$S_1 = \sum_{k=1}^{\infty} \frac{(-1)^{k-1}}{k(k+1)},$$

$$S_2 = \sum_{k=1}^{\infty} \frac{(-1)^{k-1}}{k} \sum_{n=1}^{\infty} \frac{1}{k2^n + 1}.$$

The rearrangement is valid because both S_1 and S_2 converge absolutely in k, by comparison to $\sum 1/k^2$.

To compute S_1, note that

$$\sum_{k=1}^{N} \frac{(-1)^{k-1}}{k(k+1)} = \sum_{k=1}^{N} (-1)^{k-1} \left(\frac{1}{k} - \frac{1}{k+1} \right)$$

$$= -1 + \frac{(-1)^N}{N+1} + 2 \sum_{k=1}^{N} \frac{(-1)^{k-1}}{k}$$

converges to $2 \log 2 - 1$ as $N \to \infty$, and so $S_1 = 2 \log 2 - 1$.

To compute S_2, write $\frac{1}{k2^n+1} = \frac{1}{k2^n} \cdot \frac{1}{1+1/(k2^n)}$ in the form of the geometric series $\sum_{m=0}^{\infty} \frac{(-1)^m}{k^{m+1}2^{mn+n}}$, whence

$$S_2 = \sum_{k=1}^{\infty} \sum_{n=1}^{\infty} \sum_{m=0}^{\infty} \frac{(-1)^{k+m-1}}{k^{m+2}2^{mn+n}}.$$

(This step requires $n \geq 1$, as otherwise the geometric series would not converge for $k = 1$.) This triple sum converges absolutely: we have

$$\sum_{m=0}^{\infty} \frac{1}{k^{m+2}2^{mn+n}} = \frac{1}{k^2 2^n} \cdot \frac{1}{1 - \frac{1}{k2^n}} = \frac{1}{k(k2^n - 1)} \leq \frac{1}{k^2 2^{n-1}},$$

and so

$$\sum_{k=1}^{\infty} \sum_{n=1}^{\infty} \sum_{m=0}^{\infty} \frac{1}{k^{m+2}2^{mn+n}} \leq \sum_{k=1}^{\infty} \sum_{n=1}^{\infty} \frac{1}{k^2 2^{n-1}} = \sum_{k=1}^{\infty} \frac{2}{k^2} < \infty.$$

Thus we can rearrange the sum to get

$$S_2 = \sum_{m=0}^{\infty} (-1)^m \left(\sum_{n=1}^{\infty} \frac{1}{2^{mn+n}} \right) \left(\sum_{k=1}^{\infty} \frac{(-1)^{k-1}}{k^{m+2}} \right).$$

The sum in n is the geometric series

$$\sum_{n=1}^{\infty} \frac{1}{(2^{m+1})^n} = \frac{1}{2^{m+1}(1 - \frac{1}{2^{m+1}})} = \frac{1}{2^{m+1} - 1}.$$

If we set $S_3 = \sum_{k=1}^{\infty}(-1)^{k-1}/k^{m+2}$, then

$$\sum_{k=1}^{\infty}\frac{1}{k^{m+2}} = S_3 + 2\sum_{k=1}^{\infty}\frac{1}{(2k)^{m+2}} = S_3 + \frac{1}{2^{m+1}}\sum_{k=1}^{\infty}\frac{1}{k^{m+2}}$$

(where we can rearrange terms in the first equality because all of the series converge absolutely), and so

$$S_3 = \left(1 - \frac{1}{2^{m+1}}\right)\sum_{k=1}^{\infty}\frac{1}{k^{m+2}}.$$

It follows that

$$S_2 = \sum_{m=0}^{\infty}\frac{(-1)^m}{2^{m+1}}\sum_{k=1}^{\infty}\frac{1}{k^{m+2}}$$

$$= \sum_{k=1}^{\infty}\frac{1}{2k^2}\sum_{m=0}^{\infty}\left(-\frac{1}{2k}\right)^m$$

$$= \sum_{k=1}^{\infty}\frac{1}{k(2k+1)}$$

$$= 2\sum_{k=1}^{\infty}\left(\frac{1}{2k}-\frac{1}{2k+1}\right) = 2(1-\log 2).$$

Finally, $S = S_1 + S_2 = 1$.

Solution 2. (Tewodros Amdeberhan) Since $\int_0^1 x^t\,dx = \frac{1}{1+t}$ for any $t \geq 1$, the desired sum is

$$S = \sum_{k=1}^{\infty}\sum_{n=0}^{\infty}\frac{(-1)^{k-1}}{k}\int_0^1 x^{k2^n}\,dx.$$

Again by absolute convergence, we are free to permute the integral and the sums:

$$S = \int_0^1\sum_{n=0}^{\infty}\sum_{k=1}^{\infty}\frac{(-1)^{k-1}}{k}x^{k2^n}\,dx$$

$$= \int_0^1\sum_{n=0}^{\infty}\log(1 + x^{2^n})\,dx.$$

The uniqueness of binary expansions of nonnegative integers implies an identity of formal power series

$$(1-x)^{-1} = \prod_{n=0}^{\infty}(1 + x^{2^n});$$

the product converges absolutely for $0 \le x < 1$. We thus have

$$S = -\int_0^1 \log(1-x)\,dx$$
$$= (1-x)\log(1-x) - (1-x)|_0^1$$
$$= 1.$$

Solution 3. (Serin Hong) Again using absolute convergence, we may write

$$S = \sum_{m=2}^{\infty} \frac{1}{m} \sum_k \frac{(-1)^{k-1}}{k}$$

where k runs over all positive integers for which $m = k2^n + 1$ for some n. Write $m - 1 = 2^r j$, where $r \ge 0$ is an integer and j is odd. Then the values of k are $j2^i$ for $i = 0, \ldots, r$. The inner sum is thus

$$\frac{1}{j} - \sum_{i=1}^{r} \frac{1}{2^i j} = \frac{1}{2^r j} = \frac{1}{m-1}.$$

We thus have

$$S = \sum_{m=2}^{\infty} \frac{1}{m(m-1)} = \sum_{m=2}^{\infty} \left(\frac{1}{m-1} - \frac{1}{m} \right) = 1.$$

Solution 4. (Liang Xiao) Let S_0 and S_1 represent the two summations

$$\sum_k \frac{1}{k} \sum_{n=0}^{\infty} \frac{1}{k2^n + 1}$$

with k running over all odd and all even positive integers, respectively, so that

$$S = S_0 - S_1.$$

In S_1, we may write $k = 2\ell$ to obtain

$$S_1 = \sum_{\ell=1}^{\infty} \frac{1}{2\ell} \sum_{n=0}^{\infty} \frac{1}{\ell 2^{n+1} + 1}$$
$$= \frac{1}{2}(S_0 + S_1) - \sum_{\ell=1}^{\infty} \frac{1}{2\ell(\ell+1)}$$
$$= \frac{1}{2}(S_0 + S_1) - \frac{1}{2}$$

because the last sum telescopes. This immediately yields $S = 1$.

Results

We tabulate results from the years 2001–2016 of the competition in the following forms:

- Score cutoffs for various tiers of recognition.

- Individual results: the top 5 contestants (the Putnam Fellows), in alphabetical order (the order of placement is not published) and the Elizabeth Lowell Putnam prize.

- Team results: the top 5 teams, in order of placement.

- Some additional analysis by Joe Gallian. (In addition to providing this analysis, we thank Gallian for his help with compiling the other results.)

Additional results for each year can be found in the official competition summary published in the *American Mathematical Monthly* in September or October of the following year.

Score Cutoffs

The first table on the facing page includes the following data for each of the years 2001–2016 of the competition:

- The scores of the top 5 contestants (the Putnam Fellows). Note that it is not reported which Fellow received which score.

- The minimum scores to be recognized among the top 15 and top 25 contestants (up to rounding).

The second table on the facing page includes the following data for each of the years 2001–2016 of the competition:

- The minimum scores to be recognized among the top 100[4], top 200, and top 500 contestants (up to rounding).

- The mean and median scores across all contestants.

- The percentage of contestants who scored 0 points.

---

[4]Currently, the top 100 coincides with "Honorable Mention"; during 2001–2016, Honorable Mentions formed a separate tier between the top 25 and the top 100.

Year	1	2	3	4	5	15	25
2001	101	100	86	80	80	71	68
2002	116	108	106	96	96	79	72
2003	110	96	95	90	82	77	68
2004	109	101	99	89	89	76	70
2005	100	98	89	86	80	67	60
2006	101	99	98	92	92	80	70
2007	110	97	91	90	82	71	64
2008	117	110	108	102	101	87	80
2009	111	109	100	98	97	73	70
2010	120	118	117	110	109	92	85
2011	91	87	81	71	70	55	51
2012	100	87	81	80	78	60	58
2013	99	93	91	91	88	70	67
2014	96	89	85	81	81	71	69
2015	99	90	90	89	82	74	63
2016	114	103	102	100	97	86	78

Year	100	200	500	Mean	Median	Score 0
2001	50	37	20	8.9	1	44.9%
2002	56	41	24	11.0	3	34.7%
2003	42	31	18	7.1	1	27.8%
2004	49	40	22	8.4	0	53.6%
2005	44	33	20	7.9	1	46.7%
2006	49	32	14	6.2	0	62.6%
2007	42	31	21	7.0	2	42.5%
2008	54	41	22	9.5	1	47.2%
2009	50	38	22	9.5	2	43.7%
2010	60	49	31	11.9	2	47.0%
2011	32	24	13	4.4	1	46.0%
2012	41	33	23	8.2	0	52.7%
2013	42	32	21	8.3	1	49.8%
2014	47	39	27	9.7	3	34.4%
2015	40	26	12	5.3	0	55.4%
2016	56	42	29	9.4	1	45.6%

Individual Results

The following is a list of the highest-ranking individual contestants (Putnam Fellows), in alphabetical order within each year, and the winners of the Elizabeth Lowell Putnam Prize. For further information about the career paths of these and prior Putnam Fellows, see http://www.d.umn.edu/~jgallian/putnamfel/PF.html or http://www.d.umn.edu/~jgallian/PutnamCareer.pdf.

Sixty-Second Competition — 2001

Reid W. Barton, Massachusetts Institute of Technology
Gabriel D. Carroll, Harvard University
Kevin D. Lacker, Duke University
George Lee, Jr., Harvard University
Jan K. Siwanowicz, City College of the City University of New York
Elizabeth Lowell Putnam Prize: Melanie E. Wood, Duke University

Sixty-Third Competition — 2002

Reid W. Barton, Massachusetts Institute of Technology
Gabriel D. Carroll, Harvard University
Deniss Čebikins, Massachusetts Institute of Technology
Alexander B. Schwartz, Harvard University
Melanie E. Wood, Duke University
Elizabeth Lowell Putnam Prize: Melanie E. Wood, Duke University

Sixty-Fourth Competition — 2003

Reid W. Barton, Massachusetts Institute of Technology
Ana Caraiani, Princeton University
Gabriel D. Carroll, Harvard University
Ralph C. Furmaniak, University of Waterloo
Daniel M. Kane, Massachusetts Institute of Technology
Elizabeth Lowell Putnam Prize: Ana Caraiani, Princeton University

Sixty-Fifth Competition — 2004

Reid W. Barton, Massachusetts Institute of Technology
Vladimir V. Barzov, Massachusetts Institute of Technology
Ana Caraiani, Princeton University
Daniel M. Kane, Massachusetts Institute of Technology
Aaron C. Pixton, Princeton University
Elizabeth Lowell Putnam Prize: Ana Caraiani, Princeton University

Sixty-Sixth Competition — 2005

Oleg I. Golberg, Massachusetts Institute of Technology
Matthew M. Ince, Massachusetts Institute of Technology
Daniel M. Kane, Massachusetts Institute of Technology
Ricky I. Liu, Harvard University
Tiankai Liu, Harvard University
Aaron C. Pixton, Princeton University
Elizabeth Lowell Putnam Prize: Alison B. Miller, Harvard University

Sixty-Seventh Competition — 2006

Hansheng Diao, Massachusetts Institute of Technology
Daniel M. Kane, Massachusetts Institute of Technology
Tiankai Liu, Harvard University
Po-Ru Loh, California Institute of Technology
Yufei Zhao, Massachusetts Institute of Technology
Elizabeth Lowell Putnam Prize: Alison B. Miller, Harvard University

Sixty-Eighth Competition — 2007

Jason C. Bland, California Institute of Technology
Brian R. Lawrence, California Institute of Technology
Aaron C. Pixton, Princeton University
Qingchun Ren, Massachusetts Institute of Technology
Xuancheng Shao, Massachusetts Institute of Technology
Arnav Tripathy, Harvard University
Elizabeth Lowell Putnam Prize: Alison B. Miller, Harvard University

Sixty-Ninth Competition — 2008

Brian R. Lawrence, California Institute of Technology
Seok Hyeong (Sean) Lee, Stanford University
Arnav Tripathy, Harvard University
Bohua Zhan, Massachusetts Institute of Technology
Yufei Zhao, Massachusetts Institute of Technology
Elizabeth Lowell Putnam Prize: Viktoriya Krakovna, University of Toronto

Seventieth Competition — 2009

William A. Johnson, University of Washington, Seattle
Xiaosheng Mu, Yale University
Qingchun Ren, Massachusetts Institute of Technology
Arnav Tripathy, Harvard University
Yufei Zhao, Massachusetts Institute of Technology

Seventy-First Competition — 2010

Yu Deng, Massachusetts Institute of Technology
Brian R. Lawrence, California Institute of Technology
Seok Hyeong (Sean) Lee, Stanford University
Colin P. Sandon, Massachusetts Institute of Technology
Alex (Lin) Zhai, Harvard University
Elizabeth Lowell Putnam Prize: Yinghui Wang, Massachusetts Institute of Technology

Seventy-Second Competition — 2011

Samuel (Sam) S. Elder, California Institute of Technology
Brian R. Lawrence, California Institute of Technology
Seok Hyeong (Sean) Lee, Stanford University
Xiaosheng Mu, Yale University
Evan M. O'Dorney, Harvard University
Elizabeth Lowell Putnam Prize: Fei Song, University of Virginia

Seventy-Third Competition — 2012

Benjamin P. Gunby, Massachusetts Institute of Technology
Eric K. Larson, Harvard University
Mitchell M. Lee, Massachusetts Institute of Technology
Zipei Nie, Massachusetts Institute of Technology
Evan M. O'Dorney, Harvard University

Seventy-Fourth Competition — 2013

Mitchell M. Lee, Massachusetts Institute of Technology
Zipei Nie, Massachusetts Institute of Technology
Evan M. O'Dorney, Harvard University
Robert (Bobby) C. Shen, Massachusetts Institute of Technology
David H. Yang, Massachusetts Institute of Technology
Elizabeth Lowell Putnam Prize: Xiao Wu, Yale University

Seventy-Fifth Competition — 2014

Ravi Jagadeesan, Harvard University
Zipei Nie, Massachusetts Institute of Technology
Mark A. Sellke, Massachusetts Institute of Technology
Robert (Bobby) C. Shen, Massachusetts Institute of Technology
David H. Yang, Massachusetts Institute of Technology
Lingfu Zhang, Massachusetts Institute of Technology

Seventy-Sixth Competition — 2015

Pakawut Jiradilok, Harvard University
Bumsoo Kim, Princeton University
Gyujin Oh, Stanford University
Daniel Spivak, University of Waterloo
David H. Yang, Massachusetts Institute of Technology
Yunkun Zhou, Massachusetts Institute of Technology
Elizabeth Lowell Putnam Prize: Danielle Wang, Massachusetts Institute of Technology

Seventy-Seventh Competition — 2016

Joshua D. Brakensiek, Carnegie Mellon University
Dong Ryul Kim, Harvard University
Thomas E. Swayze, Carnegie Mellon University
Samuel Zbarsky, Carnegie Mellon University
Yunkun Zhou, Massachusetts Institute of Technology
Elizabeth Lowell Putnam Prize: Simona Diaconu, Princeton University

Team Results

The following is a list of the top 5 teams, in order of placement within each year. During the years covered in this volume, schools would choose teams in advance of the competition; school ranks were obtained by summing the individual ranks (not scores) of the team members, with the lowest total being the winner. (As of 2019, a school's team score is the sum of its top three individual scores, with no advance designation required.)

Sixty-Second Competition — 2001

Harvard University:
    Gabriel D. Carroll, George Lee, Jr., Alexander B. Schwartz
Massachusetts Institute of Technology:
    Reid W. Barton, Abhinav Kumar, Pavlo Pylyavskyy
Duke University:
    David G. Arthur, Nathan G. Curtis, Kevin D. Lacker
University of California, Berkeley:
    Maksim I. Maydanskiy, James M. Merryfield, Austin W. Shapiro
Stanford University:
    Kenneth K. Easwaran, Paul A. Valiant, David T. Vickrey

Sixty-Third Competition — 2002

Harvard University:
    Gabriel D. Carroll, George Lee, Jr., Alexander B. Schwartz
Princeton University:
    Stefan L. Hornet, Mihai Manea, Radu H. Mihaescu
Duke University:
    David G. Arthur, Oaz Nir, Melanie E. Wood
University of California, Berkeley:
    Boris Bukh, James M. Merryfield, Austin W. Shapiro
Stanford University:
    Chee Hau Tan, Paul A. Valiant, Daniel Wright

Sixty-Fourth Competition — 2003

Massachusetts Institute of Technology:
    Reid W. Barton, Daniel M. Kane, Yevgeny K. Zaytman
Harvard University:
    Gabriel D. Carroll, George Lee, Jr., Alexander B. Schwartz
Duke University:
    David G. Arthur, Nikifor C. Bliznashki, Oaz Nir
California Institute of Technology:
    Zhihao Liu, Po-Ru Loh, Po-Shen Loh
Harvey Mudd College:
    David J. Gaebler, Jason Murcko, Andrew G. Niedermaier

Sixty-Fifth Competition — 2004

Massachusetts Institute of Technology:
    Reid W. Barton, Daniel M. Kane, Emanuel I. Stoica
Princeton University:
    Ana Caraiani, Suehyun Kwon, Mihai Manea
Duke University:
    Nikifor C. Bliznashki, Oaz Nir, Lingren Zhang
University of Waterloo:
    Olena Bormashenko, Ralph Furmaniak, Michael A. Lipnowski
California Institute of Technology:
    Po-Ru Loh, Mehmet B. Yenmez, Rumen I. Zarev

Sixty-Sixth Competition — 2005

Harvard University:
    Tiankai Liu, Alison B. Miller, Tong Zhang
Princeton University:
    Ana Caraiani, Andrei Neguţ, Aaron C. Pixton
Duke University:
    Nikifor C. Bliznashki, Jason Ferguson, Lingren Zhang
Massachusetts Institute of Technology:
    Timothy G. Abbott, Vladimir Barzov, Daniel M. Kane
University of Waterloo:
    Olena Bormashenko, Ralph Furmaniak, Xiannan Li

Sixty-Seventh Competition — 2006

Princeton University:
Ana Caraiani, Andrei Neguţ, Aaron C. Pixton
Harvard University:
Tiankai Liu, Alison B. Miller, Tong Zhang
Massachusetts Institute of Technology:
Oleg Golberg, Daniel M. Kane, Kuat T. Yessenov
University of Toronto:
Tianyi David Han, János Kramár, Viktoriya Krakovna
University of Chicago:
David Coley, Junehyuk Jung, Zhiwei Calvin Lin

Sixty-Eighth Competition — 2007

Harvard University:
Zachary R. Abel, Tiankai Liu, Alison B. Miller
Princeton University:
Andrei Neguţ, Aaron C. Pixton, Andrei B. Ungureanu
Massachusetts Institute of Technology:
Hansheng Diao, Eric C. Price, Yufei Zhao
Stanford University:
Serin Hong, Nathan K. Pflueger, Kiat Chuan Tan
Duke University:
Tirasan Khandhawit, Peng Shi, Lingren Zhang

Sixty-Ninth Competition — 2008

Harvard University:
Zachary Abel, Iurie Boreico, Arnav Tripathy
Princeton University:
Peter Z. Diao, John V. Pardon, Adrian I. Zahariuc
Massachusetts Institute of Technology:
Qingchun Ren, Xuancheng Shao, Yufei Zhao
Stanford University:
Young Hun Jung, Nathan K. Pflueger, Jeffrey Wang
California Institute of Technology:
Jason C. Bland, Zarathustra E. Brady, Brian R. Lawrence

Seventieth Competition — 2009

Massachusetts Institute of Technology:
  Qingchun Ren, Bohua Zhan, Yufei Zhao
Harvard University:
  Iurie Boreico, Arnav Tripathy, Alex Zhai
California Institute of Technology:
  Jason C. Bland, Samuel (Sam) S. Elder, Gjergji Zaimi
Stanford University:
  Young Hun Jung, Seok Hyeong (Sean) Lee, Jeffrey Wang
Princeton University:
  Peter Z. Diao, Adam C. Hesterberg, John V. Pardon

Seventy-First Competition — 2010

California Institute of Technology:
  Yakov Berchenko-Kogan, Jason C. Bland, Brian R. Lawrence
Massachusetts Institute of Technology:
  Sergei S. Bernstein, Whan Ghang, Jacob N. Steinhardt
Harvard University:
  Kevin Lee, Arnav Tripathy, Alex (Lin) Zhai
University of California, Berkeley:
  Shiyu Li, Evan M. O'Dorney, David D. Gee
University of Waterloo:
  Steven N. Karp, Boyu Li, Malcolm A. Sharpe

Seventy-Second Competition — 2011

Harvard University:
  Eric K. Larson, Evan M. O'Dorney, Alex (Lin) Zhai
Carnegie Mellon University:
  Michael T. Druggan, Albert F. Gu, Archit U. Kulkarni
California Institute of Technology:
  Zarathustra E. Brady, Samuel (Sam) S. Elder, Brian R. Lawrence
Stanford University:
  Seok Hyeong (Sean) Lee, Gyujin Oh, Lyuboslav N. Panchev
Massachusetts Institute of Technology:
  Vlad Firoiu, Colin P. Sandon, Jacob N. Steinhardt

Seventy-Third Competition — 2012

Harvard University:
    Eric K. Larson, Evan M. O'Dorney, Allen Yuan
Massachusetts Institute of Technology:
    Benjamin P. Gunby, Brian C. Hamrick, Jonathan T. Schneider
University of California, Los Angeles:
    Xiangyi Huang, Tudor Padurariu, Dillon Zhi
Stony Brook University:
    Thao T. Do, Dat Pham Nguyen, Kevin R. Sackel
Carnegie Mellon University:
    Michael T. Druggan, Albert F. Gu, Linus U. Hamilton

Seventy-Fourth Competition — 2013

Massachusetts Institute of Technology:
    Benjamin P. Gunby, Mitchell M. Lee, Zipei Nie
Carnegie Mellon University:
    Michael Druggan, Linus U. Hamilton, Thomas E. Swayze
Stanford University:
    Vishal Arul, Ravi K. Fernando, Sam G. Keller
Harvard University:
    Octav I. Dragoi, Evan M. O'Dorney, Allen Yuan
California Institute of Technology:
    Xiangyi Huang, Zhaorong Jin, Tian Nie

Seventy-Fifth Competition — 2014

Massachusetts Institute of Technology:
    Mitchell M. Lee, Zipei Nie, David H. Yang
Harvard University:
    Calvin Deng, Malcolm J. Granville, Xiaoyu He
Rensselaer Polytechnic Institute:
    Theerawat Bhudisaksang, Owen Goff, Wijit Yangjit
University of Waterloo:
    Kangning Chen, Sam Eisenstat, Daniel Spivak
Carnegie Mellon University:
    Linus U. Hamilton, Thomas E. Swayze, Samuel Zbarsky

Seventy-Sixth Competition — 2015

Massachusetts Institute of Technology:
  Mark A. Sellke, Robert (Bobby) C. Shen, David H. Yang
Carnegie Mellon University:
  Joshua D. Brakensiek, Linus U. Hamilton, Thomas E. Swayze
Princeton University:
  Rodrigo S. Angelo, Andre A. Arslan, Eric D. Schneider
Stanford University:
  Jie Jun Ang, Gyujin Oh, Albert R. Zhang
Harvard University:
  Calvin Deng, Ravi Jagadeesan, David W. Stoner

Seventy-Seventh Competition — 2016

Carnegie Mellon University:
  Joshua D. Brakensiek, Thomas E. Swayze, Samuel Zbarsky
Princeton University:
  Eric D. Schneider, Zhuo Qun (Alex) Song, Xiaoyu Xu
Harvard University:
  Pakawut Jiradilok, Dong Ryul Kim, David W. Stoner
Massachusetts Institute of Technology:
  Robert (Bobby) C. Shen, David H. Yang, Yunkun Zhou
Stanford University:
  Jie Jun Ang, Huy Tuan Pham, Albert R. Zhang

Analysis of Results 2001–2016 (by Joseph A. Gallian)

The William Lowell Putnam Competition is held annually for the top undergraduate mathematics students in the United States and Canada. Through 2016, there have been 148,753 participants. The number of participants between 2001 and 2016 ranged from 2954 to 4440 per year. In 2011, there were 163 participants from MIT alone. That exceeds the total number of participants in each of 1941, 1942, 1946, 1947, 1948, and 1949. Table 1 and Table 2 provide the number of participants and teams, respectively, in each of the competitions from 2001–2016.

Table 1. Number of participants in the 2001–2016 competitions.

Year	Number	Year	Number
2001	2954	2009	4036
2002	3349	2010	4296
2003	2615	2111	4440
2004	3733	2012	4277
2005	3545	2013	4113
2006	3640	2014	4320
2007	3753	2015	4275
2008	3627	2016	4164

Table 2. Number of teams in the 2001–2016 competitions.

Year	Number	Year	Number	Year	Number	Year	Number
2001	336	2005	395	2009	439	2013	430
2002	376	2006	402	2010	442	2014	431
2003	401	2007	413	2011	460	2015	447
2004	411	2008	405	2012	402	2016	415

In the period 2001–2016 the prizes for institutions with top five teams were $25,000, $20,000, $15,000, $10,000, and $5,000; while team members of the top five teams received $1,000, $800, $600, $400, and $200 and a Putnam medallion. The top five ranking individuals were designated as Putnam Fellows. Each Fellow received $2,500 and a medallion. Those ranking in the next ten[5] received $1,000, and those in the next 10 received $250. In recognition of the significantly

[5]Because of ties this is approximate.

increasing number of participants, between 2002 and 2016 the number of those designated honorable mention has gradually increased from approximately 45 to 60.

Beginning with the 23rd competition in 1962, the exams have consisted of a three-hour morning session and a three-hour afternoon session, each having six questions worth ten points apiece. Until 2018, institutions entering teams designated the three team members before the competition was held. The team score was the sum of the ranks of the three team members. Thus a team whose members finished in twenty-first, forty-ninth, and one hundred and second places would have a score of 172. Because of the method of scoring teams, an institution with many top ranking individuals did not always win the team competition. For instance, MIT had three Putnam Fellows in 2005 and 2006 but finished fourth and third in those years. (As of 2019, the team score is computed as the sum of the top three individual scores from a given institution, with no advance designation.)

In the first seventy-seven competitions (1938–2016) Harvard and MIT have had the most team success and produced the greatest number of Putnam Fellows.[6] Harvard finished in the top 5 sixty-two times to MIT's forty-five. In the years 2001–2016 both Harvard and MIT were in the top 5 fifteen times. In these years Harvard was first seven times and second four times while MIT was first six times and second three times. Two schools that rose to Putnam competition prominence in the twenty-first century are Carnegie Mellon and Stanford. After finishing in second place in 2011, 2013, and 2015, Carnegie Mellon won its first team title in 2016 in spectacular fashion by having all three team members placed in the top five. The only other institution to have achieved this amazing feat was Harvard in 1949, 1986, 1987, and 1990.[7] Carnegie Mellon's rise to prominence coincided with its hiring in 2010 of Po-Shen Loh, who was the deputy leader of the USA International Mathematics Olympiad (IMO) team, and a new scholarship program for exceptionally talented applicants. Loh's recruiting efforts and his Putnam-like problem-solving seminar immediately made CMU competitive with Harvard and MIT. Stanford placed among the top five teams nine times in the period 2001-2016 with seven of those occurring between 2007 and 2016. Stanford had four Putnam Fellows between 2008-2015 but none before 2008. After placing in the top five twenty-four times and in second place nine times prior to 2006, Princeton won its first and only team title in 2006 despite having 22 Putnam Fellows through 2016.

A complete list of the top five schools and top five individuals each year can be found at https://en.wikipedia.org/wiki/Putnam_competition. Table 3 lists every team that has placed fifth or higher in at least one competition, along

---

[6] All references to the number of Putnam Fellows in the article include multiplicity.

[7] Harvard has now done this once more, in 2018.

with the total number of Putnam Fellows from each of these institutions. Table 4 is the list of institutions that have had at least one Putnam Fellow.

Table 3. Number of teams in the top 5 in the 2001–2016 competitions.

Institution	1st	2nd	3rd	4th	5th	Total
Harvard University	7	4	2	1	1	15
Massachusetts Inst. Technology	6	3	3	2	1	15
Princeton University	1	6	1		1	9
Carnegie Mellon	1	3	2	1	2	9
California Inst. Technology	1		2	1	3	7
Duke University		1	4		1	6
Stanford University			1	5	3	9
Rensselaer Polytechnic Institute			1			1
University of Waterloo				2	2	4
U. California, Los Angeles			2			2
U. California, Berkeley				3		3
University of Toronto				1		1
Stony Brook University				1		1
University of Chicago					1	1
Harvey Mudd College					1	1

Harvard is the overwhelming champion for producing Putnam Fellows with 106 versus MIT's second place 68. But between 2001 and 2016, MIT outdid Harvard in Putnam Fellows thirty-seven to nineteen. Remarkably, both Harvard and MIT had Putnam Fellows in fifteen of the sixteen years between 2001 and 2016. MIT had an unprecedented five Putnam Fellows in 2014 (because of a three-way tie for fourth place there were six Putnam Fellows in 2014) and four Putnam Fellows in 2013.

Through 2016, there have been 292 individuals who have been Putnam Fellows for a total of 404, counting multiplicity. Only eight people—Don Coppersmith, Arthur Rubin, Bjorn Poonen, Ravi Vakil, Gabriel Carroll, Reid Barton, Daniel Kane, and Brian Lawrence—have been Putnam Fellows four times. Of these Barton, Kane and Lawrence were four-time winners and Carroll was a three-time Putnam Fellow in the years 2001–2016.

Among the twenty-two people who have been three-time winners through 2016, Aaron Pixton, Arnav Tripathy, Yufei Zhao, Xiaosheng Mu, Evan O'Dorney, Zipei Nie, and David Yang were the ones who participated between 2001 and 2016. Zhao missed being a four-time Fellow by one point in 2007. Barton is the only person ever to win four gold medals in four attempts at the IMO. Barton also

Table 4. Institutions of Putnam Fellows in the 2001–2016 competitions.

Institution	Number
Massachusetts Inst. Technology	37
Harvard University	19
California Inst. Technology	7
Princeton University	6
Stanford University	4
Carnegie Mellon	3
Yale University	2
University of Waterloo	2
Duke University	2
City College of New York	1
U. Washington, Seattle	1

won two gold medals in the International Olympiad in Informatics. O'Dorney won the U.S. National Spelling Bee.

The first woman Putnam Fellow was Ioana Dumitriu from New York University in 1996. In 2002 Melanie Wood from Duke became the second woman to be a Putnam Fellow; the third was Ana Caraiani from Princeton in 2003 and 2004. As a group, the five winners of the 2003 competition have amassed the greatest number of Putnam Fellow designations ever: Gabriel Carroll, Reid Barton and Daniel Kane won four times, Ana Caraiani won twice, and Ralph Furmaniak won once.

One might wonder about the most difficult Putnam problems over the years. By design, the 5th and 6th problems in each session tend to be more difficult than the others, but time also is a factor with the last two problems. From 2001–2016, the only problem for which no one in the top 200 received a positive score was B6 on the 2011 exam (see page 230). In fact, in 2011 only one person in the top 200 scored a positive score on A5 and B6 combined. In 2011 181 people out of the top 200 left A5 blank. In 2014, the highest score for A5 was 1.

Unlike the early years of the Putnam competition, during the period 2001–2016 many of those who have done exceptionally well in the Putnam competition have participated as high-school students in problem solving summer training camps in the United States and elsewhere in preparation for the IMO, and many of the international students who represented their countries in the IMO have come to the United States for their undergraduate degrees. As a consequence the winners of Putnam competitions now come from many countries. The 2006 Putnam competition illustrates this well. All five 2006 Putnam winners were IMO gold medal recipients, and 12 of the top 26 scorers in the competition represented countries other than the United States or Canada in the IMO. In 2007 five of the six Putnam Fellows were IMO Gold medalists and nine of the top 24 in the Putnam competition represented countries other than the United States or Canada in the IMO. In 2009 seven of the top 25 in the Putnam competition represented countries other than the United States or Canada in the IMO while in 2010 there were six in the top 25. Between 2010 and 2016 all but three Putnam Fellows were IMO Gold medalists.

Over the seventy-seven competitions between 1938 and 2016 there have been only four perfect scores—one in 1987, two in 1988, and one in 2010. The average of the top 5 scores in 2010 was 114.8. The exam median was 2.

Through 2016, there have been thirteen individual winners of the Elizabeth Lowell Putnam Award given from time to time to a female participant with a high score. Nine of these occurred in the period 2001–2016. Of these, Alison Miller won it three times and Ana Caraiani and Melanie Wood won it twice. Caraiani and Wood were Putnam Fellows. The only institution to have more than one woman win the Elizabeth Lowell Putnam award is MIT with three. The 2004 competition was a high-water year for women. In addition to Caraiani and Miller, two other women finished in the top fifteen, four more received honorable mention, and another eleven finished in the top 200. Two of Princeton's three-member team, which was second to MIT, were women.

Prior to the period 2001–2016 Harvard had always far outpaced all other schools in the number of individuals receiving honorable mention or higher status. In the 1990s, for instance, Harvard had 25 Putnam Fellows and seven team championships to MIT's one and zero. This changed dramatically when in the late 1990s the MIT math department became aware that its admissions office was rejecting many applicants who had excelled in the USA Mathematical Olympiad (USAMO) sponsored by the MAA because they weren't sufficiently "well-rounded." Following some discussions, the MIT admissions office was very cooperative in admitting applicants whom the math faculty identified as being extraordinarily strong problem solvers. This paid immediate dividends with MIT overtaking Harvard as the leader in the number of individuals receiving honorable mention status or higher in 1998. Some close watchers of the Putnam competitions believe that the legendary four-time IMO gold medal winner Reid Barton's matriculation to MIT began a trend of top performers in the USAMO and the IMO going to MIT. Between 2001 and 2005 MIT had 12 Putnam Fellows to Harvard's 7 with Barton and Kane accounting for eight instances; between 2001 and 2016 MIT had 37 Putnam Fellows to Harvard's 19. The widest margin of MIT versus Harvard in the number of individuals achieving honorable mention or higher was 34-6 in 2012. In part, the recent disparity between MIT and Harvard is due to the fact that MIT has about four times as many math majors as Harvard. Among the ten institutions in the 2012 competition that had the greatest number of people to achieve honorable mention or higher status, the number from MIT exceeded the total of the other nine. MIT's dominance reached its zenith in 2013 when it placed 57th in the top 201 finishers. During the years 2012–2014, MIT had twelve Putnam Fellows, Harvard had four, and all other schools combined had zero. In 2012 MIT had 12 who placed in the top 25 to Harvard's 3, but only one MIT team member was in the top 25 whereas Harvard had two team members in the top 5. That put Harvard in first place and MIT in second.

Exceptional performance on the Putnam exam correlates well with excellence in research in mathematics. Of the sixteen winners of the AMS-MAA-SIAM Morgan Prize for outstanding research by an undergraduate student during 2001–2016 Ciprian Manolescu, Wood, Barton, Kane, Pixton, and Eric Larson have been Putnam Fellows. Three-time Putnam Fellows Zhao and O'Dorney received Honorable Mention for the Morgan Prize. Four AMS Presidents are Putnam Fellows and one received honorable mention and sixteen members of the National Academy of Sciences are Putnam Fellows. Keeping in mind that most people in the following categories do not take the Putnam exam, it is noteworthy that six Fields Medalists, five Nobel Prize winners, three Abel Prize winners, and three MacArthur "genius" award winners earned honorable mention or better in the Putnam competition.

See also the author's other articles [**Gal1, Gal2, Gal3, Gal4**] for other analyses of results of the competition.

Additional Material

This chapter includes some additional material that may be useful for navigating this book and/or preparing to participate in the Putnam competition.

- Some strategies for the Putnam competition, both for novice solvers and for experts.

- A bibliography. For each reference, we indicate for which problem(s) does the solution cite this reference.

- A topic index. We have identified some of the most common themes among problems in this volume, and indicated which problems touch on each of these themes. This is intended to help the reader study particular topics in more detail.

- A keyword index. This includes citations of acknowledged contributors.

Strategies for the Putnam

For beginners.

- For those new to mathematical problem solving at this level, it may be worth focusing preparation on basic problem-solving strategies; any good preparatory material for Olympiad-style problems will also be good preparation for the Putnam. In addition to various books, this includes the (freely accessible) AoPS forums.

- Focus initially on A1, A2, B1, B2. These problems are intended to be easier than the others, and so are a good way to get started with Putnam-type problems. In the competition, these problems also have a disproportionate effect on most of the scores; for example, getting three out of the four is generally sufficient to place within the top 500, while getting all four is usually enough for a top-200 finish (see the historical score cutoffs on page 314).

- When using this book to study for the Putnam, remember that we have included hints in addition to the solutions. The hints are deliberately quite terse, and may not make much sense at first; be persistent!

- When participating in the competition, do not count on partial credit; most solutions are assigned a score from the set $\{0, 1, 2, 8, 9, 10\}$. For the same reason, it is worth spending some extra time writing up your solutions to make sure they score in the 8–10 range.

For experts.

- Any preparatory material for Olympiad problems is also broadly applicable to the Putnam, but is likely to omit material on college-level topics such as calculus, linear algebra, and abstract algebra. Ways to remedy this include using the topic index of this book (page 339) to identify problems on these topics; searching the AoPS forums for the tag "Putnam"; or reading the book [**AG17**], which provides a Putnam-centered approach to mathematical problem solving.

- While each set of six problems is intended to be ordered by difficulty, this is highly subjective and may not agree with your experience. When participating in the competition, you should at least attempt all of the problems.

- By comparison with Olympiad competitions, the time control on the Putnam is quite rapid (30 minutes per problem). One effect of this is that in contrast with advanced Olympiad problems, Putnam problems do not generally have multiple layers; usually only one key insight is required. If you have a complicated approach in mind, it may be worth looking for something simpler.

- A key insight is often one that transforms the problem from one subject area within Putnam-level mathematics to another. For instance, we transform 2015 A3 from algebra to number theory, 2014 B3 from linear algebra to graph theory, 2016 B4 from linear algebra to combinatorics, and 2013 A6 from combinatorics to calculus to algebra.

- Another effect of the time control is that it makes time management a more serious issue than for Olympiad competitions. When participating in the competition, try not to get hung up on any one problem; a better approach is to continually cycle through all remaining problems, moving on once you find yourself stuck.

- Yet another effect of the time control is that competitors need to be efficient about writing up completed solutions. It may help to practice writing solutions out carefully (not just solving the problem "in your head").

- Be prepared for the possibility that your final score comes in somewhat lower than you had anticipated. This is rather common, even among expert solvers!

Bibliography

[AF01]   T. Andreescu and Z. Feng, *Mathematical Olympiads 2000-2001: Problems and Solutions from Around the World*, Math. Association of America, Washington, D.C., 2003. (2003B6)

[AG17]   Răzvan Gelca and Titu Andreescu, *Putnam and beyond*, Springer, Cham, 2017. Second edition of [MR2334764]. MR3702004

[Arney] D. C. Arney, Army beats Harvard in football and mathematics! (September, 1994), *Math Horizons* 14–17.

[Berl]   Elwyn Berlekamp, *Algebraic coding theory*, Revised edition, World Scientific Publishing Co. Pte. Ltd., Hackensack, NJ, 2015. MR3380755, (2014B5)

[Bhar]   Manjul Bhargava, *The factorial function and generalizations*, Amer. Math. Monthly **107** (2000), no. 9, 783–799, DOI 10.2307/2695734. MR1792411,(2016A1)

[BM]   B. J. Birch and J. R. Merriman, *Finiteness theorems for binary forms with given discriminant*, Proc. London Math. Soc. (3) **24** (1972), 385–394, DOI 10.1112/plms/s3-24.3.385. MR306119, (2004B1)

[Birk]   Garrett Birkhoff, *Book Review: General lattice theory*, Bull. Amer. Math. Soc. (N.S.) **1** (1979), no. 5, 789–792, DOI 10.1090/S0273-0979-1979-14671-8. MR1567177, (2008A3)

[Boyd]   David W. Boyd, *Linear recurrence relations for some generalized Pisot sequences*, Advances in number theory (Kingston, ON, 1991), Oxford Sci. Publ., Oxford Univ. Press, New York, 1993, pp. 333–340. MR1368431,(2007B3)

[Bryl]   T. H. Brylawski, *A combinatorial perspective on the Radon convexity theorem*, Geometriae Dedicata **5** (1976), no. 4, 459–466, DOI 10.1007/BF00150777. MR440465, (2006B3)

[Clar]   P.L. Clark, The quadratic reciprocity law of Duke-Hopkins, http://math.uga.edu/~pete/morequadrec.pdf (retrieved Oct 2019). (2012B6)

[CK97]   Karen L. Collins and Lucia B. Krompart, *The number of Hamiltonian paths in a rectangular grid*, Discrete Math. **169** (1997), no. 1-3, 29–38, DOI 10.1016/0012-365X(95)00330-Y. MR1449703, (2005A2)

[DB62]   F. N. David and D. E. Barton, *Combinatorial chance*, Hafner Publishing Co., New York, 1962. MR0155371, (2006A4)

[DH]   William Duke and Kimberly Hopkins, *Quadratic reciprocity in a finite group*, Amer. Math. Monthly **112** (2005), no. 3, 251–256, DOI 10.2307/30037441. MR2125386, (2012B6)

[Gal1]   Joseph A. Gallian, *Notes: Fifty Years of Putnam Trivia*, Amer. Math. Monthly **96** (1989), no. 8, 711–713, DOI 10.2307/2324720. MR1541580

[Gal2]   Joseph A. Gallian, *Putnam Trivia for the 90s*, Amer. Math. Monthly **107** (2000), no. 8, 733–735, DOI 10.2307/2695470. MR1543731

[Gal3]   J.A. Gallian, The first sixty-six years of the Putnam Competition, *Amer. Math. Monthly* **111** (2004) 691–699.

[Gal4]   Joseph A. Gallian, *Seventy-five years of the Putnam Mathematical Competition*, Amer. Math. Monthly **124** (2017), no. 1, 54–59, DOI 10.4169/amer.math.monthly.124.1.54. MR3608683

[GR15]   I. S. Gradshteyn and I. M. Ryzhik, *Table of integrals, series, and products*, 8th ed., Elsevier/Academic Press, Amsterdam, 2015. Translated from the Russian; Translation edited and with a preface by Daniel Zwillinger and Victor Moll; Revised from the seventh edition [MR2360010], (2005A5). MR3307944

[Helf]   H. A. Helfgott, *Growth and generation in* $SL_2(\mathbb{Z}/p\mathbb{Z})$, Ann. of Math. (2) **167** (2008), no. 2, 601–623, DOI 10.4007/annals.2008.167.601. MR2415382, (2008A6)

[Kaji]   Hajime Kaji, *On the tangentially degenerate curves*, J. London Math. Soc. (2) **33** (1986), no. 3, 430–440, DOI 10.1112/jlms/s2-33.3.430. MR850959, (2014A5)

[KT]   Kiran S. Kedlaya and Philip Tynan, *Detecting integral polyhedral functions*, Confluentes Math. **1** (2009), no. 1, 87–109, DOI 10.1142/S1793744209000031. MR2571694, (2014B6)

[KX]   Kiran S. Kedlaya and Liang Xiao, *Differential modules on p-adic polyannuli*, J. Inst. Math. Jussieu **9** (2010), no. 1, 155–201, DOI 10.1017/S1474748009000085. MR2576801, (2014B6)

[MathWorld]   E. Weisstein et al., *Wolfram MathWorld*, http://mathworld.wolfram.com. (2006A6)

[Michael]   T. S. Michael, *Ryser's embedding problem for Hadamard matrices*, J. Combin. Des. **14** (2006), no. 1, 41–51, DOI 10.1002/jcd.20063. MR2185515, (2005A4)

[Newman]   Donald J. Newman, *Analytic number theory*, Graduate Texts in Mathematics, vol. 177, Springer-Verlag, New York, 1998. MR1488421, (2003A6)

[Page]   E.S. Page, Systematic generation of ordered sequences using recurrence relations, *The Computer Journal* **14** (1971), 150–153. (2015B5)

[PutnamI]   A. M. Gleason, R. E. Greenwood, and L. M. Kelly, *The William Lowell Putnam Mathematical Competition*, Mathematical Association of America, Washington, D.C., 1980. Problems and solutions: 1938–1964. MR588757

[PutnamII]   L. F. Klosinski, G. L. Alexanderson, and L. C. Larson, *The William Lowell Putnam Mathematical Competition*, Amer. Math. Monthly **92** (1985), no. 8, 560–567, DOI 10.2307/2323162. MR1540709

[PutnamIII]   Kiran S. Kedlaya, Bjorn Poonen, and Ravi Vakil, *The William Lowell Putnam Mathematical Competition, 1985–2000*, MAA Problem Books Series, Mathematical Association of America, Washington, DC, 2002. Problems, solutions, and commentary. MR1933844, (2005A3)

[PS09]   Alexander Postnikov and Richard P. Stanley, *Chains in the Bruhat order*, J. Algebraic Combin. **29** (2009), no. 2, 133–174, DOI 10.1007/s10801-008-0125-4. MR2475632, (2005B5)

[Ryser]   Herbert John Ryser, *Combinatorial mathematics*, The Carus Mathematical Monographs, No. 14, Published by The Mathematical Association of America; distributed by John Wiley and Sons, Inc., New York, 1963. MR0150048, (2001B1)

[Stanley]   Richard P. Stanley, *Enumerative combinatorics. Volume 1*, 2nd ed., Cambridge Studies in Advanced Mathematics, vol. 49, Cambridge University Press, Cambridge, 2012. MR2868112, (2003A5)

[Zasl]   Thomas Zaslavsky, *Extremal arrangements of hyperplanes*, Discrete geometry and convexity (New York, 1982), Ann. New York Acad. Sci., vol. 440, New York Acad. Sci., New York, 1985, pp. 69–87, DOI 10.1111/j.1749-6632.1985.tb14540.x. MR809193, (2006B3)

Topic Index

In the following index, we identify problems referring to the following topics.

- Algebra
- Induction
- Polynomials
- Inequalities
- Geometry
- Trigonometry
- Limits
- Differentiation
- Integration
- Series/Products
- Differential Equations
- Real Analysis
- Complex Analysis
- Combinatorics
- Enumerative Combinatorics
- Probability
- Pigeonhole
- Linear Algebra
- Determinants
- Number Theory

- Abstract Algebra

- Group Theory

- Finite Fields

- Functional Equations

- Generating Functions

- Recurrence Relations

- Game Theory

- Optimization

An extended version of this index can be found online at the Putnam Archive.

Year	#	Algebra	Induction	Polynomials	Inequalities	Geometry	Trigonometry	Limits	Differentiation	Integration	Series/Products	Differential Equations	Real Analysis	Complex Analysis	Combinatorics	Enumerative Comb.	Probability	Pigeonhole	Linear Algebra	Determinants	Number Theory	Abstract Algebra	Group Theory	Finite Fields	Functional Equations	Generating Functions	Recurrence Relations	Game Theory	Optimization
2001	A1																								X				
2001	A2		X																X								X	X	
2001	A3			X																									
2001	A4					X																							
2001	A5																				X								
2001	A6									X																			
2001	B1														X														
2001	B2																												
2001	B3	X							X																				
2001	B4																				X								
2001	B5	X																										X	X
2001	B6	X											X																
2002	A1		X				X																						
2002	A2			X																									
2002	A3													X															
2002	A4																		X										X
2002	A5	X																			X								
2002	A6									X																			
2002	B1														X														
2002	B2					X																							X
2002	B3			X					X	X																			
2002	B4		X																										
2002	B5																				X								
2002	B6														X						X								
2003	A1														X						X								
2003	A2					X																							
2003	A3						X		X																				X
2003	A4	X		X																									
2003	A5													X													X		
2003	A6													X							X								
2003	B1	X																X											
2003	B2	X																											
2003	B3																				X	X							
2003	B4	X		X																		X							
2003	B5					X																							
2003	B6			X									X																
2004	A1	X	X																										
2004	A2	X																											
2004	A3	X																										X	
2004	A4	X		X																									
2004	A5														X														
2004	A6					X			X												X								
2004	B1			X																	X								
2004	B2	X		X												X													
2004	B3				X																								X
2004	B4													X					X										
2004	B5						X																						
2004	B6														X														

		Algebra	Induction	Polynomials	Inequalities	Geometry	Trigonometry	Limits	Differentiation	Integration	Series/Products	Differential Equations	Real Analysis	Complex Analysis	Combinatorics	Enumerative Comb.	Probability	Pigeonhole	Linear Algebra	Determinants	Number Theory	Abstract Algebra	Group Theory	Finite Fields	Functional Equations	Generating Functions	Recurrence Relations	Game Theory	Optimization
2005	A1		■																		■								
2005	A2	■														■						■						■	
2005	A3			■										■															
2005	A4																		■										
2005	A5						■																						
2005	A6														■														
2005	B1	■																			■								
2005	B2	■			■																								
2005	B3								■			■													■		■		
2005	B4														■														
2005	B5									■											■								
2005	B6														■														■
2006	A1					■				■																			
2006	A2																				■							■	
2006	A3	■													■	■													
2006	A4	■												■															
2006	A5	■					■							■															
2006	A6					■																							
2006	B1					■																							
2006	B2	■														■		■											
2006	B3			■											■														
2006	B4														■				■										■
2006	B5									■																			
2006	B6													■													■		
2007	A1	■				■				■																			
2007	A2	■				■									■														■
2007	A3														■	■													
2007	A4			■																	■								
2007	A5														■							■	■						
2007	A6		■					■																					
2007	B1	■																	■										
2007	B2			■					■																				■
2007	B3	■			■																						■		
2007	B4		■																										
2007	B5													■															
2007	B6				■								■																
2008	A1	■																											
2008	A2																			■	■					■			■
2008	A3											■																	
2008	A4								■	■																			
2008	A5	■		■									■																
2008	A6												■		■				■		■								
2008	B1	■				■				■																			
2008	B2					■		■		■																			
2008	B3					■														■									■
2008	B4			■															■										
2008	B5								■				■						■										
2008	B6														■	■			■	■									

Year		Algebra	Induction	Polynomials	Inequalities	Geometry	Trigonometry	Limits	Differentiation	Integration	Series/Products	Differential Equations	Real Analysis	Complex Analysis	Combinatorics	Enumerative Comb.	Probability	Pigeonhole	Linear Algebra	Determinants	Number Theory	Abstract Algebra	Group Theory	Finite Fields	Functional Equations	Generating Functions	Recurrence Relations	Game Theory	Optimization
2009	A1	■																							■				
2009	A2											■																	
2009	A3																				■								
2009	A4																					■							
2009	A5																					■	■						
2009	A6								■																				
2009	B1																				■								
2009	B2									■																			
2009	B3														■														
2009	B4				■																								
2009	B5								■																				
2009	B6																				■								
2010	A1														■														
2010	A2								■																■				
2010	A3										■																		
2010	A4																				■								
2010	A5																				■						■		
2010	A6															■													
2010	B1	■				■																							
2010	B2						■																						
2010	B3														■		■												
2010	B4	■		■																									
2010	B5									■																			
2010	B6																		■										
2011	A1														■														
2011	A2										■																		
2011	A3								■	■																			
2011	A4																		■										
2011	A5											■																	
2011	A6																■		■				■						
2011	B1												■																
2011	B2																				■								
2011	B3												■																
2011	B4												■																
2011	B5												■																
2011	B6																				■								
2012	A1					■																							
2012	A2																										■		
2012	A3																								■				
2012	A4	■																											
2012	A5																				■								■
2012	A6									■																			
2012	B1	■			■																								
2012	B2						■																						
2012	B3													■															
2012	B4					■																						■	
2012	B5												■																
2012	B6																				■								

		Algebra	Induction	Polynomials	Inequalities	Geometry	Trigonometry	Limits	Differentiation	Integration	Series/Products	Differential Equations	Real Analysis	Complex Analysis	Combinatorics	Enumerative Comb.	Probability	Pigeonhole	Linear Algebra	Determinants	Number Theory	Abstract Algebra	Group Theory	Finite Fields	Functional Equations	Generating Functions	Recurrence Relations	Game Theory	Optimization
2013	A1														■			■											
2013	A2																				■								
2013	A3	■										■																	
2013	A4													■															
2013	A5					■															■								
2013	A6													■														■	
2013	B1	■																									■		
2013	B2						■																			■			
2013	B3														■														
2013	B4			■						■									■										
2013	B5														■	■													
2013	B6																												■
2014	A1																		■						■				
2014	A2																		■	■									
2014	A3											■							■										
2014	A4																■		■										
2014	A5	■								■			■																
2014	A6																		■										
2014	B1																					■							
2014	B2			■						■																			
2014	B3																					■							
2014	B4	■	■																		■								
2014	B5																				■		■	■					■
2014	B6												■								■								
2015	A1								■																				
2015	A2																				■							■	
2015	A3	■																			■								
2015	A4												■																
2015	A5																				■								
2015	A6														■	■													
2015	B1								■																				
2015	B2														■						■								
2015	B3																		■										
2015	B4	■									■																		
2015	B5														■														
2015	B6										■		■																
2016	A1			■																	■								
2016	A2						■																				■		
2016	A3										■																		
2016	A4														■									■					
2016	A5																						■						
2016	A6			■							■																		■
2016	B1								■																			■	
2016	B2						■								■														
2016	B3				■		■				■																		
2016	B4																■			■									
2016	B5	■											■														■		
2016	B6										■																		

Index